A BRIEF TEXT IN ASTRONOMY

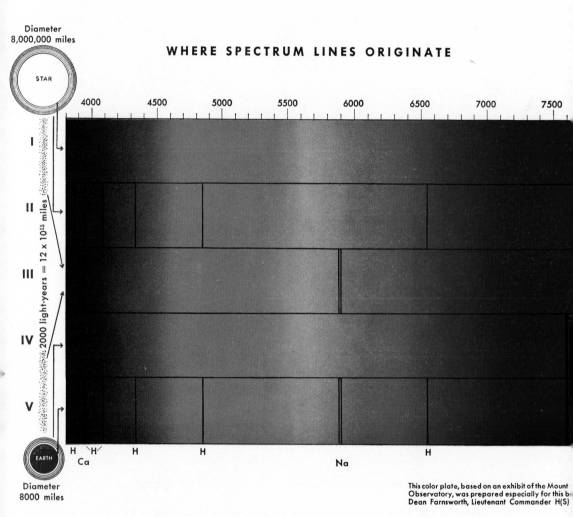

WHERE SPECTRUM LINES ORIGINATE

Diameter
8,000,000 miles

STAR

Diameter
8000 miles

2000 light-years = 12 x 10¹⁵ miles

4000   4500   5000   5500   6000   6500   7000   7500

I

II

III

IV

V

H H H H   H
Ca   Na

This color plate, based on an exhibit of the Mount
Observatory, was prepared especially for this b
Dean Farnsworth, Lieutenant Commander H(S)

ı   *Continuous spectrum from body of star*   ııı   *Calcium and sodium lines from*
ıı   *Hydrogen lines from atmosphere of star*   *gases in interstellar spaces*
                ıv   *Oxygen lines from earth's atmosphere*
                v   *Combined spectrum as actually observed*

A BRIEF TEXT IN

ASTRONOMY

WILLIAM T. SKILLING

SAN DIEGO STATE COLLEGE, RETIRED

ROBERT S. RICHARDSON

MOUNT WILSON AND PALOMAR OBSERVATORIES

HENRY HOLT AND COMPANY

February 1955

PREFACE

THE reason for a brief textbook in astronomy is that a majority of college students have time for no more than a one-semester course in the subject.

The reason for two authors of different lines of experience, in observatory and classroom, is to aid in the difficult task of deciding what *should* be given of all that is known in the observatory, and what *can* be given to students who may have little or no scientific background.

The authors of such an introductory book are faced with two correlated but opposite facts; the vastness of the universe, which supplies our subject matter, and the shortness of time at the student's disposal.

Two other opposite conditions challenge both writers and teachers to make the course more than a means of satisfying a few units of required science. First, the often feeble interest at the outset in students who have never before come in contact with the subject. Second, our conviction of the intellectual value of astronomy to all students.

The authors feel that we are expressing your gratitude and thanks, as well as our own, to the following astronomers who have, by their courteous assistance, helped us to avoid questionable statements and to include some of the advances in special fields that are so recent as not to be very generally known. We thank Edison Pettit for advice and criticism on the first half of the book dealing with practical astronomy, the planets and sun. We owe thanks to A. H. Joy for reading the part on variable stars and their motions, and the nebulae. We wish to thank Walter Baade for reading the remarks about the change in the distance scale on pp. 280–281, and for the latest revision on the diagram of the positions of stars of Pop. I and II on p. 279,

Fig. 21.5. Thanks go to H. C. Arp for the position of the Type II cepheids in Fig. 21.5. We thank Martin Schwartzschild of Princeton University Observatory for reading chapter 19 on WHAT KEEPS THE STARS SHINING. Hugh Hildreth Skilling of Stanford University, though not an astronomer, has helped by suggestion in obtaining greater clarity and understandableness in parts of the book. His books on electrical engineering are well-known for those qualities.

February, 1954   *W. T. S.*
San Diego, California   *R. S. R.*
Pasadena, California

CONTENTS

CONTENTS

INTRODUCTION

The Telescope

This is a prefatory introduction to the telescope and some of its accessory instruments. Later more remarks will be made about these instruments when the results obtained with them are discussed. Astronomical instruments are of such a specialized nature and operate upon principles so generally unfamiliar in our everyday experience, however, that there is little point in attempting to describe them in detail in an elementary book.

(1) those that focus light coming through a *lens;* and (2), those that reflect light to a focus from the silvered or aluminized surface of a *mirror.* Gathering light from celestial objects and bringing it to a focus is the main purpose of a telescope. The light from

There are two kinds of tele-scopes

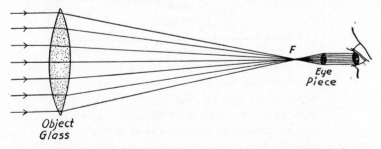

Object Glass

Fig. I-1a. The action of a simple lens is to bend the rays of light from a distant object to a focus at F. Here the image may be examined by an eyepiece or photographed by inserting a plate at the point F.

a celestial body is brought to a focus to form an image on some sensitive surface, such as the retina in the eye or the emulsion on a photographic plate. Either a convex lens (thick centered), or a concave mirror (curved in at the center like a saucer) will serve to focus

1

light and form an image. A lens type of telescope is called a "re-fractor" because the light is bent by the lens or refracted. The action

Fig. I-1b. The lens or objective in the end of a 6-inch refracting telescope. This is the kind of telescope with which most people are familiar. The lens is shaped so that the light after passing through it is brought to a focus at the eye end of the telescope. The image may be magnified by an eyepiece if the telescope is used visually, or photographed if the telescope is used as a camera.

of a simple lens type of telescope is shown in Fig. I-1a. The lens in the end of a small refracting type of astronomical telescope is shown in Fig. I-1b. A mirror type of telescope is called a "reflector" because

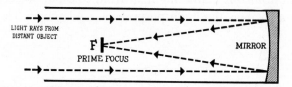

Fig. I-2a. The rays of light from a distant celestial object fall upon the surface of the concave mirror in the bottom of the telescope tube and are reflected to the prime focus in the center of the tube at F. A photograph may be obtained by inserting a plate at F in a small reflector. In the 200-inch telescope the tube is large enough so that the observer works in a cage at the prime focus.

the light is reflected to a focus (Figs. I-2a and I-2b). The largest refracting telescope in the world is the 40-inch of the Yerkes Observatory at Williams Bay, Wisconsin. The largest reflector is the 200-inch Hale telescope on Palomar Mountain. The comparative

2

Fig. I-2b. The 200-inch Hale telescope showing an observer working at the prime focus of the mirror, which can be seen beneath him. The light from the stars passes down to the surface of the mirror and is reflected back to the observer in the cage where it comes to a focus on the photographic plate. Some light is intercepted by the cage so that the full aperture of the mirror is not used. (*Mount Wilson and Palomar Observatories.*)

sizes of some of the largest refractors and reflectors are shown in Fig. I-3.

Early refracting telescopes, such as those used in astronomy for the first time by Galileo about 1609, consisted of a single lens which gave images that were badly blurred by rainbow colors if the

The telescope's imperfections remedied

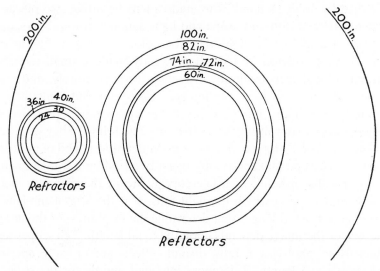

Fig. I-3. Relative diameters of some of the largest telescopes. *Refractors:* Yerkes, 40 in.; Lick, 36 in.; Allegheny, 30 in.; Lowell, 24 in. *Reflectors:* Palomar Mountain, 200 in.; Mount Wilson, 100 in.; MacDonald Observatory, University of Texas, 82 in.; Dunlap, University of Toronto, 74 in.; Victoria, B. C., 72 in.; Harvard and Mount Wilson, each 60 in.

lens was very large. Not until 150 years later was this imperfection remedied by John Dolland, who made a lens by fitting two pieces of glass together of different shape and light bending power. Telescopes that are nearly free from blurring by color are said to be "achromatic." Isaac Newton in 1668 had already made a small telescope without color defects by doing away with the lens entirely, and using a concave mirror to form the image. (Fig. I-4.) But difficulties in preparing a suitable mirror delayed the construction of reflecting telescopes for about fifty years, when in 1720 John Hadley produced a 6-inch mirror that gave images of good definition. Today unskilled amateur telescope makers usually begin by grinding a 6-inch mirror.

Aperture and length of a telescope

By the *aperture* of a telescope is meant the diameter of the lens or mirror upon which the light falls. It is the size of the lens or mirror and its focal length that determine the brightness of the image. The size of the image depends upon the focal length. Telescopes used primarily to photograph faint distant objects are of large aperture and short focal length. Telescopes intended mainly for the study of the sun and planets where there is usually plenty of light available are generally refractors of long focal length. The 200-inch Hale reflector on Palomar Mountain and the 120-inch reflector under construction at the Lick Observatory are examples of telescopes of great aperture intended for the study of faint stars and nebulae. But the 150-foot tower telescope on Mount Wilson used to study the sun has only a 12-inch lens at the top of the tower (Figs. I-5a and I-5b).

The Schmidt telescope

This is an unusual type of reflecting telescope named after its inventor, Bernard Schmidt, of Germany. Schmidt placed in the telescope tube a thin correcting lens through which the light passes before it reaches the curved mirror. This changes the direction of the light rays slightly, so that when they are reflected from the mirror, they form an image which is in good focus over a wide field of view. This instrument is really a wide angle camera, since the Schmidt telescope cannot be used to "look through." The largest Schmidt telescope in use today is located on Palomar Mountain and has an aperture of 48 inches for light to enter.

Attachments to the Telescope

People ordinarily think of an astronomer as peering through his telescope all night at the moon or Mars or some star. On the contrary, astronomers seldom look into their telescope except to focus it or to make sure it is pointed on the right star. Today practically all observations are made by some automatic recording device attached to the telescope. The photographic plate is probably the most important of these. Long exposure photographs bring out objects that cannot be seen by the eye (Fig. I-6). Photographs constitute a permanent record of the appearance of an object at a particular time. They may be stored away and compared with other photographs taken years later. Only in the study of fine planetary detail such as the markings on Mars does the eye still seem to have an advantage over the photographic plate.

Spectroscopy

The spectroscope and spectrograph

Valuable as direct photographs are for certain purposes, photographs of the *spectra* of heavenly bodies are vastly more important. In some observatories a major part of the available time of the great telescopes is given to the photographing of stellar spectra. The spectrum of a bright star can be photographed in a few minutes, but that of a dim star may require many hours.

Early astronomers devoted themselves to determination of the positions and motions of heavenly bodies, thinking that a study of their *nature* was, and ever would remain, impossible. But with the discovery by Newton of the composite nature of white light, and the much later invention by Fraunhofer of the modern form of spectro-

Fig. I-5a. The sun-tower telescope on Mount Wilson. Two mirrors and a lens at the top of the tower form an image of the sun 17 inches in diameter in the house at the base of the tower. The dome is opened and turned so that light from the sun falls on the mirrors.

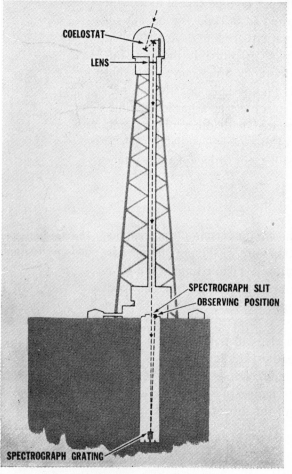

COELOSTAT

LENS

SPECTROGRAPH SLIT

OBSERVING POSITION

SPECTROGRAPH GRATING

Fig. I-5b. The 150-foot sun tower telescope on Mount Wilson. Sunlight reflected from a moving mirror or *coelostat* at the top of the tower passes through a lens which forms a 17-inch image of the sun at the ground level. To form a spectrum of the sun, the light of the image is passed through a slit a few thousandths of an inch wide to a grating 75 feet below ground. The grating reflects the light up to the ground level where the spectrum is brought to a focus. The total path of the light beam is 300 feet.

Fig. I-6. Effect of telescope aperture and exposure time. (*Mount Wilson Observatory.*)

a. 14 in., 1 min. Stars to 12th magnitude.

b. 60 in., 1 min. Stars to 15th magnitude.

c. 60 in., 27 min. Stars to 18th magnitude.

d. 60 in., 4 hr. Stars to 20th magnitude.

scope, a way was opened for learning something about objects from which light comes. "Fingerprints" of the elements of which stars are made can be found in the light coming from the star. Lines in the spectra of stars or sun give indisputable evidence that certain chemical elements exist in these bodies which radiate the light. Hydrogen, for example, in the sun or in a star produces several lines which are in exactly the same relative positions in the spectrum at which hydrogen gas in the laboratory will produce lines. In the laboratory hydrogen is sealed in a glass tube, and electricity is passed through it to make it luminous. Nothing but hydrogen will make these lines; hydrogen always does.

As is well known, a prism separates the light passing through it into spectral colors (Fig. I-7). A grating (several thousand lines

Principle of the spectroscope

to the inch ruled with a diamond point on a bright, reflecting metal film on glass) also makes a spectrum. A prism or a grating is therefore the essential part of a spectroscope, for either will divide light into its component colors. But to make a useful spectrum the light must first pass through a slit, then through a lens which is known as the collimator to bring it in parallel rays to the prism or grating. After leaving the prism in the form of a spectrum of colors these colors

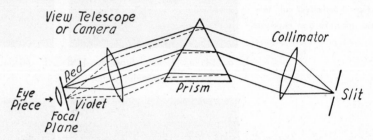

Fig. I-7. Diagram of a spectroscope, showing arrangement of parts and the way in which it separates light into its colors.

must be brought to a focus by another lens called the view telescope. A slit, a collimator, a prism (or grating), and a view telescope, then, constitute a spectroscope (Fig. I-7). If equipped with a camera so that the spectrum may be photographed, the instrument is called a spectrograph.

The general appearance of the spectrum of a glowing celestial body is shown in the color plate (see Frontispiece). The dark lines that cross the spectra are produced by elements such as hydrogen gas in the atmosphere of a star. Other dark lines are produced by elements in the space between the star and the earth.

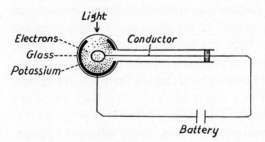

Fig. I-8. The photoelectric cell ("electric eye"). Fluctuations of light cause more or fewer electrons to fill the enclosed space to carry the battery current. In darkness there is no current.

Although all spectrographs are built upon the same basic principles they produce spectra that differ widely in appearance depending upon the purpose for which the instrument is designed. Spectrographs designed to study the sun may spread the light out into a

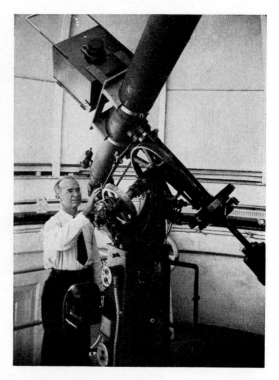

Fig. I-9. The 6-inch refracting telescope of the Mount Wilson Observatory. The south end of the polar axis is near the observer's cuff. Since the latitude of Mount Wilson is 34° N., the polar axis is inclined at an angle of 34° to the horizontal so that it is parallel to the earth's axis of rotation. The declination axis, which is attached to the telescope tube is perpendicular to the polar axis. A small camera has been mounted upon the telescope tube.

colored band several feet in length from the red to the violet since there is an abundance of light available. But spectrographs designed to study faint stars give a visible spectrum less than an inch long since it is necessary so-to-speak to "hoard" the light entering the instrument.

With a photoelectric cell it is possible to detect and record the light from a star with more accuracy than is possible by the eye or even the photographic plate. (Fig. I-8) shows the parts of a simple photoelectric cell from which we can see the principle upon which it works. Light from the telescope is focused upon the sensitive surface of the cell. The light ejects charged particles (electrons) from the photocell causing an electrical current to flow. The strength of the current varies with the changing intensity of the light entering the cell. By using cells of special design in connection with powerful amplifying systems instruments of marvellous sensitivity for detecting faint starlight have been designed.

Use of the photo-electric cell in measuring faint light

Telescopes must be mounted so that they can be easily and quickly pointed to any part of the sky. Once the telescope is pointed or "set" on the star it must move so as to keep the star steadily in view as it swings across the sky from east to west. Astronomical telescopes are mounted so as to turn on one axis that points to the celestial pole, and on another axis perpendicular to it that lies parallel with the plane of the earth's equator (Fig. I-9). Such a mounting is

Telescope mounting

said to be an *equatorial*. Telescopes are made to follow a star by a motor or clockwork. The mounting of a large reflector has to be of massive construction to provide a firm support for the optical parts (Fig. I-10). (Obviously it would be impossible to secure good photographs of the stars if the telescope shook during the exposure!) A great mirror no matter how perfectly ground would be useless unless properly mounted. In 1832 Lord Rosse produced a reflecting telescope with a mirror six feet in diameter, which would be considered a large mirror even today. But the telescope was so clumsily mounted that it was never extensively used. Three men were required to move the telescope and keep the astronomer in a position so he could look through it. There was a fourth who seems to have been a roving assistant, who stood by ready to lend a hand whenever an emergency arose. Most large modern telescopes can be operated by two men or even only one in a pinch.

Observatories are usually dome shaped structures with a shutter curving down one side which can be opened when observing with the telescope. (The telescope tube does *not* project through the slot in the dome as often shown in cartoons.) The opening must of course be somewhat wider than the diameter of the telescope. The whole dome can be rotated so that the opening for the telescope faces in any direction it is desired to observe (Fig. I-11).

The housing of a telescope

The following quotation is an extract from the address of Raymond Fosdick in 1948 at the dedication of the 200-inch Hale telescope on Palomar Mountain in California.

How astronomy ranks among the sciences

This telescope is the lengthened shadow of man at his best. It is man on tip-toe reaching for relevancy and meaning, tracing with eager finger the outlines of order and law by which his little life is everywhere surrounded.

This beautiful expression concerning the world's greatest telescope came not from an astronomer but from a lawyer. It reminds us that a study of the heavens, together with medicine and religion, have been fundamental in the minds of all thoughtful men since earliest antiquity.

1 THE PURPOSE OF ASTRONOMY

Why Study Astronomy?

ASTRONOMERS are often asked the question, "Of what use is astronomy anyhow? Why bother to study stars that are so far away they can be seen only through a powerful telescope?"

If by "use of astronomy" is meant *How will it help me to make more money?* or *How will it help me to get a better job?* the answer is that astronomy probably never will be of the slightest use to you whatever. Astronomy has a few practical applications as, for example, in celestial navigation, the determination of time, and, recently, in predicting conditions for radio transmission, but they are insignificant compared with the contributions of sciences such as physics, chemistry, and geology, to mention only a few.

1.1. Reasons sometimes cited for studying astronomy

The subject matter of astronomy is on a magnificent scale far surpassing that of any other science. Contemplation of the heavenly bodies and the vast distances involved in their study are sometimes cited as inspiring a noble and lofty attitude of mind.

It is true that our viewpoint today differs widely from that of the ancients, who thought the stars and planets were set upon the inner surface of a crystal sphere which rotated around the earth once a day as the center of the universe. Now we know that the earth is merely a speck of matter moving around an ordinary sort of star that we call the sun, and the sun itself only one of the thousands of millions of stars that compose our galactic system. Yet because the subject matter of a science is on an imposing scale does not necessarily mean that the science is correspondingly important. We can find new worlds to explore in a drop of water from a pond. And philosophers may argue the proposition that a huge conglomeration of matter such as a star cloud is of more significance than a worm that possesses the mysterious quality we call life.

Most astronomers develop a practical, matter-of-fact attitude toward their work which is far removed from the popular conception of stargazing. An astronomer preparing to observe in the evening is likely to look at the stars, not from an esthetic point of view, but to see how steadily they are shining so that he will know whether to photograph them with five hours of exposure time or six.

What, then, is the real value of astronomy? *Astronomy has given the world knowledge of the most fundamental kind concerning the properties of matter and energy.*

1.2. The value of astronomy

Certainly no one would deny the importance of mechanical or electrical engineering. Yet no real progress was made in mechanics until Isaac Newton stated his three laws of motion and developed a new form of mathematics for applying them. These constitute the real basis for practically any kind of engineering project in any field. Newton's discoveries were made as the result of an attempt to explain certain laws of planetary motion first stated by an earlier astronomer, Kepler. Kepler would never have been able to state these laws of motion if he had not had a long, accurate series of observations on the planet Mars left to him by his master, the Danish astronomer, Tycho Brahe. Yet Tycho's observations were finally halted because the Danish king considered it extravagant for the government to support such a useless piece of work!

Today as never before technicians are finding practical applications for the results of pure scientific research in fields such as television, radiology, biology, etc. Often the technical applications of pure science are so spectacular that we are apt to forget the prosaic-sounding principles upon which they are based. Real progress is impossible without pure scientific research.

Star Study without a Telescope

When a subject is approached for the first time, a general survey of the material is often helpful before the various topics are taken up individually. In this way, we obtain an understanding of the relationship of one topic to another which might otherwise be obscured by detailed study.

Ancient people fancied the stars formed patterns or CON- STELLATIONS in the sky which they named after the deities and animals familiar to them. Probably the one best known to most people today is the "Big Dipper," which is more properly known as Ursa Major, or the Big Bear, in the northern heavens. Very few constellations have the least resemblance to the objects after which they

1.3. Groups of stars or constellations

13

Fig. 1.1. Star trails recorded around the north celestial pole during an exposure of 6 hours. The 150-foot tower telescope of the Mount Wilson Observatory is in the foreground. The bright streak nearest the center was produced by the North Star, 1° from the true pole. (Photograph by Anthony Wausnock.)

were named. The constellations are thousands of years old, and their origin was lost long ago.

There are several features of interest and value which you can learn about the stars simply by observing them for a few minutes in the evening with the unaided eye. These are a knowledge of the apparent daily and yearly motions of the stars; the names and appearances of the most important constellations and the objects of special interest they contain; and the names and location of the brightest stars visible from the part of the world in which you live.

1.4. Magnitude

The word magnitude, when applied to stars, refers not to their size but to their luminosity. The first classification of stars, made by ancient astronomers, was made on the basis of their apparent brightness. Hipparchus, about 150 B.C., divided them into six classes, or magnitudes, putting about twenty of the brightest into the first-magnitude group, and all of the hundreds of those about as faint as could be seen into the sixth. Other stars of intermediate degrees of brightness were put into the second-, fourth-, and fifth-magnitude groups.

1.5. Circumpolar stars

A good place to start is with the North Star, Polaris, and its neighbors, called the *circumpolar stars* because they seem to go around the pole once a day, and more slowly, once a year. These are always visible, winter and summer, to as many degrees out from the celestial north pole as the observer is degrees north of the equator. This pole of the heavens is the point where the axis of the earth extended would pierce the sky. Polaris is within about 1° from this point (Fig. 1.1).

The pole star is in reality one of the brightest; it outshines the sun 1500 times. But to us it is only a second-magnitude star, seeming considerably less than half as bright as those classed as first magnitude. Its great distance from us, which makes it appear dim, can be better understood when we consider that its light requires about 400 years to reach us, whereas sunlight needs but 8⅓ minutes to travel from the sun to the earth.

As the earth turns on its axis each day, carrying us around a circular path, our unobserved motion makes the really stationary stars *seem* to move in similar circles, but in the reverse direction. This can be observed by watching them for a while or by photographing them with a time exposure.

The conspicuous constellations that do not set below the horizon when observed as far north as 40° north latitude are the "Little Dip-

Fig. 1.2. The stars that never set in latitude 40° N. The stars revolve around the pole daily in the direction of the arrows. Line through the two lower stars in constellation of Ursa Major, or the "Great Bear," are the "pointers" that point to the pole star.

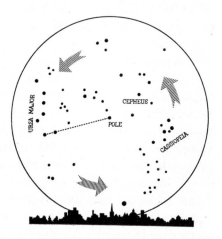

per" (Ursa Minor), with the North Star at the end of its handle; the "Big Dipper" (Ursa Major); Cassiopeia, or "Cassiopeia's Chair," beyond the North Star from the Big Dipper and at about the same distance; Draco, the "Dragon," winding between the two Dippers; and Cepheus, near his queen of classic literature, Cassiopeia (Fig. 1.2).

Outside of this area of circumpolar stars that do not set for observers at latitude 40° N. are several fine constellations that dip below the horizon for a few hours only. This region is rich with stars. The Milky Way glows in the sky beyond Cassiopeia. Perseus and Andromeda are here, two constellations associated in early literature with Cassiopeia. Ahead of them (in their circumpolar motion) Cygnus, the "Swan," is flying with outstretched wings down the

1.6. Stars that are hidden briefly

Milky Way. Deneb, meaning "tail," is a brilliant first-magnitude star close behind the wing and the far-reaching neck. Behind all these constellations comes Auriga, a pentagon in shape, with a brighter-than-first-magnitude star, Capella.

1.7. Stars south of us   Turning to the southern skies, we find that the picture is different. The south circumpolar stars are far out of sight below our horizon. But one who lives in the southern hemisphere—in Australia, South Africa, or South America—can see the brilliant Southern Cross, and other less familiar constellations, circling about the south pole of the heavens. From the extreme southern part of Florida and Texas the Southern Cross is visible when it is highest in the sky. From there we can see two-thirds of the way from the celestial equator (the great circle that in imagination is drawn in the sky directly over the earth's equator) to the south pole, but the more southerly stars never appear in our sky at all.

1.8. Stars over the equator   Stars that rise directly in the east, and set exactly west, are over the equator. As they pass our MERIDIAN (the noon point of the sun) they are south of our ZENITH, the point in the sky directly overhead. A photograph of stars on the equator, such as those in Orion, shows their paths as straight lines across the sky (Fig. 1.3).

1.9. The winter sky   The most beautiful part of our southern and central sky is the region of Canis Major, Orion, and Taurus. These constellations lie in or near the Milky Way, where stars may be expected to be numerous. They make their appearance above the eastern horizon in the fall, are up to our CELESTIAL MERIDIAN (the great circle that in imagination is drawn in the sky north and south through the observer's zenith) in the midwinter evenings, and disappear in the west in spring.

This group of constellations formed the basis of classic stories. Orion, the hunter, followed by his dog, Canis Major, chases Taurus, the bull, across the sky.

Midsummer skies are made almost equally beautiful by the stars of another part of the Milky Way, especially Scorpius and

1.10. The summer sky

WELL-KNOWN CONSTELLATIONS

The pronunciations and spellings are those recommended in the report prepared by the Committee of the American Astronomical Society on Preferred Spellings and Pronunciations.

NAME OF CONSTELLATION	PRONUNCIATION	GENITIVE *	PRONUNCIATION
Visible in Winter from the Northern Hemisphere			
Orion	o-ri'on	Orionis	o'ri-o'nis
Canis Major	ka'nis ma'jer	Canis Majoris	ka'nis ma-jo'ris
Canis Minor	ka'nis mi'ner	Canis Minoris	ka'nis mi-no'ris
Gemini	jem'i-ni	Geminorum	jem'i-no'rum
Taurus	tô'rus	Tauri	tô'ri
Auriga	ô-ri'ga	Aurigae	ô-ri'je
Perseus	pûr'sus	Persei	pûr'se-i
Andromeda	an-drom'e-da	Andromedae	an-drom'e-de
Leo	le'o	Leonis	le-o'nis
Pegasus	peg'a-sus	Pegasi	peg'a-si
Visible in Summer from the Northern Hemisphere			
Aquila	ak'wi-la	Aquilae	ak'wi-le
Cygnus	sig'nus	Cygni	Sig'ni
Lyra	li'ra	Lyrae	li're
Hercules	hûr'ku-lez	Herculis	Hûr'ku-lis
Corona	ko-ro'na	Coronae	ko-ro'ne
Borealis	bo're-a'lis	Borealis	bo're-a'lis
Boötes	bo-o'tez	Boötis	bo-o'tis
Virgo	vûr'go	Virginis	vûr'ji-nis
Scorpius	skôr'pi-us	Scorpii	skôr'pi-i
Sagittarius	saj'i-ta'ri-us	Sagittarii	saj'i-ta'ri-i
Visible all Year round from Lat. 40° N.			
Ursa Major	ûr'sa ma'jer	Ursae Majoris	ûr'se ma-jo'ris
Ursa Minor	ûr'sa mi'ner	Ursae Minoris	ûr'se mi-no'ris
Cassiopeia	kas'i-o-pe'ya	Cassiopeiae	kas'i-o-pe'ye
Draco	dra'ko	Draconis	dra-ko'nis

* The *genitive* is the possessive form of the name of a constellation. It is used when referring to the name of a star that belongs in a certain constellation. Thus the brightest star in the constellation of the Lyre is α (alpha) Lyrae; the brightest star in the constellation of Aquila is α Aquilae; the second brightest star in the constellation of Gemini is β (beta) Geminorum, etc.

17

Sagittarius. These lie farther to the south than the finest of the winter constellations. Sagittarius is sometimes pictured as an archer shooting an arrow at the scorpion.

A more modern and awe-inspiring conception of these constellations is that their great star clouds form the center of our whole system of several billions of stars, and that around this center all the stars revolve, as planets revolve around the sun.

THE TWENTY BRIGHTEST STARS

NAME	PRONUNCIATION	EQUIVALENT	PRONUNCIATION
Sirius	sir'ius	α Canis Majoris	al'fa ka'nis ma-jo'ris
Canopus	ka-no'pus	α Carinae	al'fa ka-ri'ne
		α Centauri	al'fa sen-tô'ri
Vega	ve'ga	α Lyrae	al'fa li're
Capella	ka-pel'a	α Aurigae	al'fa ô-ri'je
Arcturus	ärk-tu'rus	α Boötis	al'fa bo-o'tis
Rigel	ri'jel	β Orionis	ba'ta o'ri-o'nis
Procyon	pro'si-on	α Canis Minoris	al'fa ka'nis mi-no'ris
Achernar	a'ker-när	α Eridani	al'fa e-rid'a-ni
		β Centauri	ba'ta sen-tô'ri
Altair	al-tar'	α Aquilae	al'fa ak'wi-le
Betelgeuse	bet'el-juz	α Orionis	al'fa o'ri-o'nis
Acrux	a'kruks	α Crucis	al'fa kroo'sis
Aldebaran	al-deb'a-ran	α Tauri	al'fa tô'ri
Spica	spi'ka	α Virginis	al'fa vûr'ji-nis
Pollux	pol'uks	β Geminorum	ba'ta jem'i-no'rum
Antares	an-ta'rez	α Scorpii	al'fa skôr'pi-i
Fomalhaut	fo'mal-ôt	α Piscis Austrini	al'fa pis'is ôs-tri'ni
Deneb	den'eb	α Cygni	al'fa sig'ni
Regulus	reg'u-lus	α Leonis	al'fa le-o'nis

1.11. How the observer's latitude affects his view of the sky

An observer at the equator would be able to see all the way to the north and south celestial poles, both of which would be on his horizon. He could therefore command a view of all the stars in the sky—half of them at any hour of the night, and the other half at the same hour six months later.

As one travels north from the equator the pole of the heavens (the North Star, nearly) rises 1° in the sky for each degree of latitude traveled. Hence at 40° N. the pole is 40° high and we can see all the northern stars that are within 40° of the celestial pole.

Looking south, an observer can see the stars as far beyond the

equator as 90° minus his latitude. This is because we can see everything in the sky within 90° of our zenith, in any direction. So at latitude 40° N. we can see stars that are as much as 50° south of the
equator.

Constellations and first-magnitude stars are best studied together. The tables on pages 17 and 18 give the more important
constellations for American and European observers. Also a list of
the twenty brightest stars in the whole sky is given. All of these constellations were listed by Ptolemy in the *Almagest,* published about
A.D. 150. Forty-eight constellations had been named before that time.
Modern astronomers now recognize 88, but many of these are so
poorly marked as to be without interest to the general student. Some
are too far south to be seen from the latitude of the United States.

Constellations are often spoken of as *groups* of stars; doubtless in ancient times they were considered as such, but most of them
are only *apparent* groups. Some stars of a constellation may be many
times as far away as others. They merely form a pattern against the
sky which seemed to the poetic fancy of the ancient observer to resemble the person or thing for which he named the constellation.

In modern astronomy constellations are useful in helping to
locate stars. The sky is divided into regions, much as our country is
divided into states. As the name of a post office has the name of the
state following it in an address for the convenience of the postal department, so a star is referred to by the astronomer as belonging to
a specific constellation. Moreover the Greek letters representing the
stars of a constellation, are usually given in the order of their brightness. Thus Alpha and Beta (α and β) Ursae Minoris signify the
brightest and second brightest stars in Ursa Minor, the Smaller
Bear.

The outlines of all constellations are very indefinite as judged
by appearance; but for use in locating stars in the manner explained
above, the International Astronomical Union, in 1928, arbitrarily
fixed the boundaries of all of them. They made these boundaries in
all cases run along meridian lines and lines parallel to the celestial
equator. There is no question now as to which of two adjacent constellations contains a given star that may be near the border between
them. Boundaries are not shown on star maps as they would not be
helpful in recognizing the constellations, but lines connecting the
brighter stars are of aid in picking them out in the sky. Students are
warned, however, that learning the constellations is like learning to
swim in that you cannot do it by reading about it in a book. Probably
the best way is to ask someone who already knows the constellations

1.12. Constella-
tions

1.13. Ancient
meaning of the
constellations

1.14. Modern
meaning and use

1.15. Modern
changes in the
number and out-
lines of constella-
tions

Fig. 1.4. Southern portion of the moon photographed through the 100-inch telescope, July 30, 1921. (*Mount Wilson Observatory.*)

to point them out to you. Once you are able to identify a few of the more conspicuous constellations, it is fairly easy to learn the rest.

Astronomy with a Small Telescope

With the increasing availability of small telescopes for amateurs, a great many people have an opportunity to see some of the things in the sky not visible to the unaided eye. The observer is cautioned not to expect to see satisfactorily everything shown in photographs taken at the great observatories, but some objects are very rewarding. No photograph can give the mental impression that comes with actually seeing through even a small telescope the moon's craters, for example, or the beautiful Pleiades cluster.

1.16. Particularly interesting objects

Altogether the most easily seen and the most rewarding sight is the constantly changing moon, with its many craters, its mountain peaks and ranges, and their shadows thrown across the plains. The best time to see the moon is four or five days after the new phase, when the shadows are long. The last quarter is equally interesting but

20

Fig. 1.5. Saturn and its ring, photographed Nov. 17, 1911. The ring is not solid but is composed of small particles. (*Mount Wilson Observatory.*)

can be seen only in the later part of the night (Fig. 1.4). The moon is worth viewing at any time, but during the second quarter the contour of its surface can be seen only along a narrow strip bordering the dark portion, which corresponds with the sunrise side of the earth, where every elevation casts a shadow. Also at the full phase the "rays," to be discussed later, can be seen; they do not show at all except when the moon is almost or quite full.

Planets come next in interest, especially Jupiter, Venus, and Saturn. **1.17. Planets**

Jupiter shows four satellites (moons) almost in a straight line, although one may be absent in eclipse on some evenings. This great planet also has dark and light bands in its abundant atmosphere. **1.18. Jupiter**

Venus, which comes into the western sky at intervals of a little more than a year and a half and remains for several months, goes through phases as the moon does. It is most interesting as it comes back toward the sun after its period of greatest brightness, for then it is becoming a narrower and narrower crescent. At the same time the crescent appears larger, for the planet is coming nearer as it prepares to pass between earth and sun and go into the morning sky. **1.19. Venus**

Saturn has the charm of being unique in the possession of a ring, or rings, as a larger telescope will reveal. Both Saturn and Jupiter appear a little later each year and are visible in the evening sky for about six months at a time (Fig. 1.5). **1.20. Saturn**

Even a very small telescope is an aid in looking at objects farther away than the moon and the planets, out among the stars. A telescope pointed at the well-known cluster called "The Pleiades," or "the seven sisters," will reveal perhaps half a hundred stars, like a cluster of white jewels, instead of the scant six or seven that the naked eye brings into view. **1.21. Looking beyond the planets**

Fig. 1.6. Diffuse nebulosity around Merope, one of the bright stars in the Pleiades. Exposure 5 hours, Oct. 9, 1909, with 60-inch telescope. (*Mount Wilson Observatory.*)

Few people can see more than six stars in the Pleiades without optical aid, but in reality eight are brighter than sixth magnitude, which is supposed to be the limit of vision. The faintest star of the seven is at the east end of the group; the eighth in brightness is at the west end nearly between the end stars of the cup-shaped figure. The six brighter stars are of third and fourth magnitude. On a dark, clear night, with no competing city lights to dim the vision, a keen young eye, after being out in the dark for some time, may sometimes see more than eight. On long-exposure photographs the Pleiades appear enveloped in nebulosity (Fig. 1.6).

Another more open but less interesting cluster, not far, apparently, from the Pleiades, but really much closer to the earth, is the group called the Hyades. Its stars form a small ∨ in Taurus. The ∨ has been pictured as the face of the bull with Aldebaran as its flaming red eye, but this first-magnitude star is not really a part of the Hyades cluster, being much nearer to the earth than the Hyades. It is partly to its nearness that Aldebaran owes its greater apparent brightness. This star and two farther back (at the tips of the horns, as shown in old pictures) form a large ∨ by which the constellation is well marked. It is good practice to remember such otherwise unimportant facts as an aid in locating constellations. These stars are in the evening sky from about October to April.

An interesting spring and early summer star cluster is Praesepe, well called the "Beehive," as its many stars remind one of a swarm of bees. It is in the constellation Cancer, and is almost exactly on the ecliptic, the path described by the sun, and closely followed by the

Fig. 1.7. The great star cluster Messier 13 in the constellation Hercules. (Mount Wilson Observatory.)

moon and the planets. This group is more difficult to find for, being very distant, its stars are dim.

Globular clusters, as distinguished from open clusters, are well represented by "the great globular cluster in Hercules" (Fig. 1.7). Even though this is a good example of its kind, it is interesting chiefly for what it is rather than for its appearance, for it is little but a blur in a small telescope. On the photographic plate it is found to contain as many as 50,000 stars. But for this we would not see it at all, for, like the hundred or so of its kind, it is exceedingly far away.

1.22. Globular clusters

Double stars, of which there are many in the sky, are usually too close together or too dim to be seen well with any but great telescopes. But a few are well worth finding. One of these is the middle star of the Dipper handle, Mizar. A fairly small telescope will separate the components of Mizar.

1.23. Double stars

An even finer double is Beta Cygni, at the end of the outstretched neck of "the Swan." The component stars are well separated, 35″ apart, and have marked contrast in color; one is orange, the other blue.

A nebula is a cloud of dust and gas among the stars. The best example of one that can be seen by the amateur observer is the one at the middle star of Orion's sword. There are stars entangled in its misty light, especially four that form a little "Trapezium" in shape, and are well known by that name (Fig. 1.8). To the naked eye the nebula and all its associated dim stars look like one fuzzy star. It is

1.24. A nebula

Fig. 1.8. The constellation of Orion photographed with a small lens and an exposure of 10 hours. The star on the lower left is Sirius, the brightest in the sky. Only about two dozen stars can be readily seen in Orion by the unaided eyes. (*Mount Wilson Observatory.*)

very imposing as seen with a moderate sized telescope on a dark night away from artificial lights.

Our Outlook upon the Universe

As we ponder over the vastness of astronomical distances, it seems incredible that from our limited point of view upon the earth we have been able to attain so comprehensive a knowledge of the universe. Our situation upon the earth may be compared to that of an ant crawling over the surface of an ocean liner. It would take a most intelligent and industrious ant to determine precisely not only the size and shape of the ship upon which he lives, but also the nature of the vessels sailing the ocean in his vicinity to the limit of the visible horizon.

Our situation upon the earth is even more limited than that of an ant upon an ocean liner. Our knowledge of the earth and the universe beyond was gained almost entirely by the patient efforts of a few men, who struggled in a world that in some cases not only failed to appreciate their efforts but was indifferent or actively antagonistic to them.

In the following pages you may in a few minutes learn of facts that some of the foremost thinkers of all times devoted their lives to discovering.

THE EARTH IN ASTRONOMY   2

Size and Shape of the Earth

STARS and planets are so distant that little could be learned about them if it were not for the fact that we have one representative star and one representative planet near at hand. Astronomers can better interpret what they observe in the stars if they have first studied the sun. They can more easily explain the distant planets by first comparing them with the earth.

The fact that we are situated upon the surface of the earth is actually somewhat of a handicap in determining its true size and shape. A man is so small compared to the globe upon which he dwells that he can see only an extremely small portion of it at one time. The earth certainly *appears* to be flat and for thousands of years people thought it *was* flat; but if you could view it from some distant point in space such as the moon you would see at once that the earth is a sphere rotating on its axis.

It is probably easiest to start the study of the earth by assuming what we already know: that the earth is nearly a perfect sphere which rotates on its axis once a day. If this is true then certain consequences must follow, which we can check by observation.

It is hard to talk about the earth without first having some method of locating points upon its surface. In a city there are usually two principal streets, one running north and south and the other east and west, from which the other streets are numbered. Similarly, upon the earth there are two principal lines from which position upon the surface is counted.

2.1. Locating points upon the earth

The axis of rotation forms a natural line of reference for locating position upon the surface. The two points on the globe where the axis of rotation may be imagined to pierce the surface are the north and south geographical poles (Fig. 2.1).

2.2. The two main lines of reference

25

The line drawn around the earth halfway between the poles is the EQUATOR. The lines drawn from pole to pole perpendicular to the equator are MERIDIANS. Since all meridians look alike, we have to select one arbitrarily and call it the PRIME MERIDIAN. It has been agreed that the meridian passing through the position formerly occupied by the Royal Observatory at Greenwich, England, shall be the zero or prime meridian.

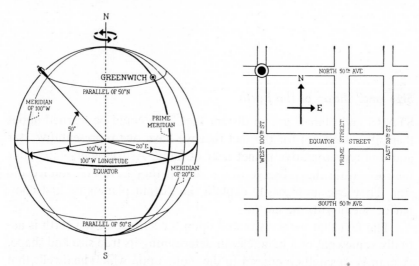

Fig. 2.1. How points are located on the surface of the earth. The meridians of longitude correspond to streets running north and south. The parallels of latitude to streets running east and west. The man is located at the point where the meridian of 100° W. longitude crosses the parallel of 50° N. latitude.

The difference in direction or *angle* between two lines drawn from a point is measured in terms of degrees (°), minutes ('), and seconds (″) of arc. The angular distances measured completely around a circle is divided into 360 equal parts or degrees. Each degree is divided into 60', and each minute is divided into 60″. Thus the angular distance around the equator is equal to 360°. The angular distance from one of the poles to the equator is one-fourth of a whole circle or 90°. An angle of 90° is often called a "right angle." The angular distance from pole to pole measured along a meridian is half a circle or 180° (Fig. 2.2).

The angular distance measured along the equator from the prime meridian to any other meridian is called LONGITUDE. Longitude is measured east and west from the prime meridian from 0° to 180°.

The angle measured from the equator along a meridian to any particular point is called the LATITUDE of that point. Latitude is

26

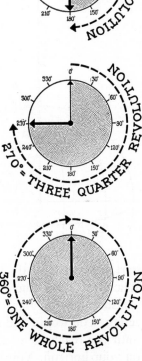

Fig. 2.2. How angles are measured. The difference in direction between the two arrows tells the
number of degrees through which the moving pointer
has turned.

measured from 0° at the equator north or south to 90° at the poles.
All points on the surface having the same latitude are said to lie on
the same PARALLEL.

We now have a definite system of reference for locating points on
the surface of the earth. In a city we say a building is located on the
corner where West 100th Street intersects North 50th Avenue. On
the earth we would simply say that a point is at 100° W. longitude
and latitude 50° N. Longitude and latitude may seem a bit compli-

cated to you at first but they are really much simpler than the haphazard network of streets found in most cities.

2.3. Proof that the earth is a sphere

Imagine yourself at the north pole in latitude 90° N. (Fig. 2.3). The North Star, Polaris, would be directly overhead in the sky, or in your zenith. (Actually it would be about 1° from your zenith, but for simplicity we will suppose it to be *exactly* overhead.) You

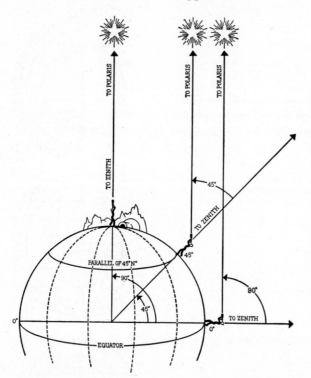

Fig. 2.3. Proof that the earth is a sphere. The zenith distance of Polaris changes by the same number of degrees that the man travels south over the surface. Polaris, assumed to be exactly at the north pole of the heavens, is so distant that it always is seen in the same direction in space.

start walking directly south along a meridian toward the equator. When you reach the parallel of latitude marked 45° you stop and measure the angular distance that Polaris has moved from your zenith. You would find it to be 45°. You continue along the meridian until you reach the equator in latitude 0°. Polaris is now just visible on your horizon. You have moved 90° in latitude from the pole to the equator. Polaris has also moved 90° from the zenith to the horizon.

If you had taken the trouble to measure the zenith distance of Polaris every few degrees of latitude you would have found that it sank toward the horizon by precisely the same number of degrees that you had moved in latitude. You need not keep to a meridian but may take any path you like toward the equator. The result would always be the same. The change in the distance of Polaris from your zenith would always equal your change in latitude. *This is true only on the surface of a sphere.* If the earth were shaped like a watermelon, for example, it is true that Polaris would be in your zenith at the north pole and on the horizon at the equator. But the change in its zenith distance would not equal the change in latitude for points in between.

As you were on your way toward the equator suppose that you measured the distance along the meridian necessary to make a change of 1° in the zenith distance of Polaris. You would have found this distance to be about 69 miles. Since there are 360° in a circle this means that the distance around the earth is 360 × 69, or about 25,000 miles. This distance corresponds to a globe about 8000 miles in diameter. This method of determining the size of the earth seems to have been known to the Greeks more than 2000 years ago.

2.4. Size of the earth

Rotation of the Earth on Its Axis

The rising and setting of the sun, moon, and stars are due to the rotation of the earth upon its axis. But their rising and setting and their motion westward across the sky could be explained equally well if the earth were fixed and these bodies moved around us. Now since we know that the stars are huge suns scattered around us at immense distances in space, this idea seems so absurd that we cannot consider it seriously. It is about as reasonable to suppose that because everyone is yelling when you walk into a stadium it is on your account rather than because one team has scored a touchdown. Nevertheless, it is desirable to have some method of proving the earth rotates that has nothing to do with the rising and setting of the stars. Such a method is the pendulum experiment first performed by the French physicist Foucault in 1851.

The principle of this experiment is easiest to understand if you imagine the pendulum suspended over one of the poles of the earth. The pendulum must be mounted so that it is free to swing back and forth in any direction. The pendulum is now started swinging. Since there are no forces acting to change its motion the pendulum will continue to swing in the same direction. But all the time the earth is turning under the pendulum. The resultant effect is that the pendulum appears steadily to shift its direction of swing performing a complete revolution in a day. Actually, of course, the pendulum has been swinging in the same direction but the earth has turned around under it (Figs. 2.4 and 2.5).

2.5. The Foucault pendulum experiment

Foucault pendulums may be seen in several planetariums in the United States where people watch them fascinated, but usually without the faintest notion of what they are supposed to demonstrate. The time required for a pendulum to make a complete revolution becomes longer the farther it is from the poles. At Los Angeles, in lati-

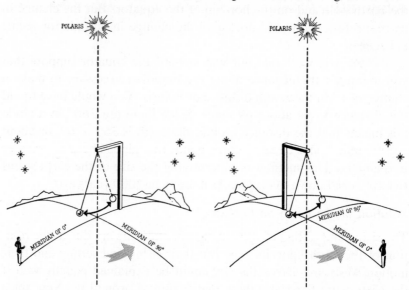

Fig. 2.4. The pendulum is started swinging over the north pole along the meridian of 0°, in line with the mountain and the triangle of stars. The earth is rotating in the direction of the arrow.

Fig. 2.5. Six hours later the earth has turned under the pendulum so that it now swings *across* the man's meridian instead of *along* his meridian. Notice that the pendulum is still swinging in the same direction relative to the stars.

tude 34° N., the time is 42 hours. At the equator the pendulum would not appear to turn at all, and south of the equator it goes in the opposite direction.

2.6. Flattening of the earth at the poles

The earth is not exactly spherical. Owing to its rotation, the earth is slightly flattened at the poles and bulged a little at the equator. The distance from the center of the earth to a point on the equator is 3964 miles. The distance from the center to one of the poles is 3950 miles. The difference is so slight that it would not be noticed if the earth were viewed from outer space. But the flattening at the poles is quite conspicuous for planets that rotate faster than the earth, such as Jupiter and Saturn.

Precession of the Equinoxes

2.7. The changing direction of the earth's axis in space

The daily rotation of the earth on its axis produces such large-scale effects in the sky that they are obvious to everyone. Few people realize that the earth has another large-scale motion which proceeds so slowly that it would never be noticed except by a *very* close observer of the stars. This motion called PRECESSION consists of a gradual change in the direction of the earth's axis in space. We have said that the earth's axis is now directed toward the star we call Polaris. But this particular star has not always been our north star

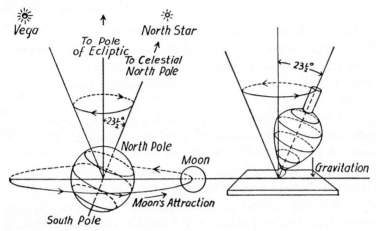

Fig. 2.6. Precession of the equinoxes and the similar motion of a spinning top. The axis of each gyrates in the form of a cone. The axis of the top moves in the direction that the top rotates; the axis of the earth in the direction opposite to that of the earth's rotation. This is because the force of the earth's attraction is tending to tip the top farther over, whereas the force of the moon's attraction upon the equatorial bulge of he earth is tending to straighten up the earth's axis. Both the earth and the top obey the law of gyroscopic motion. Since the gyration of the earth's axis is clockwise, the motion of the equinoxes is also clockwise, or westward.

nor will it always continue to be so in the future. About 12,000 years hence the bright star Vega will be our North Star or "Polaris" (Fig. 2.6). However, α Draconis, which was the "Polaris" of the early Egyptians, is the only other bright star to get about as near the celestial pole as our Polaris.

Precession is well illustrated by a spinning top, or better a toy gyroscope top. If this is set spinning vertically it will remain vertical for some time and the axis will not change its direction. But if spun on a slant the axis, extended in imagination to the ceiling, will trace a large circle. So the axis of the earth extended to the celestial pole in the sky will trace a circle of 23½° radius.

The cause of this motion of the axis is similar in both cases. The gravitational pull of the earth is tending to tip over the top; the gravitational pull of the moon (and to a less extent of the sun) is tending to decrease the 23½° slant of the earth's axis. The slant cannot be changed in either case, but what does happen is that the pole sweeps out a circle as described. Its *direction* is constantly being changed, but not its angle of inclination. This is due to a gyroscopic effect too complex for explanation here.

The Interior of the Earth

Our knowledge of conditions deep inside the earth is necessarily rather meager, since we live upon its surface and the deepest holes we can drill are mere pinpricks in the crust. Our chief source of information is derived from the way earthquake waves travel through the globe.

2.8. Conditions within the earth The average density of the earth is 5.5 times that of water. By density we mean the quantity of a substance contained in a certain volume. A pint milk bottle filled with water weighs 1.2 pounds. But if you could fill a pint bottle with material that is representative of the earth as a whole it would weigh 5.5 times as much, or 6.6 pounds. The earth is the densest of all the planets. The average density of Saturn is less than that of water. If Saturn were immersed in a giant ocean it would float.

From extensive analyses of earthquake waves the earth is believed to consist of three main parts (Fig. 2.7). At the center is a dense core 4000 miles in diameter composed of iron and nickel. The density of this nickel-iron core is probably twice that of the earth as a whole, or about 10 or 12 times the density of water. Surrounding the core is an intermediate zone 2000 miles thick which extends nearly to the surface. There is apparently a sharp boundary between the dense core and the intermediate zone as shown by the sudden increase in speed of earthquake waves about 2000 miles from the center. Overlying the top of the intermediate zone is a layer some 30 miles thick called the crust. That part of the crust which can be examined directly consists mostly of granite.

Magnetism of the Earth

2.9. The earth a great magnet A piece of iron or steel that attracts other pieces of iron or steel is said to be a magnet. There is a mineral which naturally possesses this power called a loadstone (meaning "lead stone"). If a loadstone or a bar magnet is suspended by a thread so that it is free to turn in any direction, it will come to rest in a position that is approximately north and south. The north-seeking end of the magnet is called the north pole and the opposite end the south pole.

In 1600, William Gilbert, later court physician to Queen Elizabeth, published a famous work describing his experiments on a sphere carved from loadstone. From these experiments Gilbert concluded that the earth itself is a great magnetized sphere and that its magnetism comes from *within*.

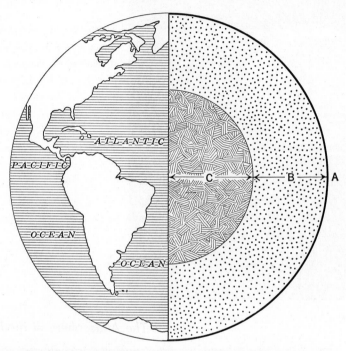

Fig. 2.7. A cross section of the earth (after Mohorovicic) as geophysicists now view it. A is the crust, from 25 to 30 miles thick; B represents the intermediate zone, 2000 miles across; and C is the central core. Adams holds that an alloy of iron with perhaps several per cent of nickel is the substance that best meets the conditions that are believed to prevail at the earth's center. (*Carnegie Institution of Washington.*)

Extensive magnetic surveys on land and sea all over the earth have established the soundness of Gilbert's results. The earth may be regarded as a magnetized sphere with its magnetic axis inclined 12° to its axis of rotation. The north magnetic pole of the earth is near Hudson Bay. The south magnetic pole is in the Antarctic continent (Fig. 2.8).

More than three centuries after Gilbert's great work we are still uncertain how the earth became magnetized in the first place and why it remains so.

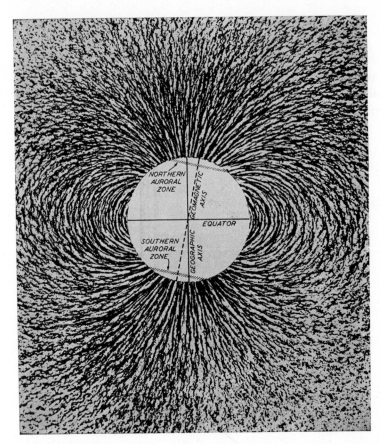

Fig. 2.8. The magnetic field about the earth. (Carnegie Institution of Washington.)

The Atmosphere of the Earth

2.10. Exploring the earth's atmospheric shell

The atmosphere is the gaseous envelope or shell surrounding the earth. The bulk of the atmosphere is within about 40 miles of the surface. The atmosphere thins out gradually so that it is impossible to state exactly where it ends, but we are probably safe in saying that "all" the atmosphere lies within 1000 miles of the surface.

We have a wide variety of methods for exploring the upper atmosphere. Manned balloons have reached 13.7 miles; sounding balloons have gone to 26.5 miles. The greatest height so far attained by any man-made object is 250 miles, an altitude achieved by a small rocket called the "Wac Corporal" fired from the nose of a V-2 rocket on Feb. 24, 1949.

One of the most powerful methods for exploring the upper atmosphere is by radio signals reflected from the electrified layers of air known as the ionosphere. The ionosphere consists of three layers at altitudes of roughly 50, 70, and 250 miles. Valuable information may also be obtained from meteor trails (50 to 100 miles) and from auroral forms from 40 to 600 miles up.

The atmosphere consists of 78 per cent nitrogen, 21 per cent oxygen, and 1 per cent argon, with minute amounts of carbon dioxide and other gases. Oxygen is the most important gas in the atmosphere to us. Without oxygen to breath a man would suffocate in a few moments. At an altitude of about 15 miles there is a trace of a rare form of oxygen called ozone. Ozone has a pungent odor, often no- 2.11. Composition of the atmosphere

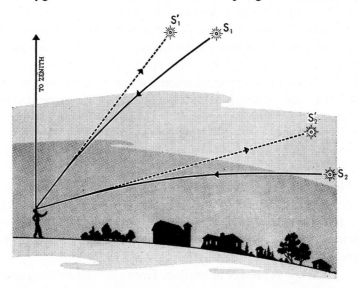

Fig. 2.9. Beam of light from a star is bent, or refracted, as it passes through the atmosphere. Refraction always makes a star appear higher in the sky (nearer the zenith) than it really is. Effect is greater near the horizon, where the beam has a longer air path. Effect greatly exaggerated in diagram.

ticeable after an electrical storm. The thin layer of ozone above us absorbs invisible ultraviolet light from the sun which, if it reached us, would blister our skin and injure our eyes. (If the ozone were *not* there, however, we would doubtless have developed a resistance to ultraviolet light in the course of the ages.) Ozone also prevents astronomers from studying the ultraviolet light of the sun and stars, which would give them much valuable information.

When a beam of light passes from one substance into another of different density, as from water to air, or from the vacuum of space into air, the direction of the beam is generally changed. Everyone must have noticed how difficult it is to judge the position of an object such as a coin on the bottom of a tank of water. This is because the light beam from the coin upon emerging from the water is bent toward the surface of the liquid. Hence we see the coin, not in its true 2.12. Refraction of light by the atmosphere position, but at the position in which the beam of light enters the eye. The effect is to make the coin appear nearer the surface of the water than it actually is. Only if we looked directly down upon the coin would we see it in its true position. This bending of light rays upon passing through substances of different density is called REFRACTION (Fig. 2.9).

Light from a star traveling in the vacuum of space is bent, or refracted, when it enters the earth's atmosphere. The atmosphere bends the ray of light down toward the surface. The ray enters the eye in such a direction that a star always appears higher in the sky than it really is. Refraction is greatest when a star is near the horizon and its light has to pass through a long thickness of air. At the horizon refraction makes a star seem more than half a degree higher than it actually is. We see the star after it has actually set. The setting sun appears flattened owing to the difference in refraction between the rays of light from its upper and lower edges.

Measurements of the apparent positions of the stars have to be corrected for refraction to get their true positions. This correction is easy to remember because refraction always makes a star appear higher in the sky than its true position. The only place in the sky where a star is not affected by refraction is at the zenith.

2.13. The twinkling of the stars The air is always in motion. Even on calm nights currents of air of different density make the stars appear to change rapidly in color and brightness or, in effect, to *twinkle*. You may see a similar effect in the shimmering of pebbles on the bottom of a stream. An object which has a disk, such as the moon or a planet, does not twinkle like a star, although its light may waver occasionally. Points on a disk twinkle like a star but there are so many of them that their light combines to form a fairly steady beam. A planet may usually be distinguished from a bright star by the fact that it shines with a steady light.

Astronomers speak of atmospheric disturbances as the "seeing." Some nights the seeing may be so bad that they cannot observe at the telescope even though the sky is perfectly clear.

2.14. Mass of the earth As we shall see later, the force of attraction between two bodies depends upon their mass and their distance apart. The mass of the earth can be determined by comparing its attraction for some object with the attraction of another body of known mass upon the same object. The experiment is simple in principle but difficult to perform in practice because the forces involved are so extremely weak. The best determination for the mass of the earth is 5.42×10^{21} tons—5.4 followed by twenty-one ciphers!

Such an enormous figure can have no meaning for us. We can only gain some notion of the mass of the earth by comparing it with other bodies in the solar system. The earth is 81 times as massive as the moon but only $\frac{1}{300}$ as massive as the largest planet, Jupiter. The sun is 746 times as massive as all the planets together.

QUESTIONS AND EXERCISES

1. On what does the length of a degree upon the surface of a planet depend?

2. How many right angles are there in a circle?

3. The diameter of the full moon is $\frac{1}{2}°$. If the angular distance between the pointers of the Big Dipper is $5\frac{1}{2}°$, how many full moons could there be between them?

4. If you saw a strange object in the sky how would you describe its size to another person? Would you say it was the size of a teacup or a dinner plate? Or would you say it was perhaps about the same size as the full moon? Which answer do you think gives the most information? Explain why.

5. Can you think of some reasons for believing the earth is a sphere besides those mentioned in the text? Do they prove the earth is a sphere or merely indicate its convex shape?

6. Does sailing around the earth prove it is a sphere?

7. Suppose that an artificial satellite were started revolving around the earth. What would be its approximate minimum distance above the surface of the earth if it is to remain in a stable orbit?

8. Why does the sun appear flattened when near the horizon? Explain.

9. Indicate different ways you might distinguish between a star and a planet.

10. Does the moon appear larger to you when near the horizon or when high in the sky? Do you think this has anything to do with refraction? Why?

11. How could you detect that the earth is flattened at the poles by measuring the altitude of Polaris in different latitudes?

12. Would the length of a degree be larger near the equator or near the poles? Explain.

3 MEMBERS OF THE SOLAR SYSTEM

The Planets and Their Paths

3.1. Size of the solar system

THE solar system is but a handful of heavenly bodies in comparison with our galactic system, estimated to contain 100,000,000,000 stars. Both in mass and in extent the solar system is comparatively small. Nearly all of its mass is in one star, the sun; and as for its extent, if we compare the space occupied by the planets with that occupied by all the stars of our galactic system it would be like comparing one square foot with the whole area of North America.

3.2. Orbits nearly in same plane

The space occupied by the solar system is not spherical but is nearly in a plane. The planes of the orbits of the planets are but slightly inclined to each other, except that of Pluto, the outermost one, whose orbit is inclined 17° to the orbit of the earth. If we omit this orbit a model of the others could be constructed of concentric wire circles, with the outer one, representing the orbit of Neptune, 5 feet in diameter, and these circles could all be enclosed in a box 5 feet across and 1 inch high (Fig. 3.1).

3.3. Scale of distances

So flat is the solar system that a two-dimensional diagram on paper or blackboard represents it almost as well as a model would do. To make a blackboard drawing, to scale, of arcs of the orbits (as in Fig. 3.2) the following distances may be used. From a dot, the sun, at one end of the board, the nearest planet, Mercury, would be 4⅝ inches, Venus 8⅝ inches, the earth 1 foot, Mars 1 foot 6 inches, the asteroids 2 feet 9 inches, Jupiter 5 feet 2 inches, Saturn 9 feet 6 inches, Uranus 19 feet 2 inches, Neptune 30 feet, and Pluto 40 feet.

This scale is a convenient one, for it makes the earth's distance from the sun one unit (one foot). The mean distance from the earth to the sun is taken by astronomers as their so-called ASTRONOMICAL UNIT. If we know that the distance to Saturn, for example, is 9½

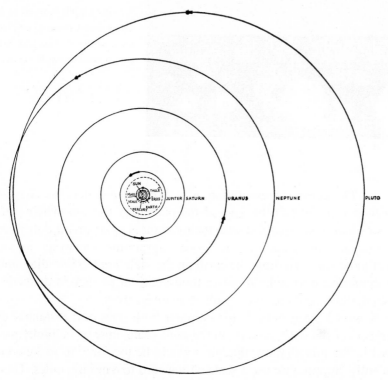

Fig. 3.1. Orbits of planets. The point of the arrow is at the position of the planet for Jan. 1, 1933; the length of the arrow indicates the distance the planet travels in one year. (*Mount Wilson Observatory.*)

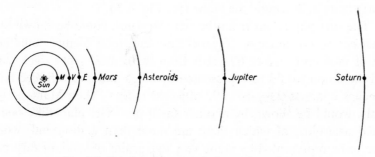

Fig. 3.2. Relative distances of planets from the sun.

units, we may find its distance in miles by multiplying 93,005,000 miles by 9½.

Since the nearest star is 270,000 times the earth's distance from the sun, it could be placed in the above model only by running the blackboard out to a length of 270,000 feet, or more than 50 miles.

39

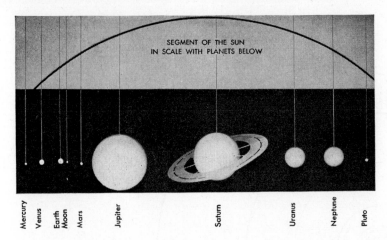

SEGMENT OF THE SUN
IN SCALE WITH PLANETS BELOW

Mercury | Venus | Earth Moon | Mars | Jupiter | Saturn | Uranus | Neptune | Pluto

Fig. 3.3. Photograph of a wood model showing relative sizes of the planets and the moon. (*Mount Wilson Observatory.*)

3.4. Distances and sizes compared

The above representation of the solar system does not suggest anything in regard to the *sizes* of the planets or the sun. Their sizes are so small in comparison with their distances apart that if dots were used to show the planets in the above diagram the dots would be too small to be seen. To draw the earth on the scale used in that diagram, we should have to make it only a thousandth of an inch in diameter. Even the sun would be but a tenth of an inch across.

A model large enough to represent both sizes and distances of members of the solar system, on the same scale, may be helpfully pictured in the imagination, though it would be too large to make conveniently. Suppose we use a scale of one yard to a million miles. Then the central body, the sun, would have to be a globe 30 inches in diameter. Imagine this globe to be placed on the ground at the center of a level, circular prairie four miles across. The planets will be shown as small objects occupying this whole plain, each moving nearly in a circle around the globe (see Fig. 3.3).

The first planet out from the sun, Mercury, could be shown by a small pea at a distance of 36 yards from the globe. Venus would be a pea of moderate size at 67 yards from the central globe. The earth and the moon would be represented by a pea and a radish seed lying 9 inches apart at 93 yards (93,005,000 miles). Then Mars, at 141 yards, would be shown by another small pea. The planetlike bodies called asteroids, of which there are more than a thousand, would have to be represented by many very fine grains of sand, or dust particles, each grain at a different distance beyond Mars, but at an average distance of about 250 yards from the globe.

As we go farther out the planets are larger (except Pluto), and the distances between them become greater for each planet. Jupiter, an orange for size, could be placed a quarter of a mile from the globe to show its approximate relative distance. Saturn, another orange, would be half a mile; Uranus, a plum, at a mile; Neptune, another plum, at a mile and a half. Pluto, of uncertain size, but probably well represented by a small pea, would have to be placed at the outer rim of the plain, at the full distance of two miles from the center.

These little objects, representing massive planets, are to be thought of as traveling at different speeds, but all in the same direction. This direction is left-handed, or counterclockwise, as one looks down upon the plane. Their time of revolution about the central globe varies from 88 days for Mercury to about 250 years for Pluto.

The most impressive fact which such a model as this makes clearer to the imagination is that of the immense distances between the planets as compared with their sizes—the fact that most of the solar system consists of empty space.

And yet, if we go a step further in the same method of representation and place some of the nearest stars in our model we find open spaces which dwarf to nothingness those within the solar system. The nearest star is so far away that it would have to be placed at a distance of 14,000 miles from our 30-inch sun. Stars would be represented by globes of various sizes, the average size being about the same as that of our sun. Stars bright enough to be visible average larger than the sun.

3.5. Stars in the model

After placing the first star in our model we should be tempted to put all about it other globes to represent the other stars that we see lying so close together against the sky. We could not do this, however, for *the stars are as far apart,* on the average (not counting double stars) *as we are from the nearest star.* We know of two stars, Alpha Centauri and Proxima Centauri, which are at the distance represented in the model; but Sirius, the Dog Star, is the only other one visible to the naked eye within twice this distance from us, and it is in quite a different direction.

3.6. Distance of the planets from Bode's "law"

There is an interesting numerical device, called Bode's "law," for fixing in mind the relative distances of the planets from the sun. The name is misleading, however, for the relationship was not discovered by Bode and it is not a law.

In 1772, J. D. Titius called attention to a rule for deriving a series of numbers that gave the distances of the six planets then known with remarkable accuracy. List the planets in the order of their distance from the sun. Write the number 4 under each one. To the first 4 add 0; to the next 4 add 3; to the next twice 3, or 6; to the next add twice 6, or 12, and so on. Then by dividing through by 10 the numbers become the distances of the planets from the sun in terms of the distance of the earth as 1.0.

	MERC.	VENUS	EARTH	MARS	—	JUP.	SAT.	URAN.	NEPT.	PLUTO
	4	4	4	4	4	4	4	4	4	4
	0	3	6	12	24	48	96	192	384	768
Bode's law	0.4	0.7	1.0	1.6	2.8	5.2	10.0	19.6	38.8	77.2
True Dist.	0.4	0.7	1.0	1.5	?	5.2	9.5	19.2	30.1	39.5

It is seen that the numbers give the distances out to Uranus, the farthest known planet at that time, quite accurately. J. E. Bode was greatly impressed by the law, particularly by the fact that it predicted a planet at a distance of 2.8 astronomical units between Mars and Jupiter. As editor of the influential *Astronomical Journal* he gave the law so much publicity that eventually it came to be named after him. Bode felt so sure there must be a small planet between Mars and Jupiter as the law predicted that he organized a group of astronomers to search for it. But before they even got to work such an object was found by an outsider, an Italian astronomer named Piazzi, on the night of Jan. 1, 1801. Piazzi's planet, which was given the name of Ceres, was later found to revolve from the sun at a mean distance of 2.8 astronomical units—exactly as predicted by Bode's law!

Discovery of the Minor Planets

The discovery of Ceres stimulated the search for other small bodies, called asteroids or minor planets. Pallas was discovered in 1802; Juno in 1804; and Vesta in 1807. But not until 1845 was a fifth disered, by Hencke, after 15 years of search. In those days hunting for minor planets was a slow and tedious process. First one made a map of the stars in a small region of the sky. Then a few nights later one checked the positions of these stars again. If a star appeared to have moved, its position would be checked closely on succeeding nights. Continued motion would tell the astronomer whether he had discovered a minor planet or merely made a mistake in plotting the stars.

About 1891 photography was applied to the method of search. On an exposure a moving object like a minor planet leaves a streak on the photographic plate, while the fixed stars will appear as points (Fig. 3.4). There is now a growing list of more than 1600 minor planets, and the task of keeping track of them has become more difficult than discovering them in the first place.

Today an asteroid is not given a name unless its orbit is well determined or is exceptional in some way. The name is usually selected by the discoverer or sometimes by the orbit computer. In the begin-

Fig. 3.4. Arrow shows trail left by the asteroid Icarus, discovered accidentally on a plate taken with the 48-inch Schmidt telescope on Palomar Mountain. Icarus comes closer to the sun than any other known asteroid.

ning feminine names were taken from classic mythology, and, when these were exhausted, from Shakespeare and the Wagnerian operas. Many asteroids have also been named after wives, sweethearts, friends, and even pet dogs and cats. The custom has been to give artificially feminized names to all asteroids except those with exceptional orbits which are given masculine names.

The diameters of only four asteroids have been measured. They are Ceres (480 miles), Pallas (304 miles), Vesta (240 miles), and Juno (120 miles). The diameters of the others can be estimated from their brightness if we assume that they reflect as much light per square mile of surface as the "big four." With this assumption we find that 500 asteroids are larger than 30 miles in diameter. Most of those discovered in recent years are between 5 and 20 miles in diameter, and a new one larger than 30 miles is so rarely found that the count is essentially complete down to that size.

Astronomers often pick up asteroid trails by accident while photographing some other object. For example, in a search for new satellites of Jupiter, 32 asteroids were found on the plates, of which only one had been previously catalogued. It is estimated that there are 44,000 asteroids bright enough to be photographed with the 100-inch telescope when nearest the earth. Today, instead of eagerly seeking asteroids as a prize, astronomers regard them as a nuisance—the "vermin of the skies." Occasionally, however, an asteroid of such unusual interest is picked up that considerable effort is made to determine its orbit accurately.

3.7. Exceptional orbits

Since 1932 several minor planets have been discovered that pass within less than 10 million miles of the orbit of the earth. The record

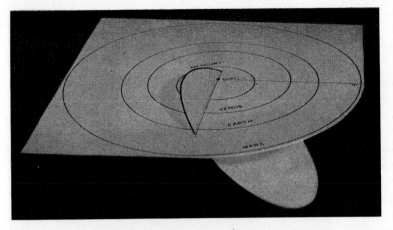

Fig. 3.5. Orbit of Icarus showing its relation to the paths of the four inner planets. Icarus travels in an orbit that is inclined at an angle of 21° to the plane in which the other planets revolve. (*Sky and Telescope.*)

close approach is held by Hermes, which on Oct. 30, 1937, came within half a million miles of the earth, closer than any celestial body except the moon and meteorites. Icarus, discovered in 1949, passes the closest to the sun of any known body in the solar system. At one extreme it passes inside the orbit of Mercury to within 17 million miles of the sun. At the other it recedes to a distance of 183 million miles from the sun, or 42 million miles beyond the orbit of Mars (Fig. 3.5).

The asteroid that goes the farthest from the sun is Hidalgo, whose orbit reaches out almost to that of Saturn.

3.8. Satellites of the planets   The sun has a family of nine planets and thousands of tiny asteroids. Some of the planets themselves have attendants called satellites, or moons. Our moon is an example of a satellite. It is larger in proportion to the planet around which it revolves than any other planet-satellite pair in the solar system. Seen from space, the earth and moon must appear like a twin planet.

Jupiter, the largest planet, has 12 known satellites. Saturn, the next largest, has 9 satellites. Uranus has 5 satellites; Neptune and Mars two each; and Mercury, Pluto, and Venus have none so far as is known.

There are seven satellites that are comparable in size to Mercury. It is possible that Pluto may once have been a satellite of Neptune.

Comets and Meteorites

3.9. Comets   Another type of body in the solar system is the comet, although it is still uncertain how many of the comets we see from time to time belong permanently to the sun. Some of them come from such a very great distance out in space that it is difficult to say whether they are visiting our system for the first time or whether they travel in closed but long drawn out orbits, returning periodically to swing around the sun.

Whatever may be the truth about comets which *appear* to travel in open, nearly parabolic orbits, there are many known comets with closed orbits. About twenty-five have been seen to make more than one passage around the sun. Their periods lie between 3.3 and 75.5 years. About forty-five other comets are known to travel in ellipses which will bring them back to our neighborhood in periods ranging up to 1000 years or more.

These tiny particles doubtless travel in orbits similar to those of comets, but they never can be seen until their orbits carry them into collision with the earth's atmosphere. Then their career is ended in a few moments.

3.10. Meteorites

In addition to the various bodies already mentioned—sun, planets, asteroids, satellites, comets, meteorites—that make up the solar system there is a cloud of dust particles (apparently) from which the zodiacal light is reflected. This cloud seems to have its center at the sun and to extend out in the plane of the earth's orbit, approximately, to a distance even beyond the earth. It appears to be lens shaped, the outer edges being thin, the center, at the sun, thick.

3.11. The zodiacal light

The presence of this cloud of scattered particles is made evident by the glow it gives after sunset and before sunrise. The brightest part of this glow, which from its spectrum seems to be reflected sunlight, is about as bright as the Milky Way. In the evening it extends up from the western horizon in a wedge shape, wide at the base and narrowing at the top. The axis of the wedge lies along the ecliptic and it reaches to a distance of some 40°. Before daylight in the morning it is similarly seen in the east.

The best time to observe the zodiacal light is in the evening during March, or in the morning during September, because at these times the ecliptic is most nearly perpendicular to the horizon. The shaft of light then reaches much higher than when it stands at a smaller angle to the horizon.

The gegenschein was discovered by Brorsen about 1853. The term "gegenschein" comes from the German word meaning "counterglow." It appears as a faint hazy path of light always exactly opposite, or "counter," to the position of the sun in the sky. Its size and brightness vary during the year, and it is obliterated completely by the moon or artificial light. According to Barnard, the gegenschein is most conspicuous in September, when it appears as a round luminous patch about forty times the width of the full moon.

3.12. The gegenschein, or "counterglow"

It has been shown that if a meteorite strayed into a region 930,000 miles from the earth in the opposite direction from the sun it would be temporarily held there by the combined gravitational at-

ELEMENTS OF THE PLANETS AND SOME COMETS AND ASTEROIDS

NAME	SYMBOL	SEMIMAJOR AXIS	MEAN DISTANCE (MILES)	PERIOD SIDEREAL (DAYS)	PERIOD SYNODIC (DAYS)	ECCENTRICITY	INCLINATION
Mercury	☿	0.3871	36,000,000	87.969	115.88	0.206	7°00'
Venus	♀	0.7233	67,270,000	224.701	583.93	0.007	3 24
Earth	⊕	1.0000	93,000,000	365.256	—	0.017	—
Mars	♂	1.5237	141,700,000	686.980 (YEARS)	779.95	0.093	1 51
Icarus	(1566)	1.0785	100,300,000	1.120	—	0.827	23 00
Ceres	(1)	2.7669	257,320,000	4.602	467	0.080	10 36
Jupiter	♃	5.2028	483,900,000	11.862	398.89	0.048	1 18
Saturn	♄	9.5388	887,100,000	29.458	378.10	0.056	2 29
Uranus	♅	19.1820	1,783,900,000	84.013	369.67	0.047	0 46
Neptune	♆	30.0577	2,795,400,000	164.794	367.49	0.009	1 46
Pluto	♇	39.5177	3,675,000,000	248.430	366.74	0.249	17 09
Encke's comet		2.21	206,000,000	3.30	—	0.85	12.4
Comet 1925 II*		6.39	594,000,000	16.47	389	0.14	9.5
Halley's comet		17.95	1,669,000,000	76	—	0.97	162.2

* Also known as Schwassmann-Wachmann (1).

NAME	DIAMETER (MILES)	MASS	DENSITY	ROTATION	ALBEDO	INCLINATION	VELOCITY ESCAPE (MI/SEC)	GRAVITY
Sun	865,400	333,400	0.26	25^d.14		7°.2	383	28.0
Mercury	3,000	0.0543	0.99	88	0.058		2.7	0.38
Venus	7,848	0.8136	0.92		0.76		6.5	0.88
Earth	7,927	1.0000	1.00 *	23^{h}56^m	0.39	23.4	7.0	1.00
Mars	4,268	0.108	0.75	24 37	0.148	24.0	3.2	0.39
Jupiter	89,329	318.4	0.245	9 50	0.51	3.1	38	2.65
Saturn	75,021	95.2	0.13	10 02	0.50	26.8	23	1.17
Uranus	33,219	14.6	0.28	10.8	0.66	98.0	14	1.05
Neptune	27,700	17.3	0.45	15.8	0.26	29.6	16	1.23
Pluto	3,600	?†	?†		0.16		?	?
Moon	2,162	0.0123	0.603	27^d.32	0.072	6.7	1.5	0.16
J I	2,090	0.0121	0.73		0.57		1.6	0.19
J II	1,870	0.0079	0.68		0.60		1.3	0.16
J III	3,100	0.0260	0.43		0.34		1.8	0.17
J IV	2,850	0.0160	0.37		0.15		1.5	0.13
Titan	2,950	0.0235	0.44		0.27		1.7	0.17
Triton	2,800	0.022	0.36?		0.2?		1.9?	0.14?

* The density of the earth is 5.52 gm/cm³.
† The mass of Pluto calculated from its gravitational attraction on other planets is 1, which would make its density 55 gm/cm³, a value that seems impossibly high.

SATELLITES OF THE SOLAR SYSTEM

NAME	DISTANCE FROM PLANET (MILES)	PERIOD (DAYS)	DIAMETER (MILES)	MASS (EARTH = 1)	DISCOVERER	DATE
Earth						
Moon	239,100	27.32	2,162	0.0123		
Mars						
I Phobos	5,830	0.32	7		Hall	1877
II Deimos	14,600	1.26	5		Hall	1877
Jupiter						
V	113,000	0.50	150		Barnard	1892
I Io	262,000	1.77	2,090	0.0121	Galileo	1610
II Europa	417,000	3.55	1,870	0.0079	Galileo	1610
III Ganymede	666,000	7.16	3,100	0.0260	Galileo	1610
IV Callisto	1,170,000	16.69	2,850	0.0160	Galileo	1610
VI	7,120,000	251	100		Perrine	1904
VII	7,290,000	260	35		Perrine	1905
X	7,300,000	260	15		Nicholson	1938
XII	13,000,000	625	14		Nicholson	1951
XI	14,000,000	700	19		Nicholson	1938
VIII	14,600,000	739	35		Melotte	1908
IX	14,700,000	758	17		Nicholson	1914
Saturn						
I Mimas	186,000	0.94	370		Herschel	1789
II Enceladus	238,000	1.37	460		Herschel	1789
III Tethys	295,000	1.89	750		Cassini	1684
IV Dione	338,000	2.74	900		Cassini	1684
V Rhea	527,000	4.52	1,150		Cassini	1672
VI Titan	1,200,000	15.9	2,950	0.0235	Huyghens	1655

SATELLITES OF THE SOLAR SYSTEM (*Continued*)

NAME	DISTANCE FROM PLANET (MILES)	PERIOD (DAYS)	DIAMETER (MILES)	MASS (EARTH = 1)	DISCOVERER	DATE
VII Hyperion	1,500,000	21.3	300		Bond	1848
VIII Iapetus	3,600,000	79	1,100		Cassini	1671
IX Phoebe	13,000,000	550	150		W. H. Pickering	1898
Uranus						
I Miranda	81,000	1.41	< 200?		Kuiper	1948
II Ariel	119,000	2.52	600?		Lassell	1851
III Umbriel	166,000	4.14	400?		Lassell	1851
IV Titania	273,000	8.71	1,000?		Herschel	1787
V Oberon	365,000	13.46	900?		Herschel	1787
Neptune						
I Triton	220,000	5.88	2,800?	0.022	Lassell	1846
II Nereid	5,800,000	785	< 200?		Kuiper	1948

tractions of the sun and earth. Thus meteorites would tend to accumulate opposite the sun in a swarm and the gegenschein is ascribed to the light reflected from these myriads of tiny bodies.

Observations by Soviet astronomers in Central Asia in 1953 indicate that the gegenschein is only 80,000 miles beyond the earth and is formed from a gaseous tail extending from our atmosphere.

The gegenschein has been photographed and otherwise observed many times. There is no doubt regarding its existence, but its nature would still seem to be uncertain.

QUESTIONS AND EXERCISES

1. Using the information in the table on page 47, mention how the terrestrial planets resemble one another. Enumerate similarities and differences among the nine planets.

2. Have you ever seen the zodiacal light?

3. How would you know where to look for the gegenschein any night? What conditions might prevent you from seeing it? Does the gegenschein always appear at the same place among the stars?

4. Do comets move according to the same laws as the planets or is their motion more erratic?

5. Can you think of some reasons why discovery of an asteroid moving very close to the earth might be more difficult than one beyond the orbit of Mars?

6. Would taking a long-exposure photograph of a faint asteroid be of help in making it easier to see on the plate? Can you think how a long-exposure photograph could be of help in making the image of the asteroid stronger?

7. Suppose that while taking a photograph of the sky near Jupiter you found the moving trail of some object on the plate. How could you tell by photographing it later whether it was an asteroid or a faint satellite of Jupiter?

LOCATING STARS UPON THE CELESTIAL SPHERE 4

The Horizon System

WHEN you look at the stars on a clear dark night they seem to be set on the inner surface of a vast celestial sphere with yourself at the center. The impression is particularly vivid if you are in an open space with an unobstructed view in all directions. Then the earth seems to recede until it meets the celestial sphere in an irregular line broken by hills and trees called the visible horizon. Although the celestial sphere is cut off from view by the earth you have the feeling that if it were transparent you could still see the stars below you.

For many purposes it is convenient to imagine that the stars *are* set on the inner surface of a celestial sphere which surrounds you on all sides. Of course, there is no real surface anywhere in the sky and the stars are at vastly different distances from us. Also, the center of the celestial sphere is not at the point on the earth's surface where you happen to be but at the center of the earth. But the celestial sphere is so enormously large compared to the size of the earth that for most purposes you can think of the center of the earth as being practically at the point where you are located on the surface. By analogy you might think of the earth as a small marble in the center of a large room which is the celestial sphere.

Before we can talk about the celestial sphere we will have to learn some technical terms pertaining to it. We shall use technical terms as sparingly as possible in this book, but there are times when they are indispensable. Technical terms are short cuts in language. We use technical terms in ordinary conversation more often than we realize because they have become so familiar to us that we no longer think of them as being technical although they might seem so to other

4.1. In defense of technical terms

51

people. For example, it never occurs to a woman that she is being technical when she remarks that her dress is cut on the bias. This is certainly much easier to say than that "it is cut on a line or seam running obliquely across the threads of the fabric." Similarly, in football we say that a team has made a touchback instead of announcing that "a player has downed the ball behind his own goal line and that the impetus that sent the ball over the goal line was given to it by an opponent."

We promise that the astronomical terms used in this book will be no more technical than those used in dressmaking or football.

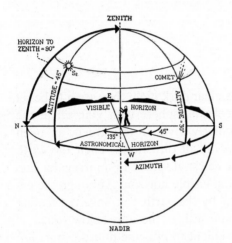

Fig. 4.1. Locating a star by its altitude and azimuth. The zenith is found from the direction of the plumb line.

4.2. Defining points and lines on the celestial sphere

The ZENITH is the point on the celestial sphere directly overhead. The zenith is harder to locate than you think. Look overhead and pick out a star that appears to be in your zenith. Then turn and face in the opposite direction. You will find that the star seems to have moved considerably. We need a method of locating the zenith that does not depend upon our personal impressions.

This can be done by a *plumb line,* which is simply a weight suspended on the end of a string. The direction of the plumb line defines "up and down" for us. By sighting along the plumb line we can locate the zenith. The (invisible) point on the celestial sphere directly underfoot is the NADIR (Fig. 4.1).

The great circle midway between the zenith and the nadir is the ASTRONOMICAL HORIZON. All points on the astronomical horizon are 90° from the zenith and nadir. If you were at sea with your eye near the water the visible horizon would nearly coincide with your astronomical horizon. Hereafter when we refer to the "horizon" we shall always mean the astronomical horizon.

Start from the zenith and draw a line on the celestial sphere straight down so that it meets the horizon vertically. This line is a VERTICAL CIRCLE. The vertical circles enable us to tell the altitude of a star, or "how high" it is in the sky. The ALTITUDE of a star is the angular distance from the horizon to the star measured along the vertical circle passing through the star. The whole distance from the horizon to the zenith is 90°. A star that chanced to be exactly at the zenith would have an altitude of 90°. If it were a third of the way to the zenith its altitude would be 30°. If halfway to the zenith its altitude would be 45°. Most people have only the vaguest notion of angular distance in the sky. If they see an object with an altitude of more than 45° they will say that it is "overhead"—a point worth remembering next time you sight a "flying saucer."

Sometimes it is handier to give the zenith distance of an object rather than its altitude. An object with an altitude of 80° would have a zenith distance of 10°; an object a third of the way from the zenith would have a zenith distance of 30°, etc.

Suppose a neighbor telephoned you one evening that he has discovered a comet. The comet has an altitude of 30°. In his excitement he hangs up without giving you any more information about its position.

4.3. Azimuth of an object

Now the fact that the comet has an altitude of 30° does give you some idea where to look for it. You would look all around the sky at an altitude of 30° and if the comet were fairly bright you might be able to find it. The altitude alone, however, does not "uniquely" determine the position of the comet upon the celestial sphere. It does not tell you in which direction—north, east, south, west—the comet lies. If our friend had said that the comet has an altitude of 30° *and is directly in the southwest,* then you would have known about where to look for it (Fig. 4.1).

We cannot always expect objects to be conveniently situated "directly" in the southwest, or the north, or the east. We need some general way of indicating direction for an object that holds regardless of its position on the celestial sphere.

The direction of an object is given by its AZIMUTH. Astronomers measure azimuth from the south point on the horizon, around the horizon toward the west, to the point where the vertical circle through the object meets the horizon. Azimuth is counted from 0° at the south point around the horizon to 360° (or 0°) at the south point again. Therefore, the azimuth of the west point on the horizon is 90°, of the north point 180°, and of the east point 270°. A star exactly southwest would lie halfway between the south and west points and have an azimuth of 45°. A star in the northwest would have an azimuth of 135°, etc.

4.4. How stars move across the sky

Suppose that you are watching the stars from some place in latitude 40° N., which is about the average latitude of the United States. How will the stars appear to move across the sky from this latitude? Let us imagine that they leave a luminous trace on the celestial sphere so that we can follow their paths during the night. By exposing a camera to the night sky for several hours you can get a photograph which shows the paths of the stars across it. (Fig. 1.3).

You will find that the celestial sphere appears to be turning around an axis that goes through you and a stationary point in the

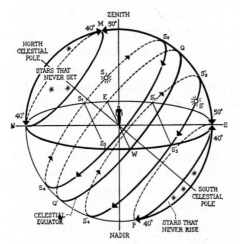

Fig. 4.2. The celestial sphere as it appears to an observer at 40° N., the middle latitude of the United States. The path of a star north of the celestial equator is shown along $S_1S_2S_3S_4$. The path of a star south of the celestial equator is shown along $S'_1S'_2S'_3S'_4$. Stars 40° from the north celestial pole never set. Stars 40° from the south celestial pole never rise.

north at an altitude of 40°. This "axis" is really the axis of the earth but the celestial sphere is so enormous in proportion to our little marble, the earth, that it makes no difference whether it goes through the center of the earth or you. The point where the earth's axis prolonged pierces the celestial sphere is the NORTH CELESTIAL POLE. (There is a corresponding point in the southern hemisphere called the south celestial pole.) The stars in the northern part of the sky appear to be circling around the north celestial pole. The closer they are to this point the smaller are the circles they describe around it. Polaris is so close to the north celestial pole that we cannot tell it is moving at all from watching it with the naked eye (Fig. 1.1).

Since the altitude of the north celestial pole is 40°, stars closer to the pole than this distance can never set. A star that is just 40° from the pole would graze the horizon as it passes beneath the pole at its

54

lowest point *N*, while its highest point would be at *M* (Fig. 4.2). Stars outside this zone but within 50° north of the celestial equator rise and set but are above the horizon more than half the time. Consider the star *S* in Figure 4.2 which is a little north of the celestial equator. It rises at S_1, crosses the meridian at S_2, and sets at S_3. After setting, the star is below the horizon out of sight from S_3 through S_4 until it rises at S_1 again.

A star within 50° south of the celestial equator, such as *S'*, is above the horizon less than half the time. It is visible only during that part of its path from S'_1 to S'_2 to S'_3. The star is out of sight during the longer part of its diurnal path from S'_3 through S'_4 to the point where it rises at S'_1.

Finally, stars that are more than 50° south of the celestial equator, or within 40° of the south celestial pole, would neither rise nor set, but would remain always below the horizon.

It must be remembered that the preceding statements are true only for an observer in latitude 40° N. Also, it should be borne in mind that the stars do not behave precisely according to geometry but are affected slightly by refraction.

The trouble with altitude and azimuth is that they fix the position of a star only for a particular place at a particular time. Each person, so to speak, carries his own horizon and zenith around with him wherever he goes. Also, the altitude and azimuth of an object are continually changing as time goes on. What is needed is a system of fixing positions upon the celestial sphere that holds good for an observer any place at any time.

4.5. Disadvantages of altitude and azimuth

The Equator System

We have seen how the position of a point upon the earth is fixed by its latitude and longitude. Imagine lines drawn upon the surface of the earth showing the meridians of longitude and the parallels of latitude. Now imagine these lines as expanding outward from the surface until they intersect the celestial sphere (Fig. 4.3). The equator of the earth will cut the celestial sphere in another circle halfway between the north and south celestial poles called the CELESTIAL EQUATOR. The parallels of latitude will cut the celestial sphere in circles, called PARALLELS OF DECLINATION, that are north and south of the celestial equator and parallel to it. The declination of a star tells us its angular distance north or south of the celestial equator. A star with a declination of 40° N., or +40°, as it is usually written, lies directly above the parallel of latitude of 40° N. on the earth. Polaris has a declination of about +89°.

4.6. Fixing the position of an object by right ascension and declination

4.7. Selecting the zero-hour circle

The meridians of longitude will intersect the celestial sphere in circles extending from pole to pole called HOUR CIRCLES. The hour circles swing across the sky from east to west like great hoops as the celestial sphere rotates. Just as there was nothing to distinguish one meridian of longitude from another on the earth so there is nothing to distinguish one hour circle from another in the sky. On the earth we had to pick out one meridian arbitrarily—the meridian through Greenwich—and call it the prime meridian. Similarly, on the celestial sphere we have to pick out one hour circle arbitrarily and call it the hour circle of zero hours (0ʰ), from which we number all the

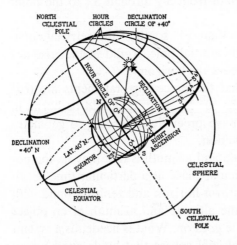

Fig. 4.3. Locating a star by its declination and right ascension. The meridians and parallels of latitude on the earth may be imagined as expanding outward until they cut the celestial sphere.

others. The best way might seem to be to select some bright star and say that the meridian through it is the zero hour circle. For various reasons which would be confusing to relate here, however, astronomers prefer to let the sun select this point for them (Fig. 4.4). The sun moves along a circle called the ECLIPTIC inclined at an angle of 23½° to the celestial equator. The point where the sun crosses the celestial equator from south to north each year about March 21 is the VERNAL EQUINOX. The hour circle through the vernal equinox is the prime celestial meridian, or the hour circle of 0°. There is no star conveniently situated near the vernal equinox, but you may think of it as being marked on the celestial sphere by the symbol ♈, representing the horns of a ram. In ancient times the vernal equinox was in the constellation of Aries, the Ram, but owing to the precession of the equinoxes it is now actually to the west of it in the constellation of Pisces, the Fishes. The point where the sun crosses the celestial equator from north to south about September 21 is the autumnal equinox marked by the symbol ♎, representing a balance.

The earth makes one complete rotation through 360° every day. If we divide the day into 24 hours, then it must rotate 360°/24, or 15° per hour. Starting on the celestial equator at the vernal equinox, we go eastward and mark off an hour circle every 15°. Thus 15° east of the vernal equinox we mark off the hour circle of 1ʰ; at 30° the hour circle of 2ʰ; and so on around to 24ʰ, or 0ʰ again.

This angular distance measured along the celestial equator to the east is RIGHT ASCENSION. Right ascension is measured either in hours and minutes of time or degrees and minutes of arc, whichever happens to be the more convenient depending upon the circumstances.

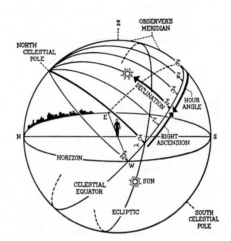

Fig. 4.4. Locating a star by its declination and hour angle. The hour circles move across the celestial sphere from east to west like great hoops in the sky. Prime hour circle is the one through the vernal equinox, where sun crosses the celestial equator from south to north about March 21.

The parallels of declination and the hour circles of right ascension are fixed upon the celestial sphere and turn with it. Therefore, once you know the right ascension and declination of a star you can find its position on the celestial sphere. The right ascensions and declinations of all the stars you can see and thousands more visible only in a telescope are recorded in star catalogues. The right ascensions and declinations of bodies that move upon the celestial sphere, such as the sun, moon, and planets, have to be calculated in advance for each day of the year. They are published by the government in books called ephemerides (singular, "ephemeris").

QUESTIONS AND EXERCISES

1. What is the zenith distance of the north celestial pole for an observer in latitude 15°? 60°? 40°? Demonstrate by a diagram.

Ans. 75°, 30°, 50°.

2. What are the azimuths of the south, west, north, and east points on the horizon? Does the azimuth of Polaris change during the day?

3. Describe how the stars would move on the celestial sphere as seen by an observer at the equator and at the poles.

4. Where on the earth are all the stars above the horizon during the course of a day?

5. When you stand facing the north, are the stars below the pole moving to your right or left?

6. The sun gains about 2 hours of right ascension per month. What is its approximate right ascension on June 21? On September 21? On November 21? *Ans.* 6 hours. 12 hours. 16 hours.

7. What is the declination of the sun on September 21?

8. Could other reference systems be devised to locate stars on the celestial sphere besides the horizon system and the equator system? Can you think of some yourself? What would be their fundamental circles corresponding to the horizon and the celestial equator?

9. The sky turns $15°$ in 1 sidereal hour. How far does it turn in 1 second? In 1 minute?

10. The declination of a star is $+ 60°$. What is its altitude when it passes above the pole for an observer in latitude $30°$ N.? What is its altitude when passing below the pole?

11. What are the altitude and azimuth of the sun when it rises on September 21?

12. What would be the approximate altitude of the sun at noon to an observer on the equator on March 21? On June 21? On December 21?

13. What would be the altitude of the sun to an observer at the north pole on September 21? What would be altitude of the sun to an observer at the south pole on December 21?

TIME AND THE CALENDAR 5

Kinds of Time

YOU have bought a telescope guaranteed to show the rings of Saturn and have invited your friends over to see the planet that evening. Suddenly it occurs to you that maybe Saturn will not be visible in the evening sky. Perhaps Saturn does not come up until three o'clock in the morning. How could you find out?

5.1. Finding how the celestial sphere stands at any moment

You consult the *Ephemeris* and find that the right ascension of Saturn that evening is about 1ʰ. Now if you only knew where the hour circle of 1ʰ is situated that evening you could tell where Saturn would be. You could do this if you have a clock which runs at the same rate that the celestial sphere turns. Such a clock that keeps time by the stars is called a *sidereal clock*.

The sidereal clock is adjusted so that it says 0ʰ when the vernal equinox, or hour circle of 0ʰ, is on your meridian. When the clock says 1ʰ the hour circle of 1ʰ is on your meridian and the hour circle of 0ʰ has moved 15°, or 1 hour, to the west. When the clock says 2ʰ the hour circle of 2ʰ is on your meridian and the hour circle of 0ʰ is 2 hours west, and so on. On a sidereal clock the hours are numbered from 0ʰ to 24ʰ. Now simply by looking at the sidereal clock you can tell how the celestial sphere is oriented at any moment.

The angular distance of a star measured *westward* along the celestial equator from your meridian is its LOCAL HOUR ANGLE. Thus when the sidereal clock says 2ʰ the vernal equinox is 2 hours west of your meridian or has an hour angle of 2 hours. Hour angle is counted from 0ʰ around to 24ʰ, or 0ʰ again. Hour angle may be counted to the east of your meridian if you are careful to specify that it is negative. Instead of saying that a star has an hour angle of 23ʰ we could say its hour angle is —1ʰ or "1 hour east" (Fig. 5.1).

5.2. Positions with respect to your meridian

Let us suppose that when your friends are assembled to look at Saturn that evening the sidereal clock says 5^h. From the *Ephemeris* you know that Saturn has a right ascension of 1^h. Therefore, Saturn must have crossed your meridian $5 - 1$ or 4 hours ago, so that it has an hour angle of 4 hours west. This means that it is getting low in the western sky and you had better hurry if you want to see the rings.

On the other hand, if the right ascension of Saturn had been 9^h then the planet would have had an hour angle of $5 - 9$ or -4 hours.

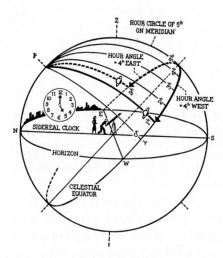

Fig. 5.1. The sidereal clock tells which hour circle is on the meridian. The sidereal time is 5 hours. If the right ascension of Saturn were 1 hour it would have an hour angle of $5 - 1 = 4$ hours *west.* If the right ascension of Saturn were 9 hours it would have an hour angle of $5 - 9 = -4$ hours *east.*

Therefore, it would have been 4 hours *east* of your meridian and rising in the eastern sky.

5.3. Time by the sun   A sidereal clock is very useful to an astronomer but it is not suited for everyday life, since our lives are regulated not by the vernal equinox but by the sun. We get up about the time the sun rises, we eat lunch when the sun is near the meridian, and we stop work and go home to dinner around sunset. It is desirable, therefore, to make the time on our watch correspond roughly with the position of the sun. That is, about sunset the watch should read 6 o'clock, meaning that the sun has an hour angle of 6 hours west.

This sounds easy enough. All we have to do is start the clock running so that it says 12 o'clock noon when the sun is on the meridian. But you would soon discover that a clock has to run at a different rate to keep time by the sun than by the stars. A day according to the sun is 3 minutes 56 seconds longer than a day by the stars. Owing to the revolution of the earth in its orbit the sun appears to move about $1°$ to the east each day. Suppose that the sun and a star cross the meridian at the same instant. After 24 sidereal hours the star will be on your meridian again. But the sun has moved 1° to the east of the star, and the earth has to turn for nearly 4 minutes to bring it onto the meridian again.

That still seems easy to fix. We will rate the clock so that it runs 3 minutes 56 seconds per day slower than the sidereal clock. But it would still fail to keep time accurately by the sun. The trouble is not with the watch but with the sun. The sun does not move eastward at a steady rate but at a rate which changes during the year.

We can understand this better if we remember that the apparent motion of the sun is merely the result of the motion of the earth around the sun. Every change in the motion of the earth will produce

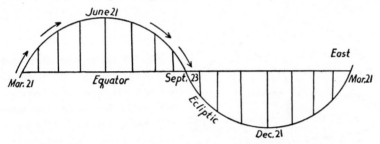

Fig. 5.2. On account of the ecliptic being oblique to the equator the sun makes more rapid eastward progress in June and December than in March and September. This is one of the reasons why the sun is fast or slow at various times.

a corresponding change in the apparent motion of the sun. The earth is moving fastest in its orbit when it is nearest the sun, about January 2, and slowest when it is farthest away, about July 3. Therefore, the sun's motion is also fastest and slowest on these dates.

Again, we have said that if you traced the path of the sun among the stars you would find that it makes an angle of 23½° with the celestial equator. This apparent path of the sun is the ECLIPTIC (Fig. 4.4). Notice that around June 21 and December 21 the path of the sun is nearly parallel to the equator so that it is moving almost due east. But about March 21 and September 21 a good deal of its motion is crossways to the equator so that there is correspondingly less motion along the equator eastward (Fig. 5.2).

The lack of uniformity in the motion of the sun during the year is small compared to ordinary standards. We could rate a clock so that it never differed more than about 16 minutes with respect to the sun on any day of the year. But this is far too great an error for precision timekeeping.

To remedy the situation astronomers have invented a purely imaginary body called the MEAN SUN that moves eastward at a steady

5.4. The mean sun

rate along the celestial equator. The mean sun makes a revolution around the equator in the same average or *mean* time that the real sun takes to make a revolution along the ecliptic. The real sun that you see shining in the sky is the APPARENT SUN.

The apparent sun is 13ᵐ 39ˢ east of the mean sun on February 1 and 16ᵐ 20ˢ west of it on November 1. You can think of the two suns as men running a race. The mean sun running on the celestial equator sets a steady pace all the way around the track, while the apparent sun running on the ecliptic falls behind its opponent and then puts on a burst of speed and passes him. But both runners always make a circuit of the track in the same time. In Figure 5.3 the

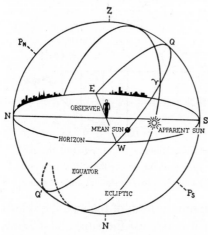

Fig. 5.3. The positions of the apparent sun and mean sun (if it were visible) as they would appear near sunset about February 12. On this date the apparent (real) sun is 14 minutes east of the mean (fictitious) sun. (The difference in right ascension is exaggerated in the figure.)

positions of the apparent sun and mean sun (if we could see it) in the sky are shown about sunset on February 12.

5.5. The determination of time

Of course we cannot observe the mean sun. If we want to set our watch we have to do it by observing the apparent sun. The difference in time between the apparent sun and the mean sun is given for every day in the *American Ephemeris*. We would observe when it is local apparent noon. Then by applying the correction given in the *Ephemeris* we could get the local mean time.

A problem still remains, however, because the sun is a large bright body difficult to observe accurately. The time can be gotten more easily and accurately from the stars. The right ascensions of certain stars are known with high precision. Suppose we observe when a star with a right ascension of 10ʰ 30ᵐ comes to the meridian. Then our sidereal clock should read 10ʰ 30ᵐ. Suppose that the sidereal clock reads 10ʰ 28ᵐ instead. Then the sidereal clock is 2 minutes slow. The time when a star crosses the meridian can be determined with a transit instrument or zenith telescope.

Once we know the correction to the sidereal clock we can easily turn the corrected sidereal time into the corresponding mean solar time, and thus find the correction to our watch or ordinary clock time.

We have said that the sidereal time is found from a knowledge of the right ascensions of the stars. But how were the right ascensions of the stars found? How did it all start in the beginning?

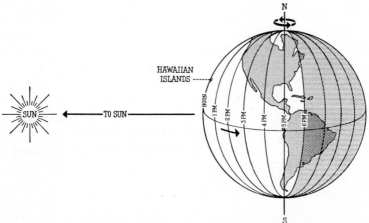

Fig. 5.4. The rotation of the earth from west to east as shown by the arrows makes the time at the eastern station later than at the western station. Here it is noon in the Hawaiian Islands, afternoon in the central part of the United States, and evening on the Atlantic coast of the United States and South America.

The process is too long and involved to explain here. All that can be said is that in the last analysis all star positions are found from observations of the sun. From observations of the sun and stars taken over many years very accurate values for the right ascensions of certain stars were eventually determined which can now be used the other way around to determine the position of the sun.

The Use of Time in Determining Longitude and Latitude

Everyone must have had the fact forced upon his attention that clocks are set to keep different time in different parts of the world. If you travel from San Francisco to New York you will have to advance your watch by three hours during the trip. Broadcasts scheduled for nine o'clock in New York are received on the Pacific coast at six o'clock. Perhaps you have never understood clearly why this difference in time exists. It is one of the few subjects in astronomy that has a direct practical influence upon our daily lives.

5.6. Difference in time equals difference in longitude

Look at Figure 5.4 showing the earth in space illuminated by the sun. The earth is rotating from west to east in the direction of the arrows. It is evening along the eastern coast of the United States and South America. The sun is setting there. This part of the globe is being carried around out of sight of the sun into the night. But the sun is still shining on the Pacific coast where it is afternoon. And farther west, in the Hawaiian Islands, the sun is nearly overhead and it is noon.

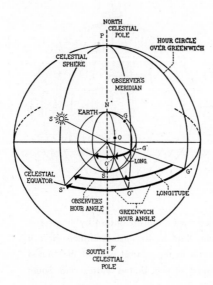

Fig. 5.5. Relation between time and longitude. The difference in hour angle of S between Greenwich and the observer corresponds to the observer's longitude.

Thus, owing to the fact that the earth rotates from west to east, it is always later at the eastern station than at the western station. How much later depends upon how many degrees they are separated in longitude.

In Figure 5.5 the earth is shown at the center of the celestial sphere. The prime meridian through Greenwich, from which longitude is counted, is NGG'. The observer at O is on the meridian of longitude NOO'. His longitude is the angular distance $G'O'$ along the equator, which corresponds to the distance $G''O$ on the celestial equator.

At the instant shown, the hour circle PG'' is over the meridian at Greenwich; the hour circle PO'' is over the observer. S is *any* object on the celestial sphere which lies on the hour circle PSS''.

The hour angle of S from Greenwich is the distance $G''S''$ measured along the celestial equator. The hour angle of S from the observer is the distance $O''S''$. The difference in the hour angle of S between Greenwich and the observer is $G''S'' - O''S''$, which equals the distance along the celestial equator $G''O''$. But $G''O''$ corresponds to the longitude $G'O'$ of the observer. Therefore, the observer can get his longitude by taking the difference in the hour angle of S measured from Greenwich and from his own station.

We said that S was *any* celestial object. Suppose it is the mean sun. Then the hour angle of S from Greenwich is the Greenwich mean time. The hour angle of S from O is the local mean time at O. Therefore, the longitude of O is simply the difference between the Greenwich time and the observer's local time. If S were the vernal equinox instead of the mean sun, then the observer's longitude would be the difference between the Greenwich sidereal time and the observer's sidereal time. It makes no difference what kind of time is used so long as it is the same at both stations.

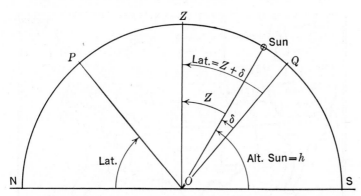

Fig. 5.6. The mariner measures the altitude of the sun, beginning a little before and after noon. When sun is on meridian its altitude is greatest, corresponding to time of local apparent noon. The measured altitude of the sun gives the zenith distance, since $h = 90 - z$. The declination of the sun is known from the *Ephemeris*. In this case, the sum of the declination and zenith distance of the sun equals the ship's latitude, which is equal to the elevation of the pole above the horizon.

5.7. Determination of local time

Greenwich time is carried on a ship's chronometer—a very accurate clock. The chronometer's time may be checked frequently by means of radio signals, which are received daily in any part of the world. The problem of finding the ship's longitude then becomes one of finding the *local* time.

Latitude and time may both be found at noon by measuring the *greatest* altitude reached by the sun (Fig. 5.6). The *Nautical Almanac* gives the distance of the sun from the equator, and from the observation its distance from the zenith can be found. Combining these two will yield the latitude. The moment the sun reaches the highest point is true local noon. The sun's altitude changes so slowly near noon that it is hard to get the exact instant of twelve.

The Time Belts

5.8. How clocks are set — In pioneer days the time of the rising and setting of the sun as given in almanacs was used in setting the clocks of the nation. This was not a very accurate method, for hills on the horizon made a dif-

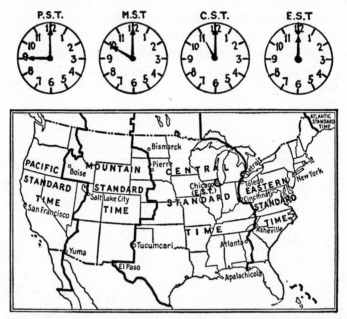

Fig. 5.7. Standard time belts of the United States. The boundaries are slightly changed from time to time. (*From Skilling's* Tours through the World of Science, *by courtesy of McGraw-Hill Book Co.*)

ference in the time of sunrise and sunset. Moreover, clocks in each different longitude would give a different time. With each degree that one goes westward the sun rises 4 minutes later; therefore the clocks would become 4 minutes slower with each degree of about 60 miles to the west. New York clocks were 11½ minutes slower than Boston clocks, and Washington clocks 12ᵐ 22ˢ still slower than those in New York when local time was used.

5.9. Standard time — In 1883, not long after the coming of transcontinental railroads, the inconvenience due to keeping local time was eliminated by dividing the whole of the United States into four standard time belts running north and south (Fig. 5.7). Each belt averaged 15° in width (though its edges were somewhat irregular) so the time from the central meridian of one belt to that of another was exactly one hour. It was agreed that each strip should keep the time that was correct for the central meridian of that belt. Thus all clocks are the same in one belt but differ by an hour from those of an adjacent belt. The longitudes of the meridians of the Eastern, Central, Mountain, and Pacific time belts are respectively 75°, 90°, 105°, and 120° W.

In the following year an international conference, called by the President of the United States, met at Washington to establish a uniform system of longitude and time for the world. There were 26 nations represented, and a majority of them favored making the meridian of Greenwich zero longitude, and fixing meridians at 15° intervals from Greenwich as prime meridians for the standard time belts. There were the time belt meridians that had already come into use in the United States and Canada.

Time *by the sun* may be (1) LOCAL APPARENT TIME, which is that given by a sundial. (2) It may also be LOCAL MEAN (or average) TIME. This is time by a sundial after correction of its reading for the amount that the sun is "fast" or "slow." (3) It may be STANDARD TIME (clock time). (4) In some parts of the country clocks are set forward an hour during the summer. Such time is called "daylight saving time," or, in some places, "summer time."

5.10. Kinds of solar time

In this age, when we can read in the daily press what has been going on only a few hours ago, or can sometimes hear broadcast by radio events as they happen in any part of the world, it becomes of interest to know the day and date at such places. If, for instance, we should read in the Monday paper that there was an earthquake in Japan on Tuesday, we wonder how that could be.

5.11. Geographic limits of "today"

We know, of course, that the turning of the earth on its axis causes one day to follow another. But it is simpler and more usual to think of the apparent westward motion of the *sun*, which is the result of the earth's rotation, as being the cause of successive days of 24 hours each. We should remember, moreover, that as the sun comes from the east so does the new day, and that therefore the farther east one is the *later* his clock will read.

By definition we say the day begins at midnight. The midnight meridian, the meridian on the opposite side of the earth from the sun, must therefore be one of the two boundaries of the day. The other boundary is the still more artificial line fixed by common consent and usage, called the international date line, which runs on or near the 180th meridian. It, like the midnight line, separates one day from another. But unlike the midnight line, it is fixed. It always remains out in the Pacific Ocean between Hawaii and the Continent of

5.12. The two boundaries

Asia. The midnight line moves westward as fast as the sun does. (By west is meant clockwise as viewed from a point out toward the north star.)

Our "today" always lies between these two lines (see Fig. 5.8). The westward motion of the midnight meridian gradually narrows down the day until it is pinched out entirely between the midnight line and the date line. Then a new day has begun, but for an instant all the world is in what had been our "tomorrow."

5.13. Need of a date line

The necessity for such a line was seen by earlier mariners, who found that after going to the west around the world and arriving at the place of starting they were one day behind the people who had not traveled. If, according to their calendar, they returned on Saturday they found people observing Sunday.

The reason for this is more easily seen if we imagine one to travel as fast as the sun in its westward passage. The sun would not have set during the whole trip and therefore, although the traveler would have been gone 24 hours, his day of week and month would not have changed. Evidently *some* line must be established where a voyager's day shall change, and it is better to have such a line in an area sparsely populated. Thus all parts of any country such as ours can have the same day and date, except when the *midnight* line moves across it.

5.14. Offsets in line

The date line has offsets in it to include island settlers who naturally prefer to have the same date as the country from which they came. For example, the Aleutian Islands were, at the time of the Alaska Purchase, brought to the American side by bending the line to the west. Islands in the South Pacific were similarly included with Australia, New Zealand, and Asia by a bend to the east.

The Calendar

5.15. Making allowance for a fraction of a day

A calendar would be very easy to make if it so happened that the length of a year were equal to any exact number of days. That is, if the earth turned on its axis exactly any whole number of times while it goes once around the sun, calendar making would give no trouble. But when the earth gets back to any certain place in its orbit where it was a year ago it has turned 365 complete times and then *nearly* a fourth of a time more.

Even if it turned *exactly* a fourth of a time more than 365 rotations, then by having a leap year once in 4 years the calendar would be correct. Or if it turned a *tenth* of a time more than a whole number a leap year once in 10 years would correct the error due to the excess.

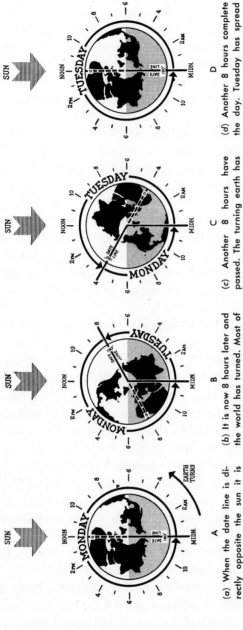

A

(a) When the date line is directly opposite the sun it is midnight at the date line. It is the same day all over the world (let us say Monday). It is 6 A.M. in Chicago and noon in London. Tuesday is about to begin.

B

(b) It is now 8 hours later and the world has turned. Most of Asia has passed the midnight line and entered Tuesday. The rest of the world is still in Monday. It is 2 P.M. in Chicago and 8 P.M. in London.

C

(c) Another 8 hours have passed. The turning earth has carried the date line to 4 P.M. and it is Tuesday on most of the earth. But in North America it is still Monday, and will be until the midnight line is reached. It is 10 P.M. Monday in Chicago and 4 A.M. Tuesday in London.

D

(d) Another 8 hours complete the day. Tuesday has spread over the whole earth. The last of Monday has just vanished and Wednesday is about to begin as the date line passes the midnight line.

Fig. 5.8. How the day changes around the world.

Our year is so nearly a fourth of a day over 365 days each year that Julius Caesar in 45 B.C., on the advice of his official astronomer, decided to overlook any discrepancy that would result from putting in a leap year once in 4 years. Caesar did not live to see the annual error thus made become augmented to noticeable size. But about 1600 years later the error of a few minutes each year had grown into an error of days and weeks. So the matter of reforming the calendar had to be considered. The sun, which in Caesar's time had crossed the equator on March 25, was in the sixteenth century crossing on March 11. The time of the vernal equinox was slowly going back into the winter months of the calendar.

5.16. The Gregorian calendar

It was in 1582 that our present system, known as the Gregorian calendar, was established. Pope Gregory, at the suggestion of a famous astronomer of the time, dropped 10 days out of that year by prescribing that the day following the 4th of October should be called the 15th instead of the 5th. He also announced that in future the centennial years—that is, those ending in two ciphers, as 1600, 1700, etc.—should *not* be leap years unless they are divisible by 400. This had the effect of dropping 3 leap years out of every 400 years, or one in about 133 years.

The reason for dropping 10 days out of the year was to bring the celebration of Easter back to the time that had been fixed for it by the famous Council of Nice, which had met in A.D. 325. The Council had decreed that Easter should be observed on the first Sunday after the first full moon occurring after the vernal equinox. When the date of Easter was thus fixed the vernal equinox was occurring on March 21. During the more than 1200 years that had elapsed since A.D. 325 the date of the vernal equinox had slipped back from March 21 to March 11. Ten too many leap years had been observed. If it had been desired to bring the date of the vernal equinox forward to March 25, where it was when the Julian Calendar was first adopted, it would have been necessary to drop four more days—14 in all, instead of 10.

In course of a long time, if the old Julian calendar had been continued, the seasons would all shift back into earlier months. In other words, the months would go forward into other seasons.

Adding one leap year every 4 years, as under the Julian calendar, was equivalent to adding 11 minutes and 14 seconds too much each year, because the true length of the year is 365 days 5 hours 48 minutes and 46 seconds instead of 365 days 6 hours. A little calculation shows that this 11 minutes 14 seconds per year would amount to a whole day in 128 years.

It would be difficult to remember when to drop a leap year if it were to be done every 128 years. Omitting 3 out of 400 years as explained above, is *almost* equivalent to omitting one at the end of each 128 years.

The Protestant countries were slow to follow the lead of Pope Gregory in this reform. When 170 years later England by act of Parliament finally did make the change it was necessary to drop 11 days. This change in the calendar of England and her colonies came in 1752, when George Washington was a young man of twenty. He was therefore born on February 11 according to the calendar then in use, although we now celebrate his birthday on February 22. For a long time dates were marked O. S. or N. S., meaning old style and new style.

Although the act of Parliament establishing the change of dates provided that neither interest nor rent could be collected for the 11 days dropped, still the people felt they were losing something that rightfully belonged to them. In Bristol there was mob violence, with the cry, "Give us back our fortnight," and several people were killed. Russia changed to the reformed calendar in 1918, dropping 13 days.

The naming of the months and the decisions on the number of days that each should have make an interesting story. Before Caesar's time March, the month in which the sun crosses the equator coming north, had been the first month of the year. Caesar made January the first month but did not change the numbers by which some of the months were known. September had been the seventh month (from March), and to this day its name indicates this. So with October, November, and December—eight, nine, and ten. But July, which had borne a name indicating "fifth," Julius changed to its present name. He also decreed that the odd-numbered months, beginning with January should have 31 days, and the even-numbered ones 30, except February, which was to have thirty only once in four years, at other times 29.

When Caesar's nephew Augustus became Emperor, the Roman Senate gave the month following July the name August to replace the number six (Sextilis) by which it had been known. But to flatter his vanity they took a day from the shortest month, February, and added it to August to make the Emperor's month as long as that of his uncle. Then to avoid having three consecutive months of 31 days they made several changes in the lengths of the months with the results which we have now.

Our calendar is constructed to endure about 3000 years before it will be necessary to give some future year two extra days instead of one. The inaccuracy in the present system is less than ½ a minute a year. If Pope Gregory's advisers had been willing to drop one leap year in 128 years instead of three in 400 years the calendar would have lasted 100,000 years instead of 3,000. But they wisely left this, among other much more imperfect conditions, to be adjusted by future generations.

5.20. The side-real year and the tropical year

The time required for the earth to revolve from some position with respect to the stars as seen by a hypothetical observer on the sun back to that same position is called a SIDEREAL YEAR. It is the actual length of time required for the earth to make one complete orbital revolution around the sun.

The TROPICAL YEAR, or "year of the seasons," is the time re-quired for the earth to move from the vernal equinox back to the ver-nal equinox again. Owing to the precession of the equinoxes (par. 2.7), however, the vernal equinox moves to the west, or backward

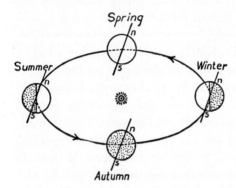

Fig. 5.9. The cause of seasons. The earth's axis always points in the same direction with reference to the stars, but not with reference to the sun.

along the equator, by such an amount that the year as measured from equinox to equinox is 20 minutes shorter than the sidereal year. It is as if the officials moved the finish line back a few feet after a race is started.

Since spring begins when the sun is at the vernal equinox, the tropical year is the one that defines the seasons for us. Therefore the tropical year is the one we always mean when we speak about a "year." If we used the sidereal year, the seasons would gradually get out of step with the calendar until after 2160 years spring would begin on February 21 instead of on March 21.

The Seasons

We have noted that the apparent path of the sun among the stars, or the ecliptic, makes an angle of 23½° with the celestial equator. Look at Figure 5.9, which shows the earth at four points in its orbit around the sun. Now except for the slight change due to precession the direction of the earth's axis of rotation always remains the same with respect to the stars. This means that as the earth revolves in its orbit its direction with respect *to the sun* is continually changing. It is this changing inclination of the axis with respect to the sun that causes the seasons.

On June 21 the north end of the earth's axis is tilted toward the sun by its full amount of 23½°. Figure 5.10a shows a man at about the average latitude of the United States of 40° N. At noon the sun passes within only 16½° of his zenith so that its rays shine

5.21. The changing slant of the sun's rays

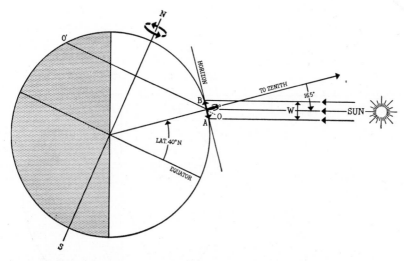

Fig. 5.10a. In summer the north pole is tilted toward the sun. On June 21 its rays fall almost vertically on the observer at 0. A beam from the sun of width W is concentrated over the distance AB on the earth. Also, the observer is in sunlight more than darkness, as shown by 00'.

down upon him almost vertically. Also, the sun is above the horizon for 15 hours out of the day. Now consider the situation when the earth is at the opposite side of its orbit on December 21 (Fig. 5.10b). Now the north pole is tilted away from the sun by its full amount of 23½°. At noon the sun passes south of the observer's zenith by 63½°, and its rays strike the surface at a much greater slant than on June 21, so that they are spread more thinly over the surface. On December 21 the sun is above the horizon for only a little more than 9 hours of the day.

At intermediate dates when the sun is at the equinoxes—on March 21 and September 21—the sun is midway between these extreme limits, and the days and nights are equal. In the southern

73

hemisphere the situation is the reverse of that in the north, so that they have summer when we are having winter and vice versa.

In the latitude of the United States, the hottest time of the year does not come on June 21 when the sun is highest and the days longest, but usually about August 1. The reason is that during late June and July the surface is receiving more heat than it can get rid of by radiation and therefore keeps growing hotter until the amount of heat received from the sun falls below that lost by radiation. In the winter the amount of heat received from the sun does not equal

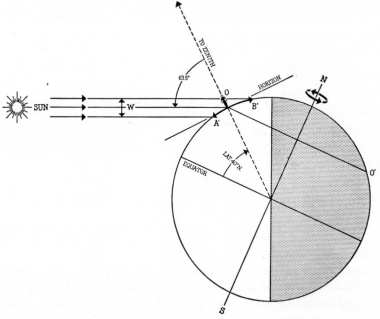

Fig. 5.10b. In winter the north pole of the earth is tilted away from the sun. A beam of width W is now spread over the distance A'B' on the surface and is less concentrated than in summer. Also, the observer spends more time in darkness as shown by OO'.

the amount of heat lost, so that after December 21 the temperature continues to drop until about February 1, which is usually the coldest part of the year.

5.22. Difference in temperature between the northern and southern hemispheres

It happens that the earth is nearest the sun when it is summer in the southern hemisphere and farthest away when it is winter there. This means that the earth as a whole receives the most heat from the sun during the southern summer and the least during the southern winter. The effect of the changing distance of the earth from the sun is therefore to make the southern summers hotter and the southern winters colder than those in the northern hemisphere. But since the total range in the amount of heat received during the year due to distance is only 6.6 per cent, the effect is of minor consequence. Owing to the precession of the equinoxes the situation will be reversed in 10,500 years, when the earth will be nearest the sun during the northern summer and farthest away in winter.

QUESTIONS AND EXERCISES

1. What kind of time is kept by a sundial? What two corrections to sundial time would be needed to make it agree with your watch?

2. Does the mean or apparent sun cross the meridian first on February 12? Which sun has the larger right ascension in Fig. 5.3? Which has the larger hour angle?

3. In what latitude would the sun be in the zenith at noon on June 21? (See Fig. 5.6.)

4. The declination of Canopus is −53°. Would Canopus ever be visible in latitude 37° N.?

5. Would there be any seasons if the inclination of the earth's axis to its orbit were 90° instead of its present value of 66½°? What would be the effect if it were 0°?

6. The axis of rotation of Mars is tilted to its orbit at about the same angle as the earth's axis. Would the seasons be different from those on the earth, and if so, in what ways?

7. There are 668.60 Martian days in a Martian year. Can you devise a calendar that would keep the Martian year dates in agreement with the seasons?

8. Suppose the earth rotated from east to west. How would it affect the difference in length between the solar and sidereal days?

9. In summer in the United States the clocks are advanced an hour to show daylight saving time. Does this change the difference in longitude between stations in the United States and Greenwich?

10. Look at Fig. 5.1. Suppose the right ascension of Saturn were 0^h. What would its hour angle be? Suppose the hour circle of 23^h in Fig. 5.1 went through the west point. Could Saturn have a right ascension of 23^h and still be visible? If so, explain how.

6

MOTION OF THE PLANETS AND THE LAW OF GRAVITATION

Apparent and Real Motions of the Planets

6.1. Apparent motion of the sun among the stars

SUPPOSE the light of the sun is dimmed until the stars become visible in the daytime, as actually happens during a total solar eclipse.

If you noted the position of the sun among the stars from day to day you would find that the sun is apparently moving eastward among them by about twice the width of its disk per day, or 1°. (This motion eastward should not be confused with the daily motion westward which the sun and stars undergo together as a result of the earth's rotation.) For example, on August 23 you would find the sun near the bright star Regulus. About October 16 the sun would be 53° east of Regulus, near the bright star Spica. On August 23 of the following year the sun would have completed an entire circuit of the heavens and would be near Regulus again.

We can explain the observed motion of the sun in two ways:

1. that the sun is stationary and the earth revolves around it from west to east in a period of one year (Fig. 6.1a); or

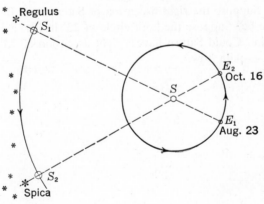

Fig. 6.1a. About August 23 an observer on the earth at E_1 would see the sun near the bright star Regulus (assuming the light of the sun dimmed so that the stars are visible). The earth moves in the direction of the arrow so that on October 16 the sun is near the bright star Spica. The motion of the earth causes a corresponding apparent motion of the sun among the stars.

2. that the earth is fixed and the sun revolves around it in a period of one year from west to east (Fig. 6.1*b*).

Either assumption will explain the observations equally well. In order to decide which is correct we must look for consequences which would follow in one case but not in the other. What are some of the consequences we might expect?

If the sun is stationary and the earth revolves around it in a vast orbit, then the stars should show slight displacements in the sky owing to the different directions from which we see them during the year. A pencil held in line with a distant tree, and viewed first with one eye and then the other, will seem to shift in position by an

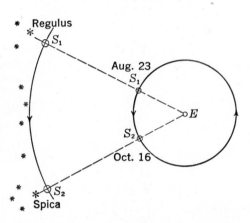

Fig. 6.1b. If the earth were stationary and the sun revolved around it the effect would be precisely the same as in Figure 6.1a where the sun is fixed. Both representations will account for the apparent motion of the sun among the stars equally well.

amount corresponding to the separation between your eyes. An apparent displacement of an object due to a change in the observer's position is called PARALLAX.

In Figure 6.2, consider the bright star at S, which is comparatively close to the earth. In the field of view of the telescope there are faint stars which presumably are so much more distant than S that they can be considered as fixed reference points.

When the earth is at E_1 in its orbit, then S will be seen as if it were at S_1 with respect to the distant fixed stars. Three months later, when the earth is at E_2, S will appear to have shifted in the opposite direction to S_2. If the position of S were measured regularly with respect to the background stars, it would apparently describe a small oval path in the sky like the orbit of the earth as seen from the star. At present reliable parallaxes are available for some 5000 stars.

Therefore, we are forced to accept one of the following conclusions:

1. The earth is fixed and the sun revolves around it. There are

5000 stars scattered over the sky each of which describes a tiny oval in the sky in exactly a year; or,

2. The earth revolves around the sun and the displacements of the stars correspond to the displacement of the earth in its orbit.

The first conclusion is so absurd that we reject it at once. There are several other proofs of the revolution of the earth around the sun but this is probably the easiest to understand without previous preparation.

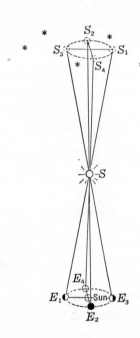

Fig. 6.2. The revolution of the earth around the sun causes the close star at S apparently to describe a small orbit among the much more distant stars. About 5000 stars show yearly displacements, constituting strong evidence that the earth revolves around the sun. The diagram is not drawn to scale.

Ancient and medieval astronomers were well aware that if the earth revolved around the sun then the stars should show a parallax. Upon finding none, they generally preferred to think that the earth was fixed and the sun moved rather than that their instruments were too crude to detect the minute motions involved. Once again our limited point of view was responsible for our inability to comprehend the true state of affairs. Centuries of observation and study were required to convince men that the earth and other planets revolve around the sun and to enable them to discover the laws that govern their motion. Then many years more passed before they discovered why the planets move in accordance with these laws.

6.2. Motion of the planets around the sun The planets, satellites, comets, and other bodies that comprise the solar system revolve around the sun at widely different distances in paths, or orbits, of different shape. The planets revolve in orbits that are nearly circular, while most of the comets move in greatly elongated paths. Despite the fact that they differ so widely in appearance, the orbits of the planets and comets are all variations of one kind of closed curve called an ellipse. The orbits of the planets are not "perfect" circles but are very slightly flattened, like a melon, although the flattening is hardly noticeable except in the case of Pluto.

Ancient astronomers thought of the circle as a perfect form, and since they mistakenly regarded the heavenly bodies as perfect, they supposed that the planets must therefore travel in circles. If they moved around the sun in circles, then their speed should be constant. Before the days of such observers and experimenters as Tycho, Kepler, Galileo, and Newton, so-called men of science were prone to imagine that nature behaves as they thought it *should* behave, rather than going to the trouble of trying to find how it actually *does* behave. It required nearly a hundred years for the world to see that Copernicus in the early 1500's was headed in the right direction when he took the first step away from the old earth-centered system of astronomy and put the sun at the center.

6.3. Early ideas about the orbits of the planets

Not until the time of Kepler in the 1600's, nearly a century after Copernicus' time, had enough accurate observations been made on the planets for the shape of their orbits to be determined. These observations were made by Tycho Brahe, a Danish nobleman, considered the greatest astronomer before the invention of the telescope in about 1609. People think of large observatories as being a modern development, but in 1572 Tycho built an observatory that in some respects has never been rivaled (Fig. 6.3). With money furnished by the King of Denmark, Tycho built an astronomical observatory that he called Uraniberg on the island of Hveen. It not only contained the finest instruments of observation then available, but also machine shops, a laboratory, library, and fine living quarters for the astronomers. It even had a jail! Tycho and his assistants worked at Uraniberg for 20 years accumulating observations of astonishing accuracy, considering that they were made without optical aid.

6.4. Discovery of elliptical orbits

When Tycho's royal patron died, the new king decided the money could be better spent in other ways than the advancement of astronomy, and Tycho was forced to abandon Uraniberg. The new king should probably not be judged too harshly. Tycho was proud and imperious by disposition; he spent money lavishly and refused to cooperate in making economies. He died a few years later in 1601. Tycho bequeathed his long series of observations on Mars to his young student assistant, Johann Kepler.

Fig. 6.3. Tycho at Uraniberg observing with his great mural quadrant. Unlike modern astronomers Tycho donned his best clothes when observing the heavenly bodies. Note the heroic size of Tycho compared with the diminutive figures of his assistants.

After an incredible amount of calculation, Kepler discovered early in the seventeenth century three laws of planetary motion that still bear his name. Kepler did not know why the planets obeyed these laws. He simply found by trial and error that they worked. In this respect he was something like a man who has found a remedy for his colds. By trying one medicine after another he finally hits upon one that gives him relief. He does not know why. He only knows that whenever he has a cold this medicine will cure it. It remained for the much greater genius of Newton to show that Kepler's laws were the result of a single fundamental law—the law of gravitation.

6.5. Kepler's laws of planetary motion

80

The first law of Kepler states that *each planet moves in an orbit that is an ellipse with the sun at a certain point within it called the focus.* An ellipse has two such focal points, F and F' (Fig. 6.4). The sun is always at one focus. The other is empty. The line AP

drawn through the foci is the major axis of the ellipse. Half the length of the major axis, the distance *OA* or *OP,* is the MEAN DIS- TANCE of the planet. The point on the ellipse closest to the sun at *P* is the *perihelion* point. The point on the ellipse farthest from the sun at A is the *aphelion* point.

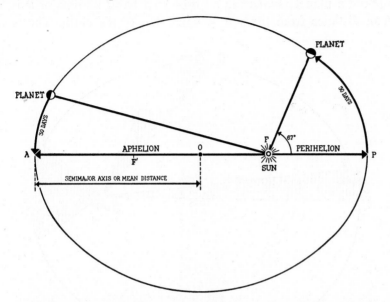

Fig. 6.4. Elliptical path of a planet around the sun. The planet moves fastest when nearest the sun at perihelion, *P;* slowest when farthest from sun at aphelion, A. The sun is always at one of two points within the ellipse called the focus. Distance between *P* and A is the major axis of the orbit. Half this length is the semimajor axis of the orbit or the mean distance. Heavy arrows show relative distances planet moves in 30 days when near perihelion and near aphelion.

The second law of Kepler states that *a planet moves in its orbit so that an imaginary line connecting it with the sun sweeps over equal areas in equal intervals of time* (Fig. 6.5). To obey the law of areas a planet must obviously move faster when it is at perihelion than at aphelion. Halley's comet moves at the rate of 100 miles per second at perihelion and less than a mile a second at aphelion. A planet like the earth has an orbit that is so nearly circular that its speed varies by only about half a mile per second.

The third law of Kepler tells us the relation between the time required for a planet to revolve around the sun and the size of its orbit. It states that *the squares of the periods of any two planets are proportional to the cubes of their mean distances from the sun.* If we take one of the planets to be the earth so that the period is expressed in years, and if we take the mean distance of the earth from the sun as unity, then the law may be written,

$$(\text{Period})^2 = (\text{mean distance})^3$$

Suppose a planet revolves in an orbit that has a semimajor axis, or mean distance from the sun, 4 times that of the earth. The mean

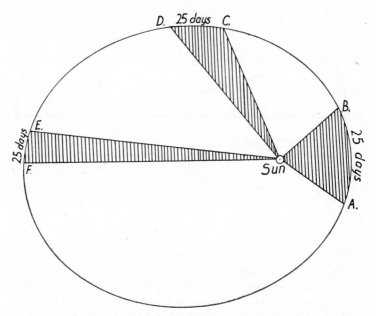

Fig. 6.5. Kepler's law of equal areas. By multiplying together the average width and length of each of the shaded areas you can show (roughly) that the areas are equal. Hence the times taken by a planet in going over the distances AB, CD, and EF should be equal.

distance cubed is $4 \times 4 \times 4$, or 64. The square root of 64 is 8. Therefore the period of revolution of the planet around the sun is 8 years.

It is rather interesting to note that the period of the planet depends only upon the *size* of its orbit and not at all upon its *shape*. One planet may revolve in an orbit that is nearly a circle and another planet in a greatly elongated elliptical orbit. Yet if the length of their major axes is the same then they will both revolve in the same period.

6.6. Orbits and motions of the planets as seen from space

If we could view the planets from a point in space millions of miles above, say, the north pole of the sun, they would all be seen revolving in the same direction counterclockwise. Think of the orbits as wire hoops and the planets as beads sliding along them. These hoops would all lie nearly in the same plane, much as if they were resting on a table top. The hoops representing the orbits of Mercury and Pluto would be tilted slightly but those of the other seven planets would lie in nearly the same plane as the earth. The planets would slide around on these hoops, moving faster the nearer they are to the sun in accordance with Kepler's laws (Fig. 6.6).

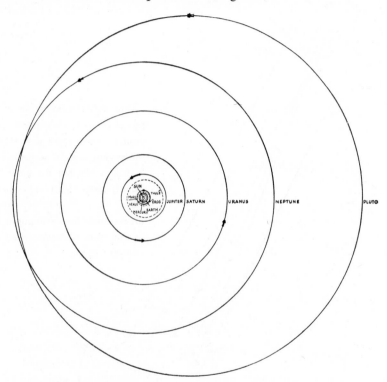

Fig. 6.6. Orbits of planets. The point of the arrow is at the position of the planet for Jan. 1, 1933; the length of the arrow indicates the distance the planet travels in one year. (*Mount Wilson Observatory.*)

6.7. Apparent motion of the planets as seen from the earth

Unfortunately we cannot view the planets from a fixed point in space but are compelled to observe them from the moving earth, and this complicates matters tremendously. A planet traces out an apparent path in the sky that is a combination of its own motion plus the motion of the earth. Trying to untangle the two was what gave the ancient and medieval astronomers so much trouble.

Let us consider the motion of a planet such as Mars, whose orbit lies outside the orbit of the earth (Fig. 6.7). As seen from the earth at E_1, the planet Mars at M_1 will appear to be among the stars at M'_1. Both planets are moving in the same direction in their orbits but the earth is moving the faster. Although Mars is moving steadily forward, as the earth gains upon it the planet seems to stop or reach a stationary point at M'_2. Then as the earth passes it at E_3, Mars appears to move backward, or retrograde, from M'_3 to M'_4. Near M'_4

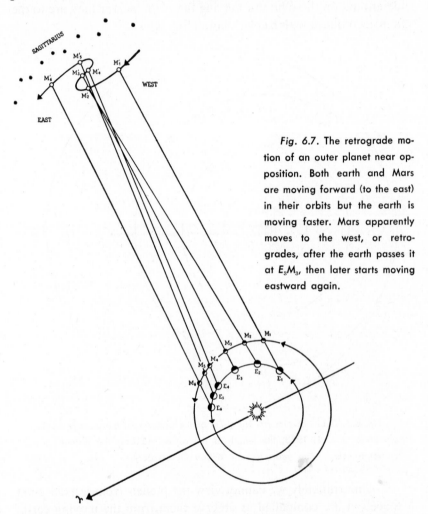

Fig. 6.7. The retrograde motion of an outer planet near opposition. Both earth and Mars are moving forward (to the east) in their orbits but the earth is moving faster. Mars apparently moves to the west, or retrogrades, after the earth passes it at E_3M_3, then later starts moving eastward again.

and M'_5 it reaches another stationary point, then starts moving forward again as the earth passes it.

6.8. Ancient theories of retrograde motion

This seemingly erratic behavior of the planets was a sore puzzle to the old astronomers. According to the Ptolemaic theory a planet was supposed to move uniformly around a small circle called an *epicycle,* the center of which was on a larger circle called the *deferent.* The planet revolved in its epicycle while its center revolved around the earth on the deferent circle. With such a combination of circles the various motions of the planets could be represented fairly well. But inevitably the planets would stray from their predicted positions and the astronomers were forced to add epicycle after epicycle in a vain effort to make theory and observation agree (Fig. 6.8).

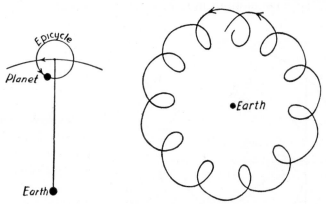

Fig. 6.8. Left: The ancient explanation of retrograde motion. Right: Motion of a planet with reference to the earth.

Mercury and Venus, whose orbits are within the orbit of the earth, also display direct and retrograde motion. Instead of describing loops like the outer planets, however, they appear to swing back and forth across the sun. Venus first appears as an evening star low

6.9. Apparent motion of an inner planet

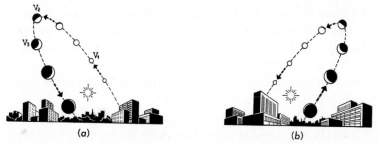

Fig. 6.9. (a) Venus as an evening star viewed after sunset in the western sky. The planet is first seen like a small full moon at V_1. It moves slowly eastward from behind the sun then turns and moves rapidly west, resembling a thin crescent moon just before it is lost from sight again. (b) After vanishing in front of the sun as an evening star in the western sky it reappears as a morning star in the eastern sky.

in the western sky, setting soon after the sun (Fig. 6.9a). The planet moves slowly from V_1 eastward, and after some 220 days, recedes to its maximum possible distance from the sun of about 46° at V_2. It is now moving east more slowly than the sun so that the sun begins to gain on it. After about six weeks Venus comes to a stationary point at V_3. It then starts moving westward, slowly at first and then more rapidly as it swings toward the earth, finally vanishing in front of the sun 72 days after passing V_2. The planet may now be seen near the sun as a morning star in the eastern sky, where it goes through the same motions in reverse order (Fig. 6.9*b*).

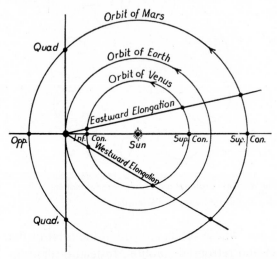

Fig. 6.10. Common designations of positions with respect to the sun as viewed from the earth.

6.10. Labeling the positions of the planets with reference to the sun

It is convenient to have names for the particular positions of the planets with reference to the sun (Fig. 6.10).

A planet in line with the earth and the sun is said to be in CON- JUNCTION. When an inner planet is on the side of the sun nearest the earth it is at INFERIOR CONJUNCTION. When on the other side of the sun it is at SUPERIOR CONJUNCTION.

When an outer planet is in the direction from the earth opposite the sun it is in OPPOSITION.

A planet seen at right angles to the sun is at QUADRATURE.

Planets in any position other than those having one of the preceding specific names are said to be at some ELONGATION, meaning that they are so many degrees east or west of the sun. The elongation may be anywhere from 0° to 180°.

The positions of the moon are given in the same way as those of the planets.

6.11. Sidereal and synodic periods of a planet

The sidereal period of a planet is the time required for it to go from a certain position with respect to the stars back to that same position *as seen from the sun*. It is the actual time required for the planet to make a complete revolution in its orbit.

The synodic period of a planet is the time required for a planet to move from a certain position with respect to the *sun* back to that same position *as seen from the earth*.

Suppose that we wish to determine the synodic period of Saturn (Fig. 6.11). We start when Saturn is in opposition with the sun at *SEP*. One year later the earth will have returned to *E* but Saturn will in the meantime have moved ahead. It will take the earth about

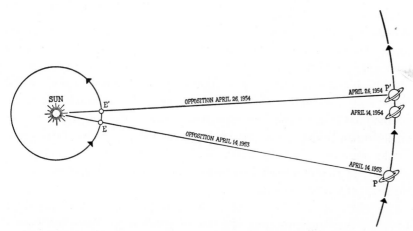

Fig. 6.11. The synodic period of a planet exterior to the earth. On April 14, 1953, the planet Saturn at P is in opposition or directly opposite the sun as seen from the earth at E. A year later the earth has returned to E and Saturn has moved on in its orbit to the position shown on April 14, 1954. It takes the earth another 12 days to catch up with Saturn so that it is in opposition again at P'. The synodic period of Saturn is therefore a year and 12 days or 377 days. (The time required for the earth to over-take Saturn varies slightly depending upon the position of Saturn in its orbit.)

13 days to catch up with Saturn so that they are in line with the sun as at *P'*. Thus the synodic period of Saturn is 378 days.

There is a simple relation between the sidereal and synodic periods of a planet. Let E be the number of degrees the earth moves per day in its orbit. Let P be the number of degrees an exterior planet moves in its orbit per day. Then $E - P$ is the number of degrees that the earth gains on a planet in 1 day. But in a synodic period the earth gains 360° on the planet. Therefore, the synodic period is the number of times $E - P$ is contained in 360°, or $360/(E - P)$.

For example, the earth moves about 1° per day in its orbit. Mars moves about 0.5° per day. Therefore, the earth gains 1° − 0.5°, or 0.5° on Mars per day. It will take the earth 360/0.5, or 720 days, to gain a whole revolution on Mars. (The synodic period of Mars is actually 780 days; our figure is not exact since we have used approximate values to simplify the illustration.)

Since an inner planet such as Mercury or Venus moves faster than the earth, we have to take the difference $P - E$. Mercury moves about 4° per day so that it gains 4° − 1°, or 3° per day, on the earth. The synodic period of Mercury is thus 360/3, or 120 days (accurately, 116 days).

The Law of Gravitation

We have told how Kepler by a prodigious amount of calculation finally found three laws that described the motions of the planets in their orbits. Although this was certainly a major achievement, he also produced a vast amount of other material that must have seemed sheer nonsense even to men of his own time. For example, he made predictions based upon the aspects of comets, cast horoscopes, and wrote down the music of the spheres that the planets sang. He even wrote popular books on astronomy! It has been said that if three-quarters of Kepler's work had been destroyed we would have a much higher opinion of him today.

6.12. What Newton did   Not until half a century after Kepler discovered his three laws did Newton announce the law of gravitation. We often have a feeling that great discoveries are only made by scientists in their later years after long study, but Newton was a young man in his early twenties when he arrived at the law of gravitation. It may be stated as follows:

Every particle of matter in the universe attracts every other particle with a force that is proportional to the product of their masses and inversely proportional to the square of the distance between them.

(By an inverse relationship we mean that as one quantity increases another decreases and vice versa. For example, as your distance from a light increases the illumination from it decreases.)

Newton discussed the law of gravitation and the general principles underlying the motion of all bodies in his great work, the *Principia,* published in 1686. The ideas which Newton set forth there form the basis of the science of mechanics; indeed, it is hard to find any science in which they are not involved in some way. People often ask what is the value of astronomy? Astronomy has been of value to the world if for no other reason than that it stimulated Newton to write the *Principia.*

Before Newton, people generally felt that to keep the planets moving indefinitely in their orbits there must be some force pulling or pushing them along. Newton showed that the only force necessary is an inward force due to the gravitational attraction of the sun. That is, if a body is somehow started moving in space, it will describe a path that depends only upon its original velocity and the inward attraction of the sun. If the original velocity exceeds a certain critical value, however, the body instead of describing a closed loop will fly away along another type of curve never to return. If a body at the earth's distance were started moving away from the sun with a velocity greater than 26 miles per second, it would fly away from the sun and never return. If the body were at rest with respect to the sun, it would move toward it in a straight line.

There is a famous anecdote that Newton was led to the discovery of the law of gravitation by the sight of an apple falling from a tree. Then glancing up at the moon it occurred to him that the same force that made the apple fall to the ground might also keep the moon revolving around the earth. This makes a good story but it is doubtful if the law of gravitation was thus revealed in a single flash of inspiration. Newton had been pondering upon the problem of planetary motion for years. Several men about that time had suggested that the planets were held in their path by an attraction between the sun and planets that varied inversely as the square of the distance but they were unable to prove it. Newton not only proved it, but showed that the three laws of Kepler also followed as a necessary consequence.

6.13. A universal law

The law of gravitation was applied with success to the solution of a wide variety of problems. Not only did it provide the answer to the motion of the planets and their satellites, but offered a solution to the motion of comets, the precession of the equinoxes, and the prediction of the tides as well. The law was found to apply to every type of body regardless of its constitution, whether it was a planet in space or an apple falling from a tree. In every case that has been studied thoroughly, the motion has been found to be in accord with the law of gravitation as slightly modified by the theory of relativity.

6.14. Correction to Kepler's third law

Newton showed that Kepler's third law of planetary motion as originally stated is not quite complete. Kepler said, "The squares of the periods of any two planets are proportional to the cubes of their mean distances from the sun." What he should have said was, "The squares of the periods of any two planets *each multiplied by the combined mass of the sun and planet* are proportional to the cubes of their mean distances from the sun."

It is easy to understand why Kepler never discovered the exact

form of the law as revealed by Newton. The masses of the planets are so insignificant compared to the mass of the sun that it makes little difference whether we use the simple form of the law according to Kepler or the exact form as revealed by Newton. For example, the mass of Jupiter, the largest planet, is less than 1 per cent of the mass of the sun. Kepler's law in its exact form is of great value in determining the mass of a planet from its satellites. The distance of a satellite from its planet and its period of revolution can be determined from observation. Then by substituting these values in the exact form of Kepler's law the mass of the planet can be determined in terms of the mass of the earth and moon. Mars has two satellites that were not discovered until 1877 by Asaph Hall at the Naval Observatory. Previously the mass of Mars had been derived from long calculations of its disturbing effects on nearby planets. But from observations of the satellites Hall was able to get an accurate value for the mass of Mars after only a few minutes of simple algebra.

6.15. The nature of gravitation

We have said that Newton by his discovery of the law of gravitation was able to "explain" the motions of the planets. Now we might in turn ask for an explanation of the law of gravitation. What causes this force of attraction between bodies? How can it be exerted across space where there is nothing to transmit it? Why does the force of gravitation depend *only* upon the masses of the bodies and their distances apart? We might expect it to depend upon whether the bodies are hot or cold, a solid or a gas. But it seems to make no difference whatever.

According to the theory of relativity as developed by Einstein, the motions of the planets have nothing to do with a "force" emanating from them. Rather a massive body such as the sun distorts the space around it so that the natural path of a body in its vicinity is usually an ellipse. Their motions therefore can have no connection with the nature of the bodies themselves, since they depend only upon the curvature of space around them (Fig. 6.12).

With very few exceptions the motions of the planets are described so accurately by Newton's laws that it is unnecessary to use the refinements of relativity.

QUESTIONS AND EXERCISES

1. A planet is discovered at a mean distance from the sun of 9 astronomical units. What is its period?　　　　　*Ans.* 27 years.

2. A comet is discovered with a perihelion distance of 1 astronomical unit and an aphelion distance of 7 astronomical units. What is its period?　　　　　*Ans.* 8 years.

3. What is the synodic period of a planet that moves 2° per day? (Assume the earth moves exactly 1° per day.)　　　*Ans.* 360 days.

4. What is the synodic period of a planet that moves 1.1° per day?　　　　　*Ans.* 3600 days.

5. What would be the synodic period of a planet that moves 0.9° per day?　　　　　*Ans.* 3600 days.

6. Newspapers sometimes speak of sending a rocket "beyond the point where the earth's gravitational attraction ends." Is there any such point? Explain.

7. What is the phase of Venus when at superior conjunction? At inferior conjunction? Can Venus ever be in opposition? Can Mars ever be at inferior conjunction? At superior conjunction?

8. Can planets outside the orbit of the earth show any phase? Which one would show the most phase? When would it occur?

9. Asteroids are often discovered accidentally by the trail they leave on a photographic plate. Is there any place in its orbit where an asteroid could not be detected by this method?

10. An asteroid trail is found on a plate about two weeks after opposition. The astronomer wants to photograph the asteroid the next night. Would he have a better chance of finding the asteroid east or west of its discovery position? Give your reason.

11. The perihelion of the asteroid Icarus lies inside the orbit of Mercury (see Fig. 3.5). Can Icarus ever be in opposition?

7 THE MOON

7.1. Its changing position against the sky

THOUGHTFUL observers of the moon ask many questions about its motions and changes. Some of these are as follows:

1. Why does the moon rise and set? Of course, as most people know, the whole sky and everything on it rises and sets because of the turning of the earth on its axis.

2. Why does the moon go through phases, from new to full and back to new? This often is a puzzle to adults as well as to children.

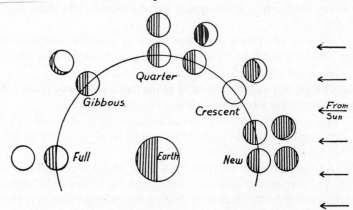

Fig. 7.1. Phases of the moon. The inner circle shows which half of the moon is illuminated; the outer circle shows how much of the illuminated side we can see.

The moon goes around the earth almost in the plane of the sun's apparent orbit, and is much nearer to us than the sun is (Fig. 7.1). When the moon is between us and the sun, we are looking against the unlighted side. If it were exactly between us and the sun, there would be a total eclipse. If the moon is a few degrees away from the sun, we see only a narrow crescent brightly lighted, and the moon is "new." When the moon is on the side of the earth opposite the sun, we see all of the brightly lighted side, and the moon is "full." The cause of the phases, then, is the monthly motion of the moon around the earth.

3. Why is the moon sometimes so far to the north, and then in two weeks so far to the south? The *sun* appears to go far to the south in winter and to re-cross the equator and come far to the north in summer as it travels around the ecliptic once a year (Fig. 7.2). The

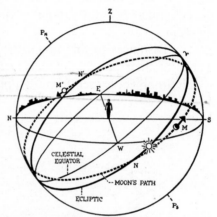

Fig. 7.2. Path of the moon shown in relation to the celestial equator and ecliptic. In winter the new moon appears far to the south, since it is south of the equator at this time in its orbit. About two weeks later, when the moon is full, it is north of the equator, and hence is seen in the northeast.

moon follows nearly in the same path of the sun, always keeping close to the ecliptic, but instead of making a circuit once a year the moon makes it once a *month*. The moon therefore swings about as far north and south in a month as the sun does in the course of a year. For example, in the winter an observer sees the new moon at *M*. The sun is south of the equator at that time, and since the moon is close to the sun, it is south of the equator, too. The new moon is therefore seen in the southwest. About two weeks later at the same time in the evening the moon has moved eastward to *M'*, where it is rising at full phase. Now the moon has moved approximately to the position that the sun occupies in the summer, and so it is north of the equator. Therefore, the observer sees the full moon in the northeast.

4. Why does the moon sometimes go farther north and south than the sun ever does? The moon's orbit is tipped about 5° from the plane of the ecliptic, the path of the sun. (This is the reason the moon is shown as a little off the ecliptic in Fig. 7.2.) Therefore, when the sun is 23½° north of the equator on June 21 the moon

may be 5° still farther north, or it may be 5° nearer the equator than the sun. It all depends upon where the nodes (crossing places) of the moon's orbit are located with respect to the vernal and autumnal equinoxes.

Owing to the gravitational attraction of the sun, the points N and N', where the orbit of the moon crosses the ecliptic, keep sliding continually westward, completing a revolution in 19 years. Thus the moon never crosses the ecliptic at precisely the same points twice in succession. For example, in Fig. 7.2 after the moon passes M' and begins to near the sun again about two weeks later, it will not cross the ecliptic at N but at a point slightly west of N, or to the left in the diagram.

7.2. The moon's distance

Distances to the moon, the sun, and the stars are found by means of their parallax, which means the *difference* in direction in which an object is seen from two places some distance apart. This is

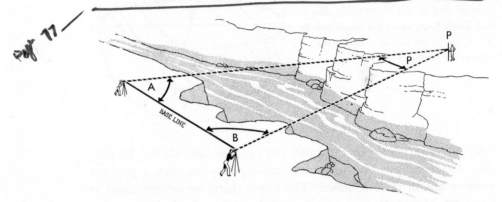

Fig. 7.3. Trigonometric method of measuring distance across a canyon. The base line AB is measured very accurately. Then by measuring the angles which the base line makes with the direction of P on the opposite bank the distance AP or BP can be found.

also the method by which a surveyor measures a distance to some inaccessible point. He lays off a "base line" somewhere nearly perpendicular to the direction to the object, measures its length, and then by sighting on the object from the two ends of the base line gets the directions in terms of angles. From these angles and the length of the base line he can compute (by trigonometry) the distance to the object.

Thus suppose that you wanted to measure the distance across a gap like the Grand Canyon of Arizona (Fig. 7.3). A surveyor would proceed by first measuring very accurately some convenient distance such as AB on one side of the canyon. This distance is his *base line*. From each end of the base line he would sight on some point P on the opposite bank and measure the angles A and B. Then knowing the length AB and the angles at A and B, he could calculate the distance across the canyon AP or BP by trigonometry.

The angular width of AB as seen from P in the diagram, is called the parallax of AB. Although the parallax is not measured directly it can be found as soon as the angles A and B are known.

It is obvious that if the base line is too short the difference in direction of P as seen from its ends will be so small that the measure-

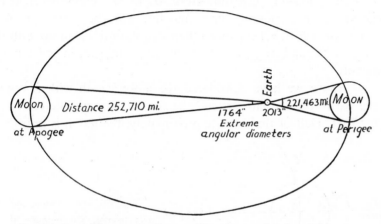

Fig. 7.4. How differences in distance affect the angular size of the moon.

ment of the distance across the canyon will not be very reliable. If the distance across the canyon was estimated to be 10 miles a surveyor would probably want a base line at least 1 mile long.

The moon is relatively close to the earth as compared with the sun or planets. Its distance is only about 30 times the diameter of the earth. It is easy to get a base line a few thousand miles long which will give a large easily measured parallax. The computations from such measurements give a distance of about 240,000 miles to the moon. The distance varies, owing to the shape of the moon's orbit around the earth, from 221,000 to 253,000 miles. This is a change in half a month of more than 14 per cent of its smallest distance. (Fig. 7.4.)

From the apparent angular diameter and the known distance to the moon, its actual diameter is found to be 2160 miles. This is somewhat more than one-fourth the diameter of the earth; more accurately, it is 0.273 as great as the earth's diameter.

7.3. Linear diameter

95

From one new moon to the next, or from full to full, is called a lunar month. Its length averages about 29½ days, more precisely $29^d\ 12^h\ 44^m\ 2^s.78$. It is the period of time taken by the moon in going once around the earth with reference to the sun. It is called by astronomers the SYNODIC MONTH. In Figure 7.5 the synodic month is the time used by the moon in going from M_1 to M_3 while the earth is going from E_1 to E_3.

There is another kind of month known as the SIDEREAL MONTH (star month), which is the period during which the moon goes from one star to the same star again. Its length is only about 27⅓ days, $(27^d\ 7^h\ 43^m\ 11^s.47)$. The time from M_1 to M_2 represents it in the diagram. After the moon comes into line with the same star, as at M_2, it must still travel for more than two days to catch up with the moving earth, and so get in line with earth and sun, in order to become full.

7.5. The moon's
path with respect
to the sun

Above we have considered the moon's path with reference to the earth, but its path around the sun has a very different shape (Fig. 7.6). Half of the time, approximately, the moon is *outside* of

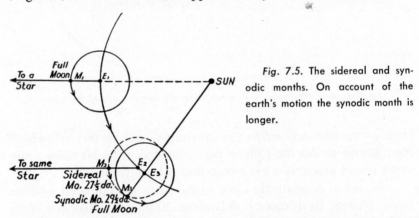

Fig. 7.5. The sidereal and synodic months. On account of the earth's motion the synodic month is longer.

the earth's orbit, the other half *inside*. While outside it travels considerably faster in its path around the sun than while on the inside, much as the upper side of a wheel travels forward faster than the lower side. For a week before and after *full* moon part or all of the moon's velocity with reference to the earth must be added to the earth's velocity to get the moon's speed with reference to the sun. While on the inside, a week before and after *new* moon, the moon moves more slowly than the earth, so the earth overtakes and passes it. With reference to the earth the moon is going nearly in a circle, but with reference to the sun it is following a wavy path. It moves, relative to the sun, with variable velocity but always forward.

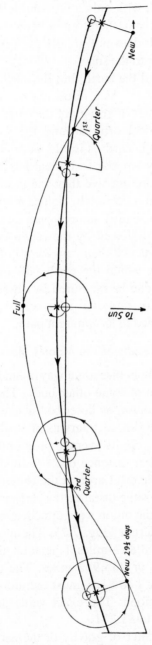

Fig. 7.6. Orbits of earth and moon with reference to the sun. The center of gravity of the two, X, travels along the heavy, smooth line. The earth is represented by a circle, the moon by a dot. It is impossible on a small scale to represent correctly the paths of the earth and moon. The moon's path with respect to the earth is not actually as shown in the diagram, but is always concave toward the sun; that is, the moon's path is rounded inward toward the sun and never outward, as shown at "New."

The earth moves with an average speed of 18½ miles a second around the sun, and the moon with only a little more than ½ a mile a second around the earth. It may therefore be seen that the motion of the moon around the earth does not greatly increase or diminish its total velocity with reference to the sun.

7.6. The earth's motion The moon goes around the earth, but the earth also shows a tendency to go around the moon. As a result, the earth does not go in a smooth orbit. It is the center of gravity of the earth-moon system that follows a smooth, elliptical orbit around the sun. When the moon is outside of this orbit the earth is inside, but only a very little way, for the center of gravity is close to the earth's center. This is because the earth is much more massive than the moon and cannot be swayed from side to side so much as the lighter moon can be.

Not only is the earth in its slightly sinuous path alternately *inside* and then *outside* of the track followed by the center of gravity, but the earth falls *behind* this point and then runs *ahead* of it, as seen in the diagram. This amount by which the earth falls behind or runs ahead of its average position can be measured by observing the sun. When the earth is advanced or retarded in its *actual* path, the sun *seems* to be advanced or retarded in its apparent path.

Results of the Moon's Mass and Position

7.7. Mass The masses of heavenly bodies are always found by the effect they produce upon the motion of some other body. The influence of the moon upon the earth's motion, as described above, gives a clue to the mass of the moon. The sun, at intervals of two weeks, seems to run forward and fall back from its average position by about 12″ of arc, corresponding to a linear distance of 2895 miles. This, then, is the radius of the earth's little orbit around the center of gravity of the earth-moon system. Or, it is the distance the earth would be from the point of balance if it and the moon were attached to the opposite ends of a rod resting on a fulcrum (Fig. 7.7). The moon's distance from this point would be 238,857 miles (the total distance from earth to moon) minus 2895, or 235,962 miles. The ratio of these distances, 2895 to 235,962 or 1 to 81.5, must therefore be the ratio of the masses of earth and moon. The exact value announced by H. Spencer Jones in 1941 is 1 to 81.271.

It will be seen that the center of gravity of the earth-moon system, or the balancing point of the two, is about a thousand miles below the earth's surface on the side next to the moon.

7.8. Density of the moon Since the moon is $\frac{1}{49}$ as large in volume as the earth, and only $1/81.5$ as heavy, its density must be $49/81.5 = 0.6$ as great as that of the earth. This seems to indicate that the moon is without any heavy iron core, such as gives the earth a density of 5.5 times that of water. If, as is supposed by some, the moon was once a part of the earth, the part removed to make it must have come from near the earth's surface, for the moon's density as compared with water is only $5.5 \times 0.6 = 3.3$. This is about the density of the basic rock just below the thin granite surface layer of the earth.

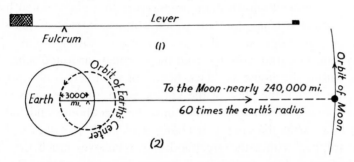

Fig. 7.7. Orbital motions of the moon and the earth center around the center of gravity of the earth-moon system. The earth and the moon, if connected by a weightless rod, would balance each other on a fulcrum at this center of gravity.

7.9. Temperature of the moon's surface

As calculated from the amount of heat that the surface of the moon radiates, the moon's temperature when it is daytime on the moon is fully as high as that of boiling water. Two weeks later, during the lunar night, when the dark side of the moon is turned toward us, the surface is colder than a piece of dry ice (frozen carbon dioxide). (Things at all temperatures above "absolute zero" radiate some heat. "Absolute zero" is 273° C below the freezing point. This is a point at which there is no motion of the molecules, and therefore no heat to radiate. It is a degree of cold almost or quite impossible to reach.)

Measures of the heat from the moon on very short radio waves (microwave radiation) indicate that the temperature of the moon several yards below the surface is always the same at about −38° F. The average temperature of the surface of the disk at new moon (the side of the moon turned away from the sun) is −198° F. Evidence was also found for a film of dust overlying the lunar surface about $\frac{1}{25}$ inch thick. Measures of the way in which light is reflected from the moon also indicate the presence of a thin dust film.

It seems reasonable to suppose that the great and sudden changes of temperature in the moon's rocky crust between day and night and during lunar eclipses should in course of time break it into powdered form. Also, meteoritic dust settling on the moon would also contribute to a dust film. Such dust would be similar to pumice. On the earth such dust soon mingles with the soil, but on the moon it might accumulate undisturbed, as fine sediment accumulates in the quietness of a deep sea bottom.

7.10. The "greenhouse effect" of an atmosphere

Air on the earth, and on other planets which possess an atmosphere, produces what is known as the greenhouse effect. The reason for the well-known high temperature in a glass-roofed house is that radiation from the sun, which consists largely of the short waves that give light as well as heat, can pass through glass quite readily. But radiation coming from the warmed earth and other materials within the house is "dark heat," of relatively long, infrared waves, for which the glass of the kind used in greenhouses is not at all transparent. When light shines into the greenhouse and falls on leaves and earth, the energy is changed from short waves to long, and is trapped within the greenhouse. Air behaves much the same way that glass does, especially if it contains water vapor. But this "greenhouse effect" is not found on the moon, for the moon has no atmosphere. That is why the moon is so hot when the sun in shining on it and so cold when it is dark.

The great length of day and night on the moon, each of two weeks' duration, helps to increase the difference in lunar temperature, though not so much as might be expected. A few hours or even a few minutes of darkness on the moon is sufficient to send the temperature to almost its minimum value, for loss of heat by radiation is very rapid where there is no air. Moreover, as mentioned above, it is now believed that the surface of the moon is finely pulverized, a condition which prevents heat from going deeply into it. Fine pumice is a good insulator, a nonconductor of heat.

7.11. The moon's surface gravity

By surface gravity is meant the gravitational force at the surface of a body—the force causing "weight." Weight is merely a measure of this force acting on the mass of the object in question. Since the mass of the moon is but $1/81.5$ as great as that of the earth, an object on it should weigh only that fraction of what it would weigh on earth, provided the surface of the moon were as far from its center as we are from the earth's center. But since the distances to the surface of moon and earth respectively are 1080 miles and 3960 miles, the attraction varies inversely as the ratio of the squares of these. The attraction at the surface of the moon, due to the smaller distance from the center is, therefore, $3960^2/1080^2 = 13.5$ times *as great* as on the surface of the earth. Hence on account of *both* mass and distance, surface gravity (weight) on the moon's surface is only 13.5/81.5 = 0.165, or ⅙ what it is on the earth.

Many interesting deductions can be drawn from this fact of the moon's relatively low surface gravity. It accounts for the absence of air, since the molecular velocity of gases is greater than could be overcome by so small a force drawing them down. If there were inhabitants on the moon they should be able to jump high enough to raise the center of gravity of the body six times as far as they could raise it on earth. They could throw a stone six times as far, and lift an object six times as massive as would be possible on earth. If one should stumble, his fall would be only one sixth as rapid as on earth. It would resemble "slow motion" in a picture.

7.12. Results of the moon's low surface gravity

To escape from the moon's attraction any body, whether a bullet or a molecule of a gas, would have to leave the moon's surface with a velocity of at least 1½ miles per second. A rifle bullet could not escape from the moon, for it travels only about ½ mile a second. It would, however, rise to a height of 139 miles before falling back to the surface. But if the gases that compose the earth's atmosphere were on the moon they would eventually escape from it, for at the temperature of the moon's surface beneath the sun many of the molecules of a mixture of oxygen and nitrogen would have speeds greater than the velocity of escape.

7.13. Velocity of escape

On the earth, where gravitational effect is stronger, the velocity of escape is correspondingly higher. A projectile would have to travel at the rate of 7 miles a second to leave the earth, and to escape beyond its control. And since molecules of oxygen and nitrogen scarcely ever attain such speed our atmosphere stays with us. Hydrogen molecules, however, travel four times as fast as oxygen molecules, and as they not infrequently exceed the velocity of escape from the earth, the earth would not be able to retain an atmosphere of hydrogen for very long.

In connection with velocities of escape the following figures are of interest. An object leaving the surface of the moon with a speed less than 1 mile a second would always fall back upon the moon. If its velocity were between 1 and 1½ miles per second it could go around and around the moon in a circular or elliptic orbit, never returning to the moon's surface, but becoming a true satellite of the moon. (This is assuming, of course, that the moon's surface did not interrupt the orbit.) The VELOCITY OF ESCAPE from the moon is 1½ miles per second. That is, a body projected from the surface of the moon with this speed or greater would never fall back

7.14. Effects of different velocities

again on the moon. Theoretically it would keep receding forever from the moon or to "infinity," as mathematicians express it.

7.15. On earth   On earth a body could become a little satellite if it had a speed between 5 and 7 miles per second, and 7 miles is the velocity of escape that would carry it away from the earth. (This does not take into account the resistance of the air.) The sun, however, would restrain it and keep it from leaving the solar system unless its speed were greater than about 26 miles a second. To escape from the *surface* of the sun, on the other hand, would require a velocity of 383 miles per second.

EAST

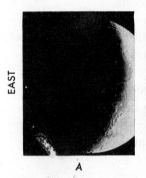  

A   B   C

Fig. 7.8. Occultation of a star (Aldebaran). (A) Just before the star is obscured by the moon's eastward motion. (B and C) After the moon has passed completely over the star. (B) was taken about an hour after (A). The suddenness of disappearance and reappearance of the star shows absence of atmosphere on the moon.

7.16. Proofs that the moon is without air   There are many lines of evidence which support the theoretical conclusion that the moon is without an atmosphere. If it had a cloudy atmosphere, the moon would be much brighter than it is. The moon's ALBEDO (the light it reflects in proportion to the light that falls upon it) is equal to about 7 per cent. A planet covered with air and clouds, as Venus is, reflects about 76 per cent of the light falling upon it.

Air, and more especially clouds, would obscure surface features. But even to the very edge of the moon, where we should have to look through the greatest thickness of air if air existed, the surface features are as sharp as they are near the center of the disk. It has been estimated that an atmosphere 1/10,000 as dense as that of the earth could be easily detected.

The moon moves eastward in the sky each hour by an angular distance about equal to its own diameter. Stars that happen to lie in the path of the moon will be occulted (hidden) as the moon's disk passes in front of them (Fig. 7.8). A star vanishes with startling suddenness when occulted; there is no gradual diminution of light and change in color such as would occur if the moon had an atmosphere. Although the test is very delicate, it is conceivable that the moon might be surrounded by a high thin gaseous envelope too highly rarified to be detected visually.

Surface Features

The most conspicuous features on the moon when viewed with a telescope are the craters, of which some 30,000 have been counted (Fig. 7.9). These circular markings range greatly in size, the diameter of the largest being 140 miles. The smallest visible with the most powerful telescopes are only a few hundred feet across.

7.17. Craters

The rim of a crater may stand as much as 10,000 feet above the surrounding country, and sometimes the floor of the crater is lower, sometimes higher, than the plain outside.

There are a few rather short mountain ranges on the moon but, unlike terrestrial volcanoes, the so-called craters of the moon do not follow these ranges. They are distributed over large areas of the lunar surface, being especially crowded in the southern portion, as seen in Figure 7.12.

7.18. Distribution of craters

Where craters are not numerous there are large dark, smooth areas mistakenly called seas by Galileo, who was their first observer with a telescope. They may once have been seas of molten lava, but if so they have long since hardened like ice on a pond, and differ from the rest of the surface only in their comparative smoothness.

7.19. Seas

Since the irregular, craterous sections of the moon scatter their reflected light in all directions, they appear more brilliant than the "seas." A smooth area sends light off at a certain angle, the direction depending on the angle of the incident light. Unless the observer happens to be in that direction a smooth area looks darker than a rough surface, though both may reflect the same total amount of light.

It is the contrast in brightness between seas and the rougher areas that gives the appearance, so noticeable to the naked eye, that is often referred to as "the man in the moon."

This is a subject which has been heatedly debated for years. The two hypotheses most often advanced are that: (1) the craters are of volcanic origin; or (2), they were produced by impact of meteorites when the moon was in a plastic condition.

7.20. Origin of the lunar craters

Evidence has been produced in support of the meteoritic hypothesis although not in the form that it was originally advanced. According to Baldwin, the craters are pits formed by the explosive impact of meteorites against the surface which need not have been plastic as formerly supposed. A meteorite would strike with such force that the portions of the meteorite and the rocky ground in con-

Fig. 7.9. The moon at the full phase. The dark "seas" and the rays are most prominent when the moon is full; the craters and mountains are difficult to discern owing to lack of shadows. The bright spot near the top of the disk is the crater Tycho. The crater Copernicus is the bright spot in the dark area a little to the lower right of center. (*Mount Wilson Observatory.*)

Fig. 7.10. The northe portion of the moon at la quarter. The mountain rang at upper left is the Apennin and that on the lower le the Caucasus. The mounta range extending along th bottom is the Alps. Larg crater near the center of th photograph is Archimede The dark oval spot near th bottom is Plato, in whi many tiny craterlets can b seen under favorable cond tions. The smooth dark are is the Mare Imbrium (Sea Showers). (*Mount Wilson O servatory.*)

Fig. 7.11. Last quarter of moon photographed with the 100-inch telescope on a night of exceptionally good seeing. Craters only a few miles across are visible on the original photograph. (*Mount Wilson Observatory.*)

Fig. 7.12. The southern portion of the moon photographed at last quarter with the 100-inch reflector. Notice the large number of craters in this region as compared with the number near the north pole as shown in Figure 7.10. The rays emanating from Tycho are not nearly so conspicuous at this phase as at full (compare with Fig. 7.9.). (*Mount Wilson Observatory.*)

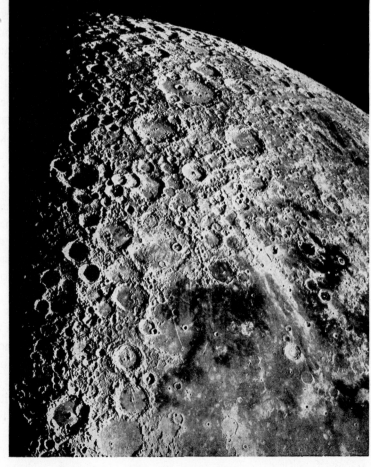

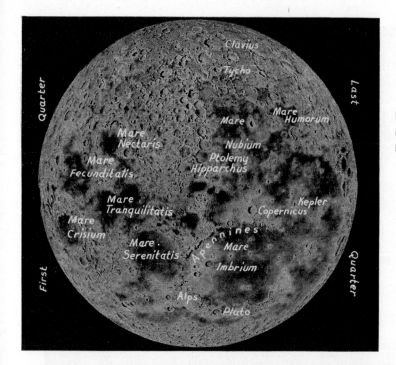

tact would be vaporized. The effect would be essentially the same as if an explosion had occurred from dropping a bomb.

Measures made on bomb craters show that there is a certain definite relationship between their width and their depth and this same relationship has also been found to hold true for the lunar craters. The craters on the moon would appear to be identical with man-made bomb craters only on a vastly larger scale.

7.21. Rills and rays Long, narrow, crooked crevices of unknown depth, apparently analogous to earthquake cracks on earth, are called RILLS, from a German word meaning small grooves.

7.22. Rays Rays are light-colored streaks which can, at full moon, be seen radiating in all directions from certain craters, especially from one in the south, called Tycho. They cast no shadows so they cannot be cracks or ridges. They run across mountains and valleys and other craters without interruption. Their arrangement makes it fairly certain that they were made by some material coming from the crater (Fig. 7.9).

7.23. Radar contact with the moon On Jan. 10, 1946, the United States Army Signal Corps made radar contact with the moon. Pulses were "beamed" toward the moon by using the directive effect of various aerial sending devices. The time required for the pulses to reach the moon and return can be timed to a small fraction of a second. Since the distance to the moon is accurately known and the pulses travel with the speed of light (186,300 miles per second), the time for the round trip from earth to moon and back to earth again can be determined in advance. The pulses should reach the moon in 239,000/186,300 or 1.28 seconds, so that the round trip should take 2.56 seconds. Therefore, since each pulse sent at a 5-second interval faithfully returned after a delay of 2.56 seconds we can feel confident that the signals actually reached the moon. (Fig. 7.14.)

The radar contact with the moon was of no particular astronomical importance but more in the nature of a very interesting experiment in electronics. It has, however, a certain philosophical significance in that it was the first time that man has reached out to touch a celestial body and received confirmation that contact was made.

The same method can be used to contact the nearer planets if radar equipment powerful enough can be developed. Venus, when closest to the earth, is 26 million miles away, corresponding to a delay of 279 seconds. Mars, at closest approach, is 35 million miles distant, which would give an echo delay of 376 seconds. It is conceivable that radar might be made to tell us something about the surfaces of the moon and planets, since the type of echo received depends upon the nature of the reflecting surface.

7.24. Moonlight

One would naturally think that a half moon would give half as much light as the full moon does. In reality it gives only a ninth as much (Fig. 7.15). When the moon is a crescent, or even when it is half full, the sunlight falls on it at such a slant that long shadows are cast. Some of these can be seen with a telescope, but many, no doubt, are too small to be seen individually. But they all reduce the total light coming to us, especially since moon shadows are much blacker than earth shadows. Air reflects a great deal of light into shadows here, but on the moon, which has no air, a shadowed place is in almost total darkness.

Also, we receive much more moonlight in winter than in summer. This is because the full moon, being always in the opposite part of the sky from the sun, is far to the north in winter when the sun is far to the south. This not only makes the moon's rays fall more nearly vertically in winter, but it gives more hours of light between the rising and setting of the moon. In summer, when the sun is in the north, the full moon is far south, and its path across the sky short.

7.25. The harvest moon

On the average the moon rises about 50½ minutes later each evening than it did the evening before, because of its eastward motion of about 12.6° a day around the earth. The full moon rises near sunset; on the following evening it does not come up until nearly an hour after sunset. The next evening would ordinarily be moonless for nearly two hours, and so on.

Fig. 7.14. The 110-foot tower of the Evans Signal Laboratory at Bradley Beach, New Jersey, on which is mounted the antenna used in the radar-moon experiments, known as the "Diana Project." Radar contact with the moon was made Jan. 10, 1946. (*Photograph by U.S. Signal Corps Engineering Laboratories.*)

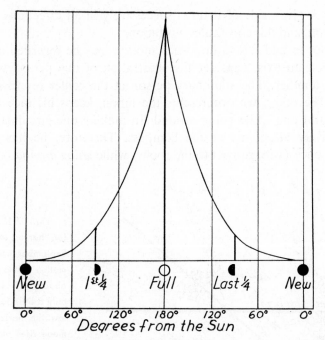

Fig. 7.15. Brightness of the moon at various phases. Notice the great difference between a half moon and a full moon, also a slight difference between first and last quarter, on account of some parts of the surface reflecting better than others.

But in September the full moon rises only a very few minutes later each evening. The difference in time, from night to night, is less the farther north one is. Hence evenings at harvest time, especially in northern latitudes, are well supplied with moonlight.

The reason for so small a change in the time of rising of the September moon is that, in September, the full moon is at a part of its orbit which runs nearly parallel to the horizon. Therefore the moon's eastward movement of about 13° a day in its orbit takes it more nearly north than east at this time of year. The consequence is that its orbital motion does not carry it much farther below the horizon from one day to another, and so it rises only a little later. Especially in high latitudes the moon's orbital motion is almost along the horizon at this time of year, and such motion retards its time of rising very much less than motion perpendicular to the horizon would do (Fig. 7.16).

With respect to the earth the moon does not rotate; it keeps the one face, with which we are so familiar, always toward the earth. But *with respect to the universe* the moon does rotate once a

7.26. The moon's rotation on its axis

month. A given side of it turns successively in all directions during the month, and this constitutes a rotation.

Better to understand how such motion may be regarded as *rotation* upon an axis, consider the illustration of one person walking around another. The stationary person at the center represents the earth. The other, who represents the moon, keeps his face toward the central one while going around. In making one circuit he faces successively all points of the compass. Therefore, he has *turned around* once (with respect to the room) while *going around* once.

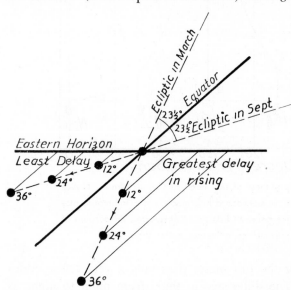

Fig. 7.16. Reason for "harvest moon." In September each day's motion of the moon of about 12° carries it only a little farther below the horizon. (The moon rises along lines parallel to the equator.)

7.27. Librations

For various reasons we do see a little more than half the moon in the course of the month. One of these reasons is that the moon's axis is tilted 6½ ° with reference to a perpendicular to the plane of its orbit around us. We therefore see 6½ ° past the pole that inclines toward us, and two weeks later 6½ ° past the other pole. This effect is called LIBRATION IN LATITUDE. It is a behavior similar to the cause of seasons, namely the inclination of the earth's axis, which enables the sun to shine 23½ ° past one pole, then 23½ ° past the other, at intervals of half a year.

But we may not only glimpse a little of the back side of the moon at top and bottom by looking over the poles, but we may look a little around the right and left sides at intervals of two weeks. This apparent rocking from *side to side* is called LIBRATION IN LONGITUDE. It is due to the fact that the turning of the moon on its axis is at a *uniform* rate, and the motion around the earth is *non-uniform*. When the moon is near perigee, and runs faster than usual, but with no change in rotation, we can see a little around the right side. When at apogee, and going more slowly, the steady *turning* brings some of the usually hidden left side into view. If the reason for this is not easily understood, imagine the moon to stop completely in its orbit, but to keep on turning on its axis. Then we should soon see all of the back side.

Thus, owing to these and other less noticeable librations, we see 9 per cent more than half the moon—59 per cent in all. There is 41 per cent never visible, 41 per cent always visible, and 18 per cent that is sometimes visible and sometimes not visible. The 9 per cent of the back side of the moon that sometimes comes into view is similar to the part always turned toward us, so it seems probable that both sides of the moon are very much alike.

If a person could view the earth from the moon, the earth would appear even brighter to him than the moon does to us, and nearly four times as wide. He would have much brighter "earthlight" than we have moonlight for two reasons. First, the reflecting surface, when full, would be 13.4 times as great, since surfaces vary as the squares of their diameters. Second, on account of the earth's atmosphere and clouds it is a better reflector than the moon's bare rock surface. Instead of reflecting about 0.07 of the light falling upon it, as the moon does (its albedo), the earth has an albedo of 0.39, so that it reflects about six times as much. Because of its greater surface and higher reflecting power the full earth gives 78 times as much light to the moon as the full moon gives to the earth. At new moon, when the dark side of the moon is turned toward us, the earth would be full. We can easily see the earthshine that illuminates the otherwise dark surface at new moon. This appearance is fancifully spoken of as "the old moon in the new moon's arms."

7.28. Earthshine on the moon

Effects of the Moon upon the Earth

The moon's attractive force is the chief cause of the tides, which have an important effect upon coastal navigation by altering ocean currents and changing the depth of water.

The moon also exerts a minute but definitely measurable effect upon the compass needle. It is too small to be taken into account in navigation but is of great value for the investigation of the high layers of the atmosphere, where these magnetic variations are produced. They arise from tidal forces of the moon acting upon the atmosphere in the same way that the rise and fall of the water in the oceans are produced, only the atmospheric tides are much more regular than those in the oceans.

Many people are still convinced that the moon influences the growth of crops. The U. S. Department of Agriculture has investigated the question and failed to find any such influence. Neither can the U. S. Weather Bureau discover any connection between phases of the moon and rainfall.

QUESTIONS AND EXERCISES

1. Does full moon come at the same time in all parts of the world? Support your answer with an argument.

2. Can you answer the questions at the beginning of this chapter?

3. Why is the synodic month longer than the month by the stars? What is the root meaning of the two words synodic and sidereal?

4. What point in the earth-moon system goes around the sun in a smooth curve? What part of a lever does this point correspond to?

5. Does the moon's smaller density suggest anything about the moon's origin? Do you think it is a conclusive proof?

6. Why should some parts of the moon be hotter and some colder than any part of the earth? Why are there no rainstorms or dust storms on the moon?

7. What evidence is there that the moon is covered with fine, pulverized material? What do you think is the most probable way in which such a surface was made? (If your answer sounds reasonable no one can deny it.)

8. How would common conditions be changed for us if the earth's surface gravity were as little as that on the moon? How would expansion of the earth to a much larger size affect its surface gravity? How would contraction to, say the size of the moon change it? (The figure representing your numerical answer would be about 13. Why?)

9. What indications argue for or against volcanic origin of the moon's craters? Have you an opinion as to which arguments are stronger?

10. Why is the full moon more than twice as bright as the half moon? If there were air on the moon why would the difference be less than it is?

11. The average distance to the moon is 238,857 miles. Show that the sun is nearly 390 times as far away.

12. Name all the effects you can think of that might cause changes on the surface of the moon.

13. The diameter of the moon as seen from the earth is $\frac{1}{2}°$. What is the apparent diameter of the earth as seen from the moon?

14. Would the positions of the stars relative to one another be the same as seen from the moon as from the earth?

15. The moon always keeps the same face turned toward the earth (very nearly). How would the earth appear in the sky as seen from the moon? Would the earth appear to be moving against the background of the stars?

16. Could the earth ever rise and set to an observer on the moon? (See par. 7.27.)

17. If the craters on the moon were caused by the impact of meteorites why are there not similar craters on the earth?

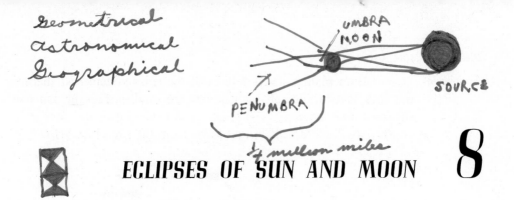

Geometrical
astronomical
Geographical

UMBRA
MOON

PENUMBRA

SOURCE

½ million miles

ECLIPSES OF SUN AND MOON   8

II.

Reason for Eclipses

ECLIPSES of the sun result from the moon coming between us and the sun, cutting off its light from us. The moon is eclipsed when it passes into the shadow of the earth, where it can receive very little sunlight to reflect to us. Eclipses of the moon occur only at full moon, and eclipses of the sun only when the moon is new.

There are several other cases of one heavenly body partly or wholly obscuring another. Satellites of Jupiter, like our moon, frequently pass through the shadow of Jupiter and so are lost to view for a while. Its satellites sometimes cast a shadow on the planet. This spot of darkness on Jupiter's surface is too small to be referred to, by us, as an eclipse of Jupiter. But if anyone were in the shadow spot on Jupiter, the sun would be totally eclipsed to him.

8.1. Phenomena similar to eclipses

Both Venus and Mercury occasionally make a "transit" across the face of the sun, but this appearance as viewed with a telescope is merely that of a very small, black dot drifting slowly across the sun's disk. Double stars, revolving around each other, sometimes suffer eclipse. One component of the pair may hide the other if its orbit lies in the right plane to make it pass between us and its companion star. Stars are often *occulted* by the moon. A star will be thus hidden for about an hour if the moon passes centrally across it.

A novel method of finding whether stars have planets has been *proposed*. If the plane of revolution of such a planet happens to bring the planet between us and the star, it would cut down the star's light as it passes. If a star the size of the sun has an eclipsing planet the size of Jupiter, the star's light would be reduced by $1/100$ of its usual amount. Such a difference could now be measured with a modern photoelectric photometer. It only remains to find a favorable example of such a stellar planet.

8.2. Do stars have eclipsing planets?

113

8.3 Shadows in space

Both planets and satellites of the solar system cast shadows out into space. Since all such bodies are smaller than the sun their shadows must be conical in shape, and the point of the cone is, of course, always directed straight away from the sun (Fig. 8.1).

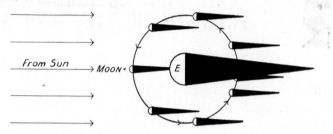

Fig. 8.1. Planets and satellites always cast cone-shaped shadows. They are not usually observable.

These shadows are invisible except when they fall upon some object, darkening it. The moon's shadow may thus fall upon the earth and the earth's shadow upon the moon.

8.4. Lengths of shadows

The mean length of the earth's shadow is 859,000 miles. (There is no possibility of the moon escaping eclipse by going around its end.) But the moon's mean shadow is only 232,100 miles in length; so it does not reach the earth at the earth's mean distance from the moon of about 239,000 miles. The moon must be nearer the earth than its mean distance in order that its shadow may reach us and cause a total solar eclipse.

8.5. When and where eclipses occur

Many of the facts concerning eclipses may be illustrated by such a diagram as that shown in Figure 8.2. It will be seen from the diagram that solar eclipses must occur only at new moon, lunar

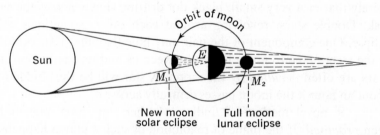

Fig. 8.2. Eclipses of sun and moon.

eclipses at full moon. Another fact shown is that all lunar eclipses may be observed anywhere on the night side of the earth. Only observers in the relatively small area upon which the moon's shadow falls can see the total solar eclipse.

Another thing that may be inferred from the diagram is that the lunar eclipse may be of long duration, and that the sun's eclipse is short. The thickness of the shadow cone of the earth, where the moon passes through it, is 5700 miles. Since the moon travels about 2000 miles an hour it may remain at least partly in the shadow nearly 4 hours. It is totally eclipsed more than 1 hour if it passes centrally through the shadow.

The moon's shadow falling vertically upon the earth is, at most, only 167 miles across. The shadow moves with the moon at an average of about 2000 miles an hour, but at noon an observer on the equator of the earth moves in the same direction 1000 miles an hour. The net relative speed of the eclipse shadow is therefore 1000 miles an hour. A total solar eclipse never lasts more than about 7½ minutes, for in that short time the small shadow, moving so rapidly, would pass any given point.

8.6. Duration of eclipses

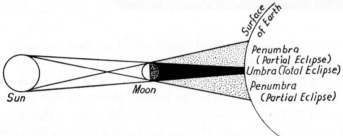

Fig. 8.3. Umbra and penumbra.

If an eclipse occurs near sunrise or sunset the observer's motion is not directly *with* that of the shadow, so the shadow's net motion is more rapid, and the eclipse is shorter.

The relative frequency of solar and lunar eclipses may also be inferred from Figure 8.2. To be eclipsed some part of the moon must pass through the shadow cone at M_2. To eclipse the sun, the moon, or at least one edge of it, must pass through some part of the wider *extension* of the shadow cone at M_1. The relative size of these two spaces is 1.5 to 1, and therefore the relative frequency of solar and lunar eclipses is 1.5 to 1. Although there are 50 per cent more eclipses of the sun than of the moon, we see fewer of the sun. Only a few observers who happen to be in the relatively small shadow made by the moon on the earth can see a solar eclipse, while everyone on the night side of the earth can see an eclipse of the moon.

8.7. Relative frequency of solar and lunar eclipses

Figure 8.2 shows only the region where no direct light reaches the earth from the sun. This darkened area is called the "shadow," or, more technically, the UMBRA. In this region the eclipse is total. Figure 8.3 shows also the region of the PENUMBRA, partial

8.8. A partial eclipse of the sun

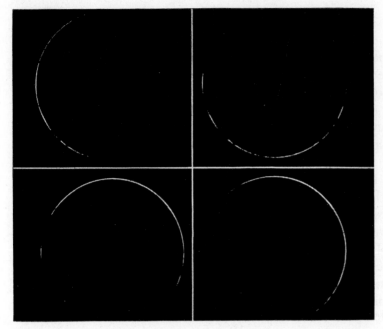

Fig. 8.4. Four exposures in quick succession of an annular eclipse of the sun. The circles are not complete, because the observer was a little to one side of the extended axis of the shadow cone. (Yerkes Observatory.)

shadow. Within this area an observer would see that the moon covers one edge of the sun. The eclipse would be partial.

8.9. Reasons for an eclipse being partial

All eclipses of the sun begin as a small, partial eclipse, for the penumbra entirely surrounds the umbra. Some eclipses fail ever to become total. There are two reasons for this. One is that the moon may be so far to one side of a line joining the center of the sun with the center of the earth that it covers only one edge of the sun, as it passes over it. The other reason is that although the moon may be central over the sun it may be too far away from the earth to cover the entire sun. If the shadow cone is not long enough to reach the earth, observers under the point of the cone see a ring still uneclipsed (Fig. 8.4). The eclipse is partial, but is called an ANNULAR ECLIPSE, from the Latin word *annus,* a ring.

8.10. Appearance of a solar eclipse

The atmosphere surrounding the sun, especially that part of the atmosphere called the corona, extends out so far in all directions that it can never be completely covered by the moon. Hence, there is a beautiful glow surrounding the eclipsed sun. This glow is red close to the surface of the sun, where the chromosphere and prominences are found. Farther out from the surface, in the lower corona, the glow is of a light yellowish color, which changes to pearly white in the upper corona.

8.11. An eclipse of the moon

The moon may pass centrally through the earth's shadow and be totally eclipsed, or one edge of the moon may go through the shadow, in which case a circular notch is darkened on the north or south side of the moon. Even when the eclipse is central there is a partial phase before the total phase begins and again after it is ended. The moon moves about its own width in an hour; hence it takes about an hour for the moon to bury itself completely in the shadow before the total phase begins, and another hour to emerge from the shadow after the total phase is ended. The distance through the shadow of the earth is about 1⅔ times the diameter of the moon; so the total phase *may* last 1 hour and 40 minutes.

During the time when the moon is wholly within the shadow it is usually quite visible, though of a dull copper color, for the shadow of the earth is not wholly dark. Sunlight grazing the earth, and passing through the atmosphere it refracted inward, partly illuminating the shadow with a dull glow from which blue and violet light have been removed in coming through the air.

Prediction of Eclipses

Eclipses far in the future can be predicted, and the dates of eclipses thousands of years in the past can also be computed. This is possible because the relative positions of the three bodies involved in an eclipse—sun, earth, and moon—can be found for any past or future date.

The prediction of eclipses would be a very simple matter if the moon's orbit around the earth lay in the same plane as the earth's orbit around the sun. Then an eclipse of the sun would occur at *every* new moon, and an eclipse of the moon *every* time the moon became full. All the eclipses of the moon would be total, for the earth's shadow is too long for the moon to pass beyond the tip of the cone, and large enough at the place where the moon would have to pass through it to much more than cover the whole moon. The sun's eclipses would be total or annular, depending on the moon's distance from the earth at the time.

To understand eclipses it is necessary for the student to picture clearly in mind the *plane* in which the earth goes around the sun, as shown in Figure 8.5, which is a photograph of a model. (If time permits, such a model may be made, which will make the matter clearer than an illustration can do.) The sun and the earth always lie in this plane, with the sun at the center of it. The axis of the earth's cone-shaped shadow also lies in the same plane and always points in a direction exactly opposite to the direction of the sun. (Except that there is an insignificant bend in the shadow due to the finite velocity of light.) The line where the plane of the earth's orbit cuts the sky is called the "ecliptic." It is along this line in the sky that the sun *seems* to travel in its apparent annual eastward motion around the earth.

8.12. Plane of ecliptic, where eclipses occur

117

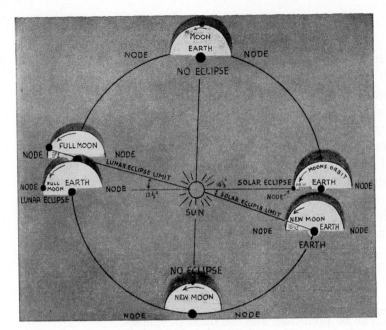

Fig. 8.5. Photograph of a model showing the earth's orbit and the moon's orbit (in a different plane), the nodes, near which eclipses must come, and the angular limits beyond which eclipses are impossible.

The moon is not always in this plane which contains the sun, the earth, and the earth's shadow.

8.13. The moon's motion in relation to the ecliptic

The plane of the ecliptic is so called because the moon must be in or near it in order for an eclipse to take place. During half of each lunar month the moon is north of the plane of the ecliptic; during the other half it is south. Twice a month when the moon passes through the plane of the ecliptic at the points called nodes there may be an eclipse if the moon happens to be full or new at the time. But a week after passing each node the moon, in its inclined orbit, is carried about 21,000 miles north or south of the plane where eclipses can occur.

If, at a time when the moon is new, it happens to lie 21,000 miles or more north of the line joining the earth and sun, its shadow will fall beyond the north pole, in empty space. Similarly when the moon is far south of the plane of the ecliptic its shadow invades empty regions beyond the south pole and so is not seen.

Exactly the same argument applies to the time when an eclipse of the moon is possible. It, also, occurs only when the moon is near a node. Otherwise the full moon, behind the earth from the sun, would pass far to the north or south of the earth's shadow.

8.14. Eclipses come in series; the interval is called a saros

Every eclipse of either sun or moon nearly repeats itself at intervals of 6585⅓ days, or 18 years 10⅓ days. The Greek word *saros* signifies the interval of 18 years 10⅓ days between two successive eclipses of the same series. Each eclipse of either sun or moon can be expected to repeat itself after that length of time. The people of Babylon and Chaldea knew of this repetition and were on the lookout for the returns, as is known from their records dating back to at least 300 B.C. There are about 120 series of eclipses going on all the time, and so it is not necessary to wait 18 years to see an eclipse; the total number is several a year.

The reason for the repetition of an eclipse is, briefly, that there will be an eclipse whenever the sun and the moon are at the same node at the same time. The moon returns to a node each 29.53 days (the synodic month). The sun returns to a node each 345.62 days (the nodal year). The saros of 6585.32 days is exactly 223 synodic months and almost exactly 19 nodal years, as can be seen by dividing. Hence there is an eclipse at each saros.

Because the saros is not an *exact* multiple of the nodal year (it misses by nearly half a day), eclipses in a series fall successively farther to the south. Eventually the shadow of the moon misses the earth entirely (or the shadow of the earth misses the moon) and that particular series has come to an end. A series of lunar eclipses lasts about 865 years; a series of solar eclipses about 1260 years. New series begin as frequently as old series end.

T. Oppolzer, an Austrian astronomer, computed the times and places of past and future eclipses. His records of the past reach back to 1207 B.C. and forward to A.D. 2162. This great work was published in the last century. It shows maps of the approximate paths taken by important solar eclipses.

One of the most exciting events in the life of an astronomer is journeying with a cargo of apparatus, perhaps halfway around the world, to witness an eclipse. Most of the work of observing is photographic, for the time is too short for visual observation. An eclipse is never longer than about 7 minutes, and is usually much shorter. The length of time that the "flash spectrum" is visible is measured in seconds, not minutes. It is the climax of the eclipse. The *dark* lines of the solar spectrum become *bright* lines. This short period of time, combined with the known rate of motion of the moon gives a clue to the depth of the innermost layer of the sun's atmosphere, the "reversing layer," which is the chief source of the spectral lines, dark or bright, of the sun. (More information on the spectrum will be given in Chapter 16.)

8.15. Observation of eclipses of the sun

QUESTIONS AND EXERCISES

1. Mention several examples of the cutting down of light that corresponds to eclipses.

2. Why can we not usually see the shadows in space thrown by planets and the moon?

3. How long would be the shadow of an object as large as the sun?

4. Why does not the moon go through the shadow of the earth every month? Why could it not miss an eclipse by going around the tip of the earth's shadow? What happens to an eclipse of the sun when the tip of the moon's shadow fails to reach as far as to the earth?

5. Why cannot an eclipse of the moon follow within less than two weeks of an eclipse of the sun? (See Figures 8.2 and 8.5.)

6. Why must the moon be new or full for an eclipse to take place?

7. What is the "flash spectrum"? Why is not the atmosphere of the sun covered when the sun itself is totally eclipsed?

8. On the average there are three eclipses of the sun and two of the moon each year. Which is a person the more likely to see—a solar eclipse or a lunar eclipse? Why?

9. What other instances can you think of in which one body passes in front of another in the sky?

9

Nature and Cause of the Tides

IT SEEMS strange that the moon, so far overhead, can exert such an influence as to lift millions of tons of water and all the tonnage of shipping that floats on its surface, and later let it all quietly sink back to its former low-water mark.

To make it seem stranger still, it can be computed that on each pound of water raised the tide lifting force that the moon overhead exerts is only $\frac{1}{282,000}$ of a pound. The earth pulls down on any mass of water or any other material 282,000 times as hard as the moon pulls up on it. Nor is this the full story, for only the *difference* be-

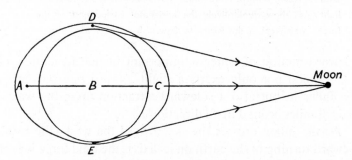

Fig. 9.1. Various directions in which the moon's attractive force is exerted at different parts of the earth's surface.

tween the moon's pull on the water and the moon's pull on the earth is used in creating a tide. Why does the water rise?

Think of the mass of the water directly under the moon, at C in Fig. 9.1, and that of the water on the opposite side from the moon, at A, and of the earth between them, at B, as each being a separate body, all three going around the sun.

121

Now think of the effect of the moon. The moon will draw on each of the three and will pull them all toward itself. But *C*, the nearest water, will be drawn hardest, *B*, the earth, less hard, and *A*, the farthest water, least of all. These three unequal forces will tend to separate the three parts, leaving them as shown in the diagram. The tide at *C* is called the "direct tide"; the one at *A* the "opposite tide."

It does not take as great a force to move an object that is suspended in space as it does to lift the object. Thus a slight pull by the moon can move the water over the surface of the earth. The moon does not need to lift the whole weight of the water. Consider a weight held up by a steel spring, such as a spring balance; the least touch of the finger tip will lift it.

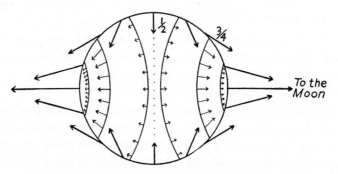

Fig. 9.2. Tide-producing forces exerted by the moon. Heavy lines represent relative magnitudes and directions of the forces. The light lines show qualitatively the horizontal components of these forces, which cause the water to flow.

Sideward motion of water is important in tide formation (Fig. 9.2). The moon not only exerts a slight upward pull on the water directly under it, but also a sideward attraction upon the water for hundreds of miles around in all directions.

9.2. Lag of the tide   As the moon crosses the sky toward the west (the result of the eastward turning of the earth on its axis), the tidal force is exerted on water farther and farther to the west. If the seas were deep enough, a *tidal wave* would roll westward across the ocean, always under the moon. Such a tidal wave would have to travel a thousand miles an hour at the equator. There is actually such a tidal wave, but it lags behind the moon because of the solid bottom below the sea. The more shallow the water the slower the wave. The sea would have to be about 13 miles deep at the equator for a tidal wave to remain always under the moon, and there could be no continents or shallow places to interrupt the steady flow.

Actually, the continents guide the motion of the surging tidal water as it is drawn by the moon. A tidal wave cannot follow the moon about the earth, but it may swing back and forth across a sea from shore to shore, oscillating in time with the impulses given by the moon.

Thus the tides are so complex that we cannot expect to find the tide high just as the moon passes overhead. But there is a fairly definite interval between the time of the moon's passage over the meridian and the time of the next following rise of the tide, known as the "establishment of the port." At the Golden Gate at San Francisco the tide becomes high 11 hours and 40 minutes after the moon has crossed the meridian.

The tide-raising force of the moon is almost the same on the side of the earth opposite the moon as it is directly under the moon. If the moon acted alone, there would be only a few inches difference in the heights of the direct and opposite tides. The sun, however, has an important effect on the tides.

9.3. Opposite tides

Since the tide-raising effect is due to the *difference* in attraction on the two sides of the earth, the nearer the attracting body is, the greater is the tide. Although the sun weights 28 million times as much as the moon does, its distance is so great that its actual tide-raising force is only about half that of the moon. The sun's total attraction for the earth is much greater than the attraction of the moon for the earth; but being so far away, the sun's attraction is nearly the same at the center of the earth as it is on water upon the earth's surface. Attraction is powerless to raise tides unless there is *difference* of attraction.

9.4. The sun's tide-raising force

That the moon is the chief tide maker is shown by the fact that the high tide averages 51 minutes later each day, just as the moon is 51 minutes later each day in passing over our meridian. This 51 minutes has been spoken of as the moon's "earmark" on the tides, as sheepmen notch the ears of their sheep to show ownership. But the position of the sun with respect to the moon makes a great difference in the height of the tide. Thus at some times of the month there may be 6 or 8 feet between high and low water, while at another time there may be only a foot or two between high tide and the following low tide, depending upon whether the sun and moon are acting in unison or not.

9.5. Moon tide versus sun tide

To understand the sun's effect on the tides we may think of the moon's tide and the sun's tide separately, the sun's tide being about half as high as the moon's tide. When moon and sun are together, at new moon, or opposite to each other, at full moon, the high tides of

123

both moon and sun fall together, and so build each other up to un-usual height. But when the sun is 90° from the moon (first or third quarter), the sun tide falls in the trough of the moon tide and makes the variation of water level less. That is, at full moon the sun will heighten the moon's high tide and deepen the moon's low tide, and a week later it will pull down the moon's high tide and partly fill up the moon's low tide. The very high tides of new and full moon are spoken of as "spring tides," and the ironed-out tides are called "neap tides."

Tidal Evolution

9.6. Effects of tides on earth and moon

The natural place for a tide is directly under the moon and on the opposite side (Fig. 9.1). But instead of forming there, friction with the earth carries it forward—there is a "lag" in the time of the tide's rising. In Figure 9.3, the distance from the moon to tide *a* is

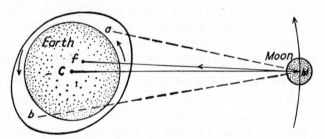

Fig. 9.3. Tides dragged forward by the rotating earth. As a result the moon is drawn forward; also the earth's rotation is retarded. Without friction tides would stand as in Figure 9.1.

less than to tide *b*, and therefore the moon has greater attraction for *a* than for *b*. This tends to check the rotation of the earth and to speed up the motion of the moon, causing it to spiral outward.

Tidal theory predicts that 4000 million years ago the moon and earth were only 8000 miles apart; the earth rotated on its axis in 4 hours, and the moon revolved around the earth in 4 hours. Tidal action caused the moon to recede from the earth and the day to lengthen until they attained their present value. Darwin suggested that the earth and moon originally formed one body. Its rapid rotation of only 4 hours plus the tides raised by the sun caused a chunk to separate which we now call the moon. Jeffries, however, has shown that although the tides raised by the sun would have been more than a hundred miles high they could never have been large enough to cause a piece of the earth to fly off and become the moon. The moon and earth seem to have originated very close to each other in some way, but were never one body.

QUESTIONS AND EXERCISES

1. Why does the moon draw differently upon the water of the near and far sides of the earth? State Newton's law of gravitation.

2. Explain why the moon does not have to lift the whole weight of the water to raise a tide.

3. Why is the relatively small moon a better tide producer than the sun?

4. It has been computed that the tides are pushing the earth and the moon apart at the rate of 5 feet a century. Why may this be so?

5. Tide-raising effect varies inversely as the cube of the distance to the attracting body. What would the tidal effect of the moon be if it were as far away as the sun?

Ans. About 1/64,000,000 as much as it now is.

6. What would be the tide-raising effect of the sun if it were condensed to a sufficiently small size to be placed where the moon is?

Ans. Approximately 64,000,000 times what it now is.

7. Tidal evolution continues to lengthen the day, but the length of the year remains the same. What changes in our daily life might this cause after millions of years? Will the calendar be the same?

10 THE SUN

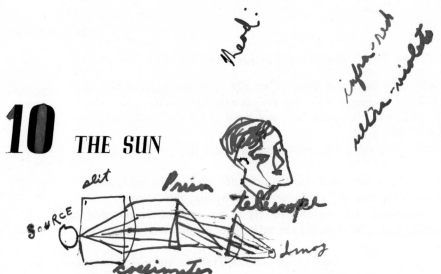

THE light from a star that enters a telescope consists of rays from all parts of its surface combined into a single beam. Even in the largest telescopes a star never shows a true disk as a planet does. In studying a star we must take it as a whole or not at all.

The sun is the only star in the heavens close enough so that we can examine its surface. In a sense, we can actually be in physical contact with the sun, since there is good evidence that the earth is occasionally enveloped in particles emitted from the solar surface, which cause auroras and disrupt radio transmission. Therefore, not only is the sun important to us astronomically as the nearest star, but also geophysically as the source of several types of terrestrial disturbances.

The Sun among the Stars

10.1. Luminosity
Although the sun is not an average star, neither is it an exceptional one. When compared with all the stars in our neighborhood the sun is found to be considerably brighter than most of them; in fact, it is some 13,000 times as bright as the commonest type of star. If the sun were removed to the distance of the nearest star it would be the third brightest star in the sky. By a coincidence, the nearest star to the earth, named Alpha Centauri, happens to be practically identical in type with the sun. By looking at Alpha Centauri we can tell how the sun would look at the same distance.

If the sun were removed to the distance of Rigel, the fifth apparently brightest star in the sky, we could not see it without the aid of a small telescope. Evidently the stars must differ enormously in their luminosity. Rigel is really an exceptionally luminous star, about 16,000 times brighter than the sun. On the other hand, stars a million times fainter than the sun are known.

Compared with naked-eye stars of moderate brightness, the sun is about 30 times fainter than those most familiar to us.

10.2. Size

The sun falls roughly midway between the largest and smallest known stars. The star known to astronomers as VV Cephei has the largest dimensions of any so far known. The most reliable determination gives it a radius 1220 times that of the sun. The smallest stars are roughly the same size as the earth or $1/100$ that of the sun.

10.3. Mass

The most massive stars known have one hundred times the mass of the sun, and there may be some two or three hundred times as great. The least massive stars have about $1/60$ the mass of the sun. The extreme range in mass for which reliable data are available is $6000/1$.

10.4. Density

The average density of a body is the average mass contained in a unit of volume. A star such as Betelgeuse has a volume millions of times that of the sun, yet it mass is only about 30 suns. Its density is therefore extremely low, about $1/2000$ that of air at sea level.

The smallest stars have nearly as great a mass as the sun, so that their density is correspondingly high. The density of the smallest known star is so high that a cubic inch would weigh 620 tons. The sun has an average density 40 per cent greater than water. There are stars ten million times denser than the sun and others one ten-millionth as dense. From which it is seen that the sun is an average star as regards size, mass, and density.

Study of the Solar Atmosphere

10.5. Radiation and temperature

We are all familiar with the fact that as a body becomes hotter and its temperature rises the body radiates more heat and often undergoes marked changes in color. When we turn on an electric heater the wires first glow a dull red, then turn to orange and yellow as their temperature rises. The stove also gives out much more heat when the wires are white-hot than when red. Evidently the temperature of a body, its color, and the quantity of heat it radiates are all related in some way to one another.

10.6. The temperature of the sun

By 1900 the laws of radiation were sufficiently well understood so that they could be used to determine the temperature of the sun. The rate at which a body radiates heat or *radiant energy* was known to increase rapidly as its temperature went up. Doubling the temperature of a body increased its rate of radiation by 16 times; trebling its temperature increased its rate of radiation by 81 times, etc. Also, the law governing the rate of radiation in the various colors had been found. At a low temperature a body radiates red light the strongest, but as the temperature rises the radiation becomes strongest in the orange, yellow, and green. At high temperatures of several thousand degrees, a body radiates so much light of all colors that it has no definite color, and we say it is "white-hot."

We can find the temperature of the sun by measuring the intensity of radiation in the different colors of a beam of light from it. The measures are complicated by the fact that the beam has to pass through our atmosphere before it reaches the measuring instruments. The atmosphere weakens some of the rays so that the beam which finally reaches the instruments does not have the same intensity in the different colors as the beam which left the surface of the sun. But when all corrections are made the various methods give a temperature for the bright surface of our sun of 10,300° F, or 6000° K on the absolute scale of temperature used by scientists.

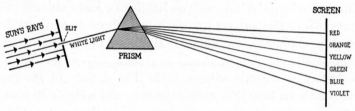

Fig. 10.1. A ray of white light from the sun upon passing through a prism is spread out on the screen into a series of rainbow colors or a *spectrum*. The violet light is bent the most by the prism; the red light the least.

There is geological evidence that the sun has been shining at its present rate for several hundred million years. What is its source of heat? What keeps it shining? If it were merely burning up like a chunk of coal it could not have lasted for more than a few thousand years. We will talk more about the source of the sun's heat later on. Right now we will simply plant the thought that its heat is derived by some source quite outside our ordinary range of experience.

10.7. The spectroscope If you let a beam of sunlight pass through a triangular-shaped piece of glass, or *prism*, the white beam emerges as a series of rainbow colors merging insensibly into one another from red at one end through orange, yellow, green, blue, and violet at the other (Fig. 10.1). Such prismatic pieces of glass make pretty ornaments dangling from chandeliers and other light fixtures. Few people realize that a prism is also one of the astronomer's most valuable tools for obtaining information about the sun and stars.

10.8. Newton's experiments in optics The first truly scientific study of light began in 1666 with some experiments which Isaac Newton, then 23 years old, performed in his room at Cambridge, England. These experiments were of a simple kind which could be repeated today with little effort or expense.

One of Newton's foremost discoveries was that a beam of white light, such as sunlight, consists of a mixture of rainbow-colored rays. This sounds commonplace today, but it created a sensation among scientific men three hundred years ago. Newton admitted a beam of sunlight into his darkened room through a hole in the shutter of the window. This beam, after passing through a triangular piece of glass or prism, was spread out upon the opposite wall in a colored strip. He noticed that the white beam of sunlight was bent or REFRACTED by the prism, the violet rays being bent the most and the red rays the least. The rainbow-colored strip consisted apparently of overlapping colored images of the hole in the shutter. If one color such as yellow was isolated from the others by allowing it to pass through another slit and onto a second prism, the yellow beam was bent again by the second prism but not split into additional colors.

Newton eventually succeeded in obtaining a purer series of colors by using a narrow slit instead of a round hole, thus reducing the effect of overlapping. By inserting a lens between the prism and screen he was able to focus the colors sharply on the wall, thus producing a true SPECTRUM. This crude apparatus was the beginning of the first SPECTROSCOPE, or instrument for analyzing light into its separate components. The spectroscope as used today (or rather the SPECTRO-GRAPH, since all observations are taken photographically) is, next to the telescope itself, the most powerful research tool at the astronomer's command.

10.9. *Discovery of the Fraunhofer lines in the sun's spectrum*

It seems curious that for a century and a half after Newton's experiments practically nothing seems to have been learned about the spectrum of the sun. Finally a German optician, Fraunhofer, made a capital discovery, one that must barely have escaped Newton probably owing to the poor quality of the glass from which his prisms were made.

In 1802, Wollaston had sent a beam of sunlight through a narrow slit before allowing it to pass through a prism and observed that the colored spectrum band was crossed by seven dark lines. He failed utterly to realize the significance of his observation, supposing that the five strongest lines marked the natural divisions among the simple colors. The dark lines were forgotten until Fraunhofer in 1814 began an investigation of the solar spectrum with first-class optical instruments. He made a map of the solar spectrum in which he carefully marked the positions of the dark lines, designated them by letters, and measured the wave lengths of those that were most prominent. Owing to the fundamental importance of his work, the dark lines in the solar spectrum are known as the FRAUNHOFER LINES (Fig. 10.2).

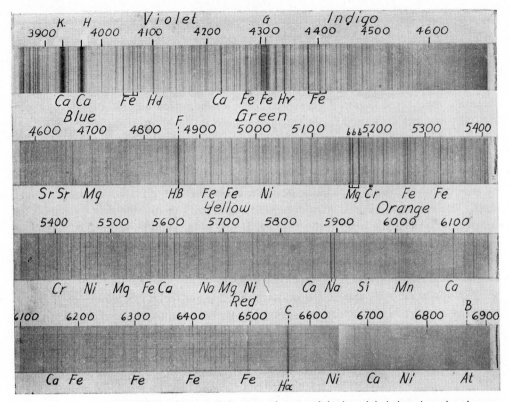

Fig. 10.2. A spectrum of the sun with some of the lines labeled to show the elements in the sun's atmosphere causing them. This spectrum as seen in the spectroscope before being photographed was colored as indicated by the labeling. (*Mount Wilson Observatory.*)

Later it was found that common elements such as iron and sodium when heated to a vapor give bright spectrum lines which match so closely with the dark Fraunhofer lines in the solar spectrum that there can be no doubt that they are both produced by the same substances. Here, then, was a means of finding what chemical elements exist in the sun and even in the stars. We need only to match the lines in their spectra with those known to be produced by glowing elements in the laboratory. Elements which produce many strong spectrum lines, such as iron, nickel, calcium, and others, are easily identified. Identification is much more uncertain, however, for elements which produce only a few weak lines in the sun, such as tin and gold. At present out of the 92 naturally occurring elements found on the earth there are 66 that have been identified in the sun, most of them with certainty.

10.10. Other uses of the spectrum lines

We can get much more information from the spectrum lines, however, than mere identification of the elements that produce them. From the strength and shape of the lines we can obtain information about the abundance of the elements in the star's atmosphere, the pressure and temperature, the electric and magnetic conditions present, and whether the gas is approaching or receding and how fast. Indeed, the amount of information that can be extracted from a study of spectrum lines in the celestial bodies would seem to be limited only by our own ingenuity.

We have said that it is possible to tell whether a celestial body is approaching or receding, and how fast, from the behavior of the lines in its spectrum. This behavior of the lines is known as the DOPPLER-FIZEAU EFFECT, after the two physicists who, in about 1840, first drew attention to its possibilities. If a source of light and an observer are approaching each other, the lines in the spectrum of the source are shifted slightly toward the violet end of the spectrum relative to the lines in a stationary source of light on the earth. If the sources are receding from each other, the lines are shifted to the red instead of the violet. *How much* the lines are shifted depends upon *how fast* the source is approaching or receding.

10.11. The Doppler-Fizeau effect

The Doppler-Fizeau effect is far too small to be noticed in any light sources that we commonly encounter upon the earth. But there is a similar effect in sound that is readily apparent. If a train is standing still the pitch of the locomotive whistle sounds steady. But if the whistle is blowing as the train approaches rapidly, the pitch of the sound seems high and then it drops abruptly as the train sweeps past. The reason is that when the train is approaching more vibrations from the whistle enter the ear per second than when the train is receding. The more vibrations the higher the pitch; the fewer vibrations the lower the pitch.

In the case of light waves, more vibrations per second corresponds to a rise in pitch, or a shift toward the violet; fewer vibrations per second corresponds to a shift toward the red, or a lower pitch.

The Doppler-Fizeau effect is our most powerful means for detecting motion in the celestial bodies. We have to wait many years for a star to move enough in the sky so that we can detect the change in its position. But from a photograph taken in a single night we can measure the shift of its spectrum lines and tell immediately how fast it is moving with respect to the earth. Keep the Doppler-Fizeau effect in mind for we shall refer to it again and again.

Objects on the Surface of the Sun

If you view the sun through moderately dark glasses it appears to be a uniformly bright shining disk. This bright surface is the photosphere, or "light sphere." Its temperature, as we have seen, is about 10,300° F. The gases that emit the light of the photosphere are

10.12. The photosphere of the sun

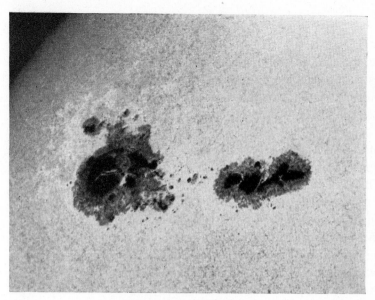

Fig. 10.3. The great spot group of February, 1946. This is the second largest spot group recorded since Galileo first turned a telescope upon the sun in 1611. Photographed at the 60-foot tower telescope of the Mount Wilson Observatory on Feb. 2, 1946. Note darkening toward the limb and granulations. Also bright patches of foculae on side of larger group toward the limb.

probably at a pressure of 1 per cent of that of the atmosphere at the surface of the earth.

If the glare from the sun is reduced enough so that it can be viewed with comfort, the disk is seen to be conspicuously brighter at the center than at the edge, or *limb*. This darkening of the sun's disk toward the limb is attributed mostly to the diffusion and scattering of light emerging from different depths in the sun's atmosphere. At the center of the disk we can look directly down into the atmosphere. Here light emerges by the shortest path and with the least diffusion. Hence we can see down into the deep, hot layers. At the limb we look through the solar atmosphere at a slant. The rays are more affected by diffusion and, in order to reach us, must come mostly from the higher, cooler levels. The change in brightness from the center to the limb of the sun corresponds to a change in temperature of roughly 10,300° to 8000° F. (Fig. 10.3).

When the air is steady so that the disk of the sun is sharp and clear, the photosphere, instead of being uniformly bright, is seen to be speckled, or covered with granulations, which are most conspicuous at the center of the disk and which fade out near the limb. The granulations continually come and go and merge into one another, so that it is hard to follow one for more than a minute or two. The width of an average granule is about 1500 miles—somewhat larger than the over-all size of the British Isles. The granules are believed to be the tops of chaotic currents of gas rising and falling in the solar atmosphere (Fig. 10.3).

Near the limb large irregular bright patches called *faculae* (torches) can usually be seen. They seem to be clouds suspended

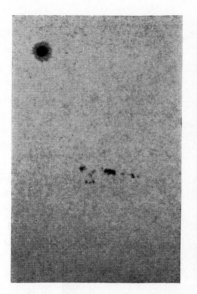 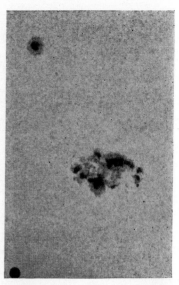

Fig. 10.4. Twenty-four-hour development of a spot group. Disk at lower left represents comparative size of earth. Aug. 18 and 19, 1917. (Mount Wilson Observatory.)

above the photosphere, and are a few hundred degrees hotter than the surface below.

Sunspot Groups and Their Characteristics

By far the most conspicuous objects on the sun's disk are the dark areas called spots; or better, *spot groups,* since they almost invariably occur in clusters (Figs. 10.3 and 10.4). Spot groups range all the way in size from tiny flecks barely distinguishable from the granulations up to huge areas visible to the unaided eye through smoked glass. The great spot group of April, 1947, which was the largest of which we have a reliable record, covered an area equal to 140 times the equatorial cross section of the earth (Fig. 10.5).

All except the smallest spots consist of two portions which differ sharply in their degree of darkness. The darker portion situated near the center of the spot is called the UMBRA. The umbra appears black to the eye but this is purely an effect of contrast due to the brilliance of the surrounding photosphere, for actually the umbra is brighter than an electric arc light. Surrounding the umbra is the lighter PENUMBRA. Large irregular groups may include several umbrae within a single large penumbra.

10.13. Visible structure of spots

Large, stable spots are sometimes surrounded by a light ring, about 3 per cent brighter than the photosphere. The bright ring resembles the faculae but is visible across the entire disk instead of only near the limb.

An observer on the earth at E (Fig. 10.6) sees a large spot as it crosses the central meridian of the sun at S. After one solar rotation the spot returns to S. Meanwhile the earth has moved in its orbit to

10.14. Rotation of the sun from long-lived spots

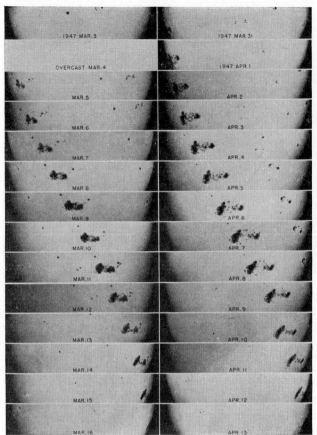

Fig. 10.5. Varying aspects of the great spot group of March and April, 1947, as it was carried across the disk of the sun by the solar rotation. In April this group attained the largest size of any ever photographed. The group was first seen on Feb. 5, 1947, when its spots were quite small. They grew rapidly, however, until by February 7 they were large enough to be seen without a telescope. When after a solar rotation the group reappeared on March 3, it was composed primarily of one huge spot, the largest single spot on record, with an area of 5 billion square miles.

When the group reappeared on March 30 for its third transit, it had separated into several groups and increased in area. At maximum size it covered 7 billion square miles of the sun's surface.

On its fourth and last transit, the group was much smaller and was last seen on May 11, having endured for 95 days. (*Mount Wilson and Palomar Observatories.*)

E', from which position the central meridian of the sun appears to be at *S'*. Therefore, the observer will not see the spot on a line through the center of the disk until the sun has turned through the extra distance needed to bring the spot in line with the earth again. For a spot near the sun's equator this apparent or synodic period of rotation is 27 days. When correction is made for the revolution of the earth in its orbit, the true or sidereal period of rotation comes out about 25 days *for spots near the equator*. It is necessary to specify the latitude when speaking about the rotation of the sun, since the sun does not rotate as a solid body. The sun rotates fastest near the equator and more slowly toward the poles, so that a spot in latitude 30° takes 1.5 days longer to make a rotation than one in latitude 5°. It is impossible to get reliable values for the solar rotation in higher latitudes by this method, since for some unknown reason spots rarely appear above latitude 30°. But by means of the Doppler-Fizeau effect we can measure the velocity of rotation up to as far as 80° from the equator, after which the displacements of the spectrum lines become too small to attempt to go farther. At the limb of the sun that is turn-

ing toward us, the spectrum lines are shifted to the violet relative to
their position at the center of the disk. At the opposite or receding
limb, the lines are shifted to the red. (We should expect the shift at
the two limbs to be equal in amount but in opposite directions. For
some reason not clearly understood the shift toward the red at the
receding limb is always slightly greater.) From the total amount of
the shift we can determine the speed of rotation. The spectroscopic

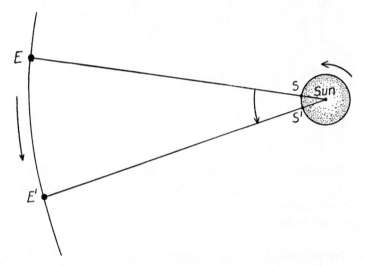

Fig. 10.6. Use of sunspots in measuring time of solar rotation.

method gives a period of rotation in latitude 75° of 33 days—more
than a week longer than at the equator.

Tracings made of the positions of spots throughout the year
will show that at certain times they move across the disk in nearly
straight lines, but at other times the paths are slightly curved. This is
due to the inclination of the sun's equator to the plane of the earth's
orbit. In March, the sun's north pole is tilted away from the earth,
and the spots move across the disk in paths that are curved toward
the north (Fig. 10.7). In September, the north pole of the sun is inclined toward the earth, and the paths are curved to the south. Halfway between, in June and December, the spots appear to move across
the disk in straight lines. From observations of long-lived regular
spots the angle of inclination of the sun's equator to the plane of the
earth's orbit has been found to be 7°10′.5.

10.15. Inclination of the sun's axis

On Oct. 30, 1825, Heinrich Schwabe, of Dessau, Germany,
began observations on the sun in the hope of catching a planet inte-
rior to the orbit of Mercury upon the solar disk. He found the chang-

10.16. Periodicity of sunspots

ing appearance of the spots so fascinating that his original plan was soon forgotten. Schwabe showed the true scientific spirit by keeping a *systematic record* of all the spots he could see upon the disk on every day that weather permitted observations. At the end of 12 years of persistent observation his counts showed good evidence of a rise and fall in the degree of sunspot activity over a period of about 10

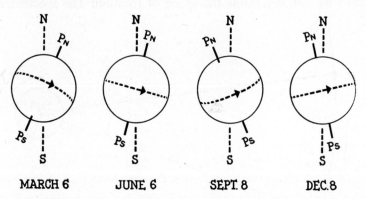

| MARCH 6 | JUNE 6 | SEPT. 8 | DEC.8 |

Fig. 10.7. Straight and curved paths of spots across the sun's disk at different seasons and changing tilt of the solar axis with respect to north and south in the sky.

years. He published a brief summary of his results but did not feel justified as yet in announcing the discovery of a 10-year period. Not until 1843, after he had observed two maxima and two minima, did he publish the momentous discovery of the sunspot cycle (Figs. 10.8 and 10.9).

Schwabe's article attracted not the slightest attention. Apparently nobody read it. When Humboldt mentioned it eight years later in his famous book, *The Cosmos,* scientific recognition finally came. And then it was hailed chiefly for demonstrating that there was still something new to be found in the supposedly "exhausted" subject of astronomy! (This was a few years before Bunsen and Kirchhoff opened up a limitless field for exploration in the spectrum analysis of the heavenly bodies.)

Schwabe's discovery of the sunspot cycle, one of the most important astronomical events of the nineteenth century, was made with two telescopes little bigger than spyglasses.

The average interval between successive minima from 1755 to the last one at 1944.2 is 11.1 years, or about one year longer than the two cycles that Schwabe observed. The interval has been as short as 9.0 years and as long as 13.6 years. Spots probably have no defi-

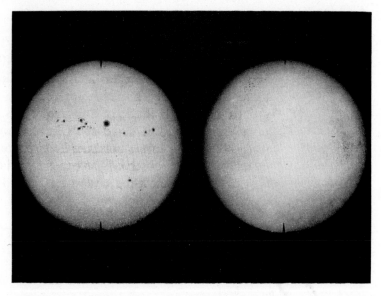

Fig. 10.8. Comparison of direct photographs of the sun soon after maximum sunspot activity on Nov. 30, 1929; and approaching minimum on June 22, 1931, when no spots are on the disk. (*Mount Wilson Observatory.*)

nite period of variation in the same sense that the earth has a definite period of revolution around the sun. During a cycle the number of spots undergoes large and rapid variations. The smooth appearance of the sunspot curve is obtained only after taking averages over a period of a year. Occasionally near maximum there may be a day when not a single spot can be discerned on the visible surface of the sun, while at minimum large spot groups sometimes occur.

10.17. Spoerer's law of sunspot latitudes

In 1858, Carrington called attention to the fact that at minimum the spots are distinctly separated into two groups—one confined to latitudes less than 20°, and later another group between latitudes 20° and 40°. The general decrease in average latitude with progress of the cycle was not announced until 1879 by Spoerer, and is generally known as Spoerer's law of sunspot latitude.

Two or three years before the end of the old cycle a few small spots may be recorded above latitude 30°. They are so small and short-lived that it is very hard to tell whether they are spots of the old cycle in exceptionally high latitude or possibly the first faint indications of the new cycle. Six months or a year before the old-cycle spots finally disappear for good, spots of the new cycle begin to become fairly plentiful in high latitudes, or between about 25° and 35°. The zone of activity soon widens out in the direction of the equator, and as the cycle progresses the average latitude of the spots steadily decreases, until at the end it is about 8° (Fig. 10.10).

Minimum usually occurs when spots of the old and new cycles are equal in number. Thus at minimum there will be four zones of activity upon the sun—two in latitude 8° on either side of the equator and two between latitudes 25° and 35°.

Spots are extremely rare above latitude 40°, and they also seldom appear closer to the equator than 5°. They do not avoid the region of the equator entirely, however, for there are many examples of spot groups that had latitudes of a degree or less. There is even one case of a group that had some spots in the southern hemisphere and some other spots in the northern hemisphere. On August 13, 1953, a small spot was observed for one day in latitude 52° North. This spot appears to mark the onset of a new 11-year cycle of solar activity.

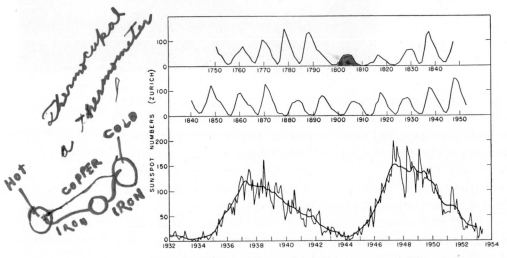

Fig. 10.9. Variations in the sunspot cycles from 1749 to 1953. The values in the two upper lines have been smoothed to eliminate short-period fluctuations. The lower curve for the last two cycles shows the short-period fluctuations as well as the smoothed values.

10.18. Characteristics of spots

The umbra of a spot looks black because it is at a lower temperature than its surroundings and therefore emits less light per unit area. The easiest way to measure the temperature of the umbra is to compare its luminosity with that of the neighboring photosphere. Knowing the temperature of the photosphere and the relative luminosity of umbra to photosphere for a certain color, we can find the temperature of the umbra by the laws of radiation.

Measures by different observers yield temperatures for the umbra ranging from 7300° to 8200° F. The chief source of error arises from tremors in the image due to atmospheric disturbances which scatter bright photospheric light into the umbra. In fact, all the errors combine to make the temperature of the umbra too high rather than too low. It is possible that spots may differ considerably in temperature among themselves. This may account for the exceptionally low temperature of only 6200° F that was found for a certain spot.

Most spot groups are only a few thousand miles in width and disappear after about a week. But a few become large enough to be visible to the unaided eye and endure for several months. Thus a spot group may be carried across the disk by the solar rotation, disappear

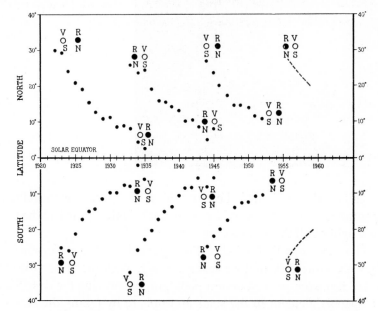

Fig. 10.10. The change in latitude and corresponding magnetic polarities of spot groups in the northern and southern hemispheres from 1922 to 1953. V and R refer to the direction of the Zeeman displacement of the spectrum lines used to determine the magnetic polarity of the spot group. If toward the violet V, the spot has a negative polarity like that of a south-seeking S magnetic pole upon the earth. If toward the red R, it has a north-seeking N magnetic pole.

onto the back side of the sun for a couple of weeks, and then appear again around the approaching limb (see Fig. 10.5). Exceptionally stable groups may survive for two and even three rotations. The spot group of longest bona fide life is one that first appeared on July 26, 1919, and did not disappear from the disk until 134 days later. Although much longer records are often quoted, they are not authentic returns of the same spot group.

Imagine a huge electric sign composed of many red, yellow, and blue lights set closely together. Viewed from a distance the individual lights would blend together to produce some particular design. Now suppose the sign were examined through a red filter which

10.19. The sun photographed in the light of a single element

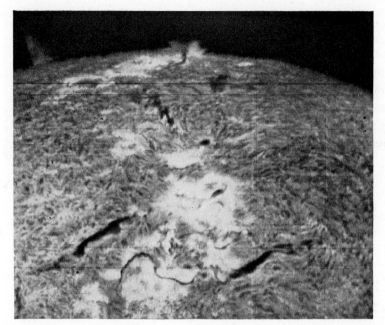

Fig. 10.11. An enlarged portion of a hydrogen spectroheliogram showing bright and dark flocculi near the limb. (*Mount Wilson Observatory.*)

transmitted the red light but cut out the yellow and blue entirely. The appearance of the sign would now be quite different than when seen in the light of all three colors together.

The sun emits light of all colors mingled together to produce the yellowish white disk that we see in the sky. With the SPECTROHELIO-GRAPH, however, we can obtain photographs showing the distribution of a specific element in the solar atmosphere by taking the exposure in the light of some strong Fraunhofer line. Making a photograph in the *light* of what appears to be a *black* line seems impossible. But the Fraunhofer lines produced by atoms in the solar atmosphere are actually *dark* rather than black. They merely seem black because of the contrast with the brilliant continuous spectrum. Actually considerable light issues from hydrogen atoms even in the center of the broad (apparently) black lines. The spectrum lines most commonly used for this purpose are those of hydrogen and calcium. The resulting photographs or spectroheliograms show the sun in the light of hydrogen and calcium only, and look very different from direct photographs of the sun taken in the usual way (Fig. 10.11).

Filters have recently been constructed that are nearly monochromatic in that they transmit only an extremely narrow band of colors. With such a filter attached to a telescope it is possible to see features upon the sun formerly visible only during a total solar eclipse or revealed photographically by the spectroheliograph.

Spectroheliograms taken in hydrogen light reveal a structure around spot groups resembling the lines of force formed by a bar

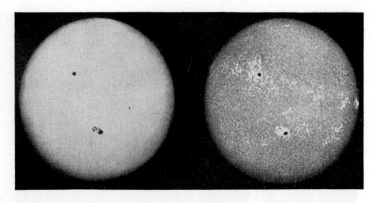

Fig. 10.12. At left is a photograph showing the sun much as it appears when viewed directly through a telescope. At right is spectroheliogram taken on the same day, showing calcium flocculi. Note bright and dark flocculi around the upper spot. (Mount Wilson Observatory.)

magnet in iron filings or the lines of flow in a whirlpool. Near the spot there are usually bright clouds of gas called FLOCCULI. On calcium spectroheliograms the bright areas near the limb visible directly to the eye called faculae (10.12) are seen to be nearly identical in structure with the bright flocculi. There may also be long streaks of dark flocculi on the disk not necessarily associated with the spot groups (Fig. 10.11).

On the calcium spectroheliograms the most conspicuous feature is the irregular bunches of bright flocculi surrounding the spot groups, through which the umbrae can be discerned like raisins in a cooky. The vortex structure, which is so striking on the hydrogen spectroheliograms, is absent. The long, dark flocculi can still be discerned but are much weaker than in hydrogen (Fig. 10.12).

In 1896, Pieter Zeeman, of Holland, discovered one of the most famous of the numerous "effects" in physics and astronomy.

10.20. The magnetic field in sunspots

He found that when a luminous vapor is placed between the pole pieces of a powerful electromagnet, the spectrum lines, instead of having their normal appearance, are split into several components. The way in which a line is split depends upon the strength of the magnetic field and upon how the light is viewed with respect to the direction of the field. Thus a spectrum line when viewed in a certain way may appear split into three distinct components. Viewed from another angle or with a weaker field the line may appear only widened slightly (Fig. 10.13).

Now the earliest observers had noticed that lines in the sunspot spectrum are almost all wider than the same lines in the spectrum of the disk. About 1905, Hale and his associates launched an intensive investigation of solar activity at Mount Wilson, with the result that three years later he was able to announce that the widening of lines in the spot spectrum is due to the presence of a magnetic field as shown by the Zeeman effect. That is, each spot is the center of a magnetic field, the strength of which increases with the size of the spot, and to a lesser degree with their darkness.

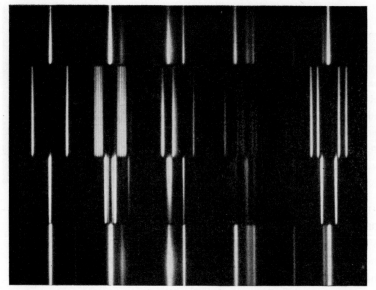

10.21. The law of sunspot polarity

As previously noted, spot groups almost always consist of two clusters or components separated by a few degrees in longitude. Hale found that the direction of the magnetic field, or its *polarity,* was opposite in the leading and following members of the spot group, like the two poles of a horseshoe magnet. Moreover, spot groups in the northern and southern hemispheres were of opposite polarity. Thus, in 1908, the leading spot in groups of the northern hemisphere

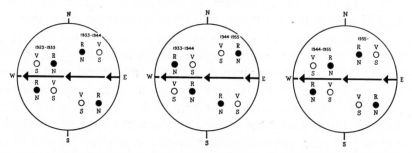

Fig. 10.14. The latitudes and magnetic polarities of spot groups at the beginning and end of a cycle in the northern and southern hemispheres of the sun.

had a polarity like that of the south-seeking pole of a magnet on the earth, and the following spot a polarity like that of a north-seeking magnetic pole. But in the southern hemisphere, the polarity of the leading spot was north and the following spot south.

When in 1912 spot groups of the new solar cycle began to appear in high latitudes, the observers were astonished to find that they had polarities which were the reverse of groups of the old cycle. At first they feared some systematic error had crept into their work, but a

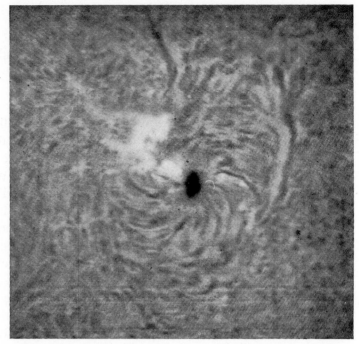

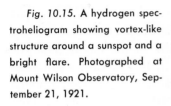

Fig. 10.15. A hydrogen spectroheliogram showing vortex-like structure around a sunspot and a bright flare. Photographed at Mount Wilson Observatory, September 21, 1921.

careful check failed to shake its validity. This reversal in polarity of spot groups at the beginning of a new cycle has been observed at the minima of 1922, 1933, and 1944, so there can be no question that it is another of the fundamental characteristics of the solar cycle (Fig. 10.14).

The significant period of the solar cycle is, therefore, from minimum to minimum, when the reversal in polarity occurs, the interval from maximum to maximum being of no particular consequence. Also, the magnetic period between the appearance of spot groups of the same polarity in the same hemisphere is twice the 11-year period.

Sunspots are often described in highly dramatic terms as great vortices or cyclonic storms whirling across the surface of the sun. It is true that on the hydrogen spectroheliograms the spots sometimes present a vortex-like structure (Fig. 10.15), but more often it is missing or poorly defined. Also, there has never been any actual whirling motion observed in the markings around a spot. As a matter of fact, only about 2 per cent of the spot groups show definite hydrogen whirls. Instead of comparing spots to violent storms on the solar surface, they seem more analogous to cool springs of water overflowing onto a desert.

Sunspots display such seemingly varied and diverse characteristics that we can only have admiration for those bold enough to devise a theory to explain them. So far none of the theories advanced have proved generally acceptable to astronomers. Although we now have detailed observations of sunspots extending over nearly a century, their origin is still unknown.

Prominences

**10.22. Appear-
ance and gen-
eral structure**

During a total solar eclipse, brilliant rose-colored clouds are often seen projecting outside the dark disk of the moon. The first definite report on prominences was made by the Swedish astronomer Vassenius, who saw them at the eclipse of May 13, 1733. Although prominences were observed and described at half a dozen later eclipses, the scattered reports seem to have made little impression upon the astronomical world and were soon forgotten.

The eclipse of July 8, 1842, was seen under exceptionally favorable circumstances in Europe. The quiet political situation of that time stimulated travel and the exchange of ideas. As a result, many of the most noted astronomers of the age traveled great distances for that time to witness the spectacle. At totality the prominences were so brilliant and unexpected that many observers did not recover from their surprise soon enough to make accurate drawings of their appearance or even their position.

As a result of the numerous observations made along the eclipse path in 1842 it was generally concluded that the prominences are real, definite objects that belonged to the sun and were not mountains of the moon, that there were no observable changes during the eclipse, but it was uncertain whether they were permanent objects or not. These conclusions were not accepted by all astronomers, however; for example, 10 years later Faye, of the Paris Observatory, maintained that the prominences were optical illusions or mirages produced in some way by the moon(!)

**10.23. Modern
methods of
observation**

The prominences may be photographed without an eclipse at any time with the spectroheliograph in the light of hydrogen or calcium, the bright image of the sun being covered by a disk of the same size. They may also be photographed or viewed directly with the coronograph or Lyot telescope, with a spectrohelioscope, or with a special type of monochromatic filter attached to a telescope.

When the prominences are viewed with the spectrohelioscope or through a monochromator in the red light of hydrogen, they appear much as the observers in 1842 described them—as rose-colored mountains or clouds projecting from the limb. The hydrogen spectroheliograms show the prominences on the disk of the sun as long, dark plumelike markings roughly parallel to the solar equator (Fig. 10.16).

A prominence resembles a sheet of flame standing on edge near

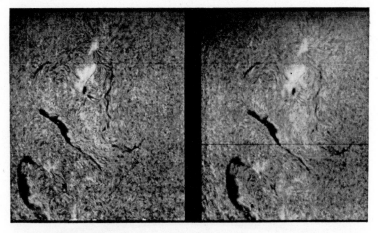

the chromosphere similar to the thin sheet of flame issuing from a fishtail burner in the laboratory. The average prominence is 6000 miles thick, 125,000 miles long, and 30,000 miles high. Its volume is 93 times that of the earth and its mass equal to a cube of water nine miles to a side (Fig. 10.17). Small prominences may have a lifetime of only a few days. The long dark markings after they become stable and acquire a definite shape may last for several months. About 10

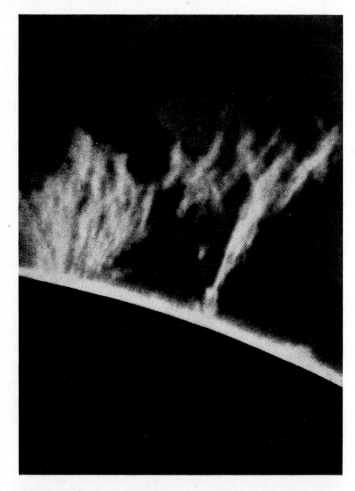

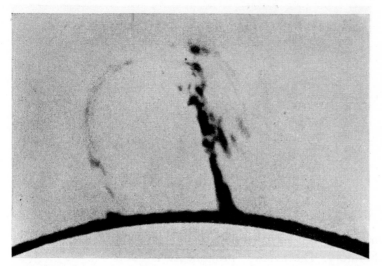

Fig. 10.18. A tornado prominence one third of a solar radius high photographed at Mount Wilson on July 7, 1940. The material seemed to be swirling up out of the chromosphere, finally breaking into fragments which moved outward along the prominence. The long column on the left is probably bending over into a center of attraction.

per cent survive for more than five rotations, 5 per cent for more than seven rotations.

10.24. Motion pictures of prominences

A special type of spectroheliograph has been developed for photographing prominences on motion-picture film. By magnifying the motion this instrument shows the prominences moving and twisting about in a startling manner as if under the influence of powerful forces. Prominences have also been photographed directly with the coronograph through a dark red filter.

Occasionally, for no visible reason a prominence starts moving rapidly upward from the sun and attains a great height and speed. One prominence extended outward from the limb of the sun to a distance of a million miles. The fastest-moving prominence on record attained a velocity of 450 miles per second. Contrary to what one might suppose from the appearance of prominences, however, the predominant direction of motion in them is *downward* toward the solar surface (Fig. 10.18).

A prominence becomes active by first pouring streamers into a center of attraction. It then starts to expand; rises rapidly, and disappears while in motion. During the whole of the eruption it sends streamers back into the original center of attraction and to others nearby.

The Solar Corona

10.25. Form and structure of the corona

The corona is an extensive gaseous envelope surrounding the sun. To the naked eye it is visible only during a total solar eclipse, appearing at the instant of totality with a splendor that is truly magnificent. The corona is, of course, always present, but its feeble light is hidden by the diffuse glare from scattered sunlight in our atmosphere. Measurement shows that the corona gives about one millionth

as much illumination as sunlight, or about half the light of the full moon.

The form of the corona varies with the sunspot cycle. At maximum it is nearly circular, while at minimum it is expanded at the equator and contracted into short streamers at the poles. Near maximum certain structural features called *arches* or *hoods* are conspicuous. The INNER CORONA extends out to about one third the diameter of the sun and resembles a brilliant white or pale yellow ring. The spectrum of the inner corona is mainly continuous with a few bright lines. The Fraunhofer lines do not appear (Figs. 10.19 and 10.20).

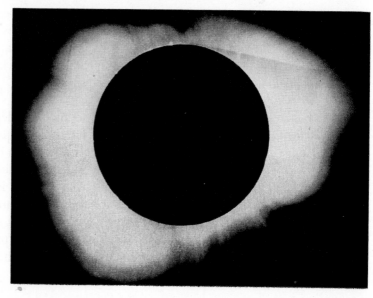

10.26. Observations of the corona without an eclipse

Bernard Lyot succeeded in 1930 in photographing the corona for the first time without an eclipse. His success was due in part to the clear sky above his observatory on the Pic du Midi, a mountain in the Pyrenees 9400 feet high. But mostly it was the result of painstaking effort to reduce to an absolute minimum the scattered light in the lens system of his telescope. Another coronograph has been installed at an elevation of 6700 feet at Arosa, Switzerland. The Harvard College Observatory maintains a coronograph in its station at Climax, Colorado, at an altitude of 11,520 feet.

All observers agree that observations of the corona without an eclipse are very difficult even under the most favorable atmospheric conditions. For example, a sky clear enough to study the details of the innermost part of the corona existed at the Arosa Observatory during only 5 hours in a period of 100 winter days.

For years the most mysterious feature of the corona was the origin of the bright lines in its spectrum, of which 26 are now known. They do not occur in the chromosphere or any other part of the solar atmosphere. The strongest lines are in the green and in the red.

In 1911 it was suggested that the coronal lines were produced by a hypothetical element called "coronium," but the idea was never taken very seriously. Despite an intensive investigation of every reasonable possibility, however, the substance producing the lines defied detection. Not until 1939 were the coronal lines finally identified with certain spectrum lines which under ordinary conditions are "forbidden." That is, they are spectrum lines which can originate only under the extraordinary conditions that prevail in the corona, where we have an exceedingly thin gas at a temperature of 2,000,000° F! Thus in the end the mysterious coronal lines were found to originate in common elements such as iron, nickel, and calcium, but in a peculiar state that cannot be reproduced in the laboratory.

Solar and Terrestrial Relationships

10.27. Known relationships

All life and energy upon the earth depend for existence upon radiation from the sun. It is of interest to inquire whether the sun may also have some terrestrial effects other than the obvious ones of supplying the earth with light and heat. In particular, sunspots would appear to be promising objects to investigate in this connection, since they vary widely in size and number from month to month, as well as in cycles of approximately 11 years. Many noted astronomers have studied sunspots—not because they were particularly interested in the spots themselves, but to see whether they could correlate them with effects upon the earth.

Of the many solar and terrestrial relationships that have been announced in the past, only a few may be considered as well established. These are as follows:

There is a close parallelism between terrestrial magnetic activity and sunspot activity, such that disturbances in the earth's magnetic field are more frequent and more intense during sunspot maximum than sunspot minimum. The relationship becomes apparent only when averages are taken over a long period, such as a year. When averages are taken for shorter periods, such as a month, the relationship is much poorer (Fig. 10.21).

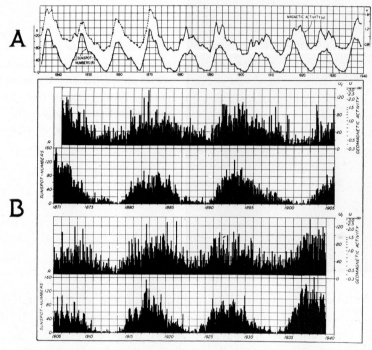

Fig. 10.21. Geomagnetic activity and sunspot numbers. (A) average annual values for the past century; (B) monthly means 1872–1939.

Occasionally the earth's magnetic field will be violently disturbed by a MAGNETIC STORM, which usually begins suddenly and at practically the same time over the entire surface of the earth. Magnetic storms can be correlated more often than would be expected by chance with the presence upon the sun of very large spot groups. The most likely position of a large spot group upon the disk with respect to the time the storm commences is from two days before central meridian passage to four days after central meridian passage. The most

149

favored time of all is about one day after central meridian passage.

There is a correspondence between the frequency of auroras and sunspots similar to that between magnetic activity and sunspots. During magnetic storms auroras may become unusually conspicuous, and visible in low latitudes. The intensity of auroral disturbances increases from low latitudes up to about 23° from the *magnetic poles,* so that magnetic latitude 67° is the zone of most frequent occurrence of auroras. The intensity then decreases toward the magnetic poles but still remains considerable.

Fig. 10.22. Greatly enlarged image of a photograph of the sun taken on motion-picture film in the light of hydrogen, showing intense flare over a spot group. Figures were written in ink on film to record time of exposure. (*Mount Wilson Observatory.*)

Auroras are attributed to collisions of the charged particles ejected from the sun with the gases of the atmosphere, roughly between elevations of 50 and 100 miles. It is believed that as the charged particles approach the earth they spiral around the lines of force of the earth's magnetic field and are guided toward the polar regions.

Brilliant FLARES (formerly called BRIGHT CHROMOSPHERIC ERUPTIONS), which are seen most often near large active spot groups of irregular magnetic polarity, occur simultaneously with sudden fade-outs in high-frequency radio transmission over the daylight side of the earth. The effect was discovered as the result of research initiated in 1935 by J. H. Dellinger (Fig. 10.22).

The flares are most easily seen with the spectrohelioscope or with a monochromatic filter in the light of the red hydrogen line. The bright flocculus usually reaches maximum brightness within less than 15 minutes of its first appearance, then fades away more slowly. Around an active spot group several small flares of a few minutes' duration may be seen within the course of an hour. The intense flares that last for an hour or even longer are rather rare. During the two weeks in which a large spot group is in transit across the disk, an observer will be lucky if he catches one or two.

Radio Waves from the Sun

The extensive use of radar during the war resulted in some developments quite different from those for which the equipment was intended. The receiver and transmitter on a radar set operate upon waves only a few feet or even inches in length, in contrast to the waves several hundred yards long used on the ordinary commercial broadcast band. Very short waves instead of being reflected back to earth will pierce the ionosphere and be lost in space forever. *Conversely,* extremely short waves from outer space can pierce the ionosphere and be received upon the earth.

10.28. Study of the sun by radio methods

In February, 1942, army radar stations in England experienced severe interference due to a high level of radio noise in their receivers. When bearings were taken on the source of interference they were found to point in a direction close to the sun. It was concluded that the noise was created by a large spot group then in transit across the disk. Here appeared to be a new method of exploring the solar atmosphere by means of waves short for radio but a million times longer than the longest infrared rays we can photograph.

Although microwave technique has only been applied systematically to solar research since the war, already valuable results have been obtained. One of the most startling was the discovery that the fairly steady constant emission from the quiescent sun corresponds to a temperature of 2,000,000° F! Since the surface of the sun that we see in the sky is known to have a temperature of only 9600° F, such a figure might seem preposterous if we did not already have good reasons for believing that the temperature of the corona is about two million degrees. Hence the source of radio noise was tentatively identified with the corona, and later work has confirmed this view (Fig. 10.23).

The radio noise usually rises sharply while a large spot group is crossing the solar meridian, and in addition there may be "bursts" when the intensity of emission increases by ten or a hundred times in less than a minute. Enough bursts have been recorded almost in coincidence with flares to show that there is undoubtedly some connec-

Fig. 10.23. The 600-inch radio telescope of the United States Naval Research Laboratory in Washington, D. C. The huge curved reflecting surface intercepts microwave radiation from the sun, stars, and planets. The radiation is focused onto the rodlike antenna projecting from the center, where it is collected and transferred to the receiver for amplification and study. (*Naval Research Laboratory*)

tion between them, although all flares cannot be associated with bursts. As a general rule, the bigger flares are most likely to be associated with bursts, but the relationship is not a simple one.

Many other effects have been blamed on sunspots, such as the weather, wars, epidemics, and financial panics, but they still lack confirmation.

QUESTIONS AND EXERCISES

1. How would you distinguish between a small round sunspot and a planet such as Mercury on the disk of the sun?

2. To get the true rotation period of the sun, it is necessary to correct observations of sunspots for the revolution of the earth around the sun. Would the same correction have to be applied to values for the rotation of the sun made with the spectrograph?

3. Tell what criteria you would use in attempting to identify a spot group that you think has survived a rotation or two around the sun.

4. What characteristics of sunspots make it difficult to determine the rotation period from spots? What type of spots would you choose for this problem?

5. Near the end of a sunspot cycle a spot group appears in latitude 15° N. What would help you in deciding whether it belonged to the old cycle or the new cycle? (See Fig. 10.14.)

6. The average length of the sunspot cycle is 11.1 years. From Figure 10.9, how accurately could you predict the time of minimum ten cycles in advance, starting from the minimum of 1810?

7. The gases of the earth's atmosphere produce black lines in the solar spectrum closely resembling the Fraunhofer lines produced in the atmosphere of the sun. Name two ways you could distinguish atmospheric lines from true solar lines.

8. Spot groups at the sun's equator have a rotation period of 25 days. The period of solar rotation in latitude 50° is 30 days. If a spot appeared in latitude 50°, how long would it take the spot on the equator to gain a whole rotation on the spot in latitude 50°?

Ans. 150 days, which is longer than the lifetime of any known spot group.

9. Would the sun appear black if the temperature of its surface were the same as that at the center of a sunspot?

11 THE TERRESTRIAL PLANETS

BEFORE proceeding to the study of the planets in detail, let us first look at their general physical characteristics.

The planets can be naturally divided into two distinctly different groups—the TERRESTRIAL planets and the MAJOR planets. The terrestrial planets, as their name implies, have physical characteristics similar to those of the earth although we find puzzling differences when considering them in detail. They are Mercury, Venus, the earth, Mars, and Pluto. Little is definitely known about Pluto except that it has a mass about the same as that of the earth. The major planets are much more massive than the terrestrial planets. They are Jupiter, Saturn, Uranus, and Neptune.

Mercury

Very few of the students who read this will remember ever having seen Mercury. At its brightest it is more brilliant than a first-magnitude star. But it is only occasionally that it can be seen at all, and then only for a little while during the evening or morning twilight. Even first-magnitude stars do not appear at their best during twilight.

The early Greeks, being more observant of the heavens than we are, often noticed this planet, both as an evening star and as a morning star. But they did not recognize it in the east as the same object they had seen about two months earlier in the west. Mercury was their name for the evening star, and they called the morning star Apollo.

The reason why Mercury is never seen throughout the night, as some of the other planets are, is that it makes such a small circuit around the sun that it is always near it. It sets soon after the sun does (if not before), and it never rises in the morning much before the sun. Twenty-eight degrees, against the sky, is as far as it can ever get away from the sun, and this distance is never straight up from our horizon but along the ecliptic, at an angle to the horizon. Mercury's orbit is inclined 7° to the earth's orbit. This is far greater than the inclination of any other planetary orbit except that of Pluto, but even this inclination does not take Mercury very far from the apparent path of the sun.

11.3. Eccentricity of orbit

Mercury goes back and forth across the sun, swinging east or west to a distance of anything from 18° to 28° either way. This difference is due to the rather eccentric orbit of Mercury. Mercury's orbit has an eccentricity of 0.2, which causes the planet's distance from the sun to vary from 28,600,000 miles at its perihelion point to 43,400,-000 miles at aphelion. The mean distance is 36,000,000 miles.

11.4. Transits

As the planet traverses the half of its orbit that lies this side of the sun, it *may* cross the face of the sun. It does so once in several years. This is not called an eclipse, because Mercury is too small to obscure enough of the sun to make it noticeable without a telescope. The crossing is known as a "transit" of Mercury. A small black circle about 1/150 the diameter of the sun creeps slowly across the bright background of the sun's disk. No name is given to the corresponding passage behind the sun, this being wholly without interest.

The transits furnish a valuable opportunity to make a very accurate check on the position of Mercury with respect to the sun. They also enable us to check upon how steadily the earth rotates on its axis. The rotation of the earth is our standard clock upon which we depend for time, and the motions of all the other heavenly bodies are predicted upon the assumption that the earth is always right. If the earth does not rotate at a steady rate, then all the other bodies will seem to get out of step with it. From irregularities in the motions of the sun, moon, Jupiter's satellites, and the transits of Mercury it has been found that the period of rotation of the earth is slowly increasing about enough to lengthen the day by one second in 100,000 years. This has been satisfactorily explained as the result of the tidal drag (par. 9.6). There are, in addition, sudden irregularities called "fluctuations," apparently resulting from abrupt changes in the rotation of the earth which are of unknown origin.

11.5. Phases

It is interesting to notice that as Mercury passes around the sun it goes through a series of phases as the moon does, from full to new. Like all the planets, Mercury owes its light to the sun. When it is nearly on this side of the sun we see only a crescent-shaped portion of the illuminated part. But when the planet is beyond the sun (but not quite behind it) the whole side illuminated by the sun is turned toward us; consequently it is "full" (Fig. 11.1).

11.6. Time to observe Mercury   The most favorable time to see Mercury in the evening is when its angular distance east of the sun is near its maximum. Even then the planet is low in the western sky at sunset. If its greatest eastern elongation occurs in March or April it is more favorably placed than at other times, for then the ecliptic, near which the planet must be, is most nearly vertical to the horizon.

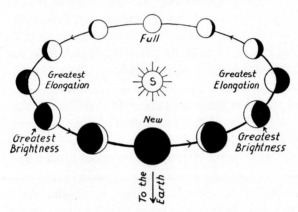

Fig. 11.1. Schematic representation of the phases of Venus and Mercury. The much greater actual difference in size is shown for Venus in Figure 11.3 where photographs are used.

Whether the planet is full or new makes less difference in its brightness than might be expected, for when it is full it is much farther away than when new.

11.7. Daytime observations   Astronomers do not confine their study of Mercury to the twilight hour, when it is visible to the naked eye. By suitably shading their telescopes from sunlight they can see the planet at any time of day whenever it is well to one side of the sun. This not only extends the time of observation but enables them to see it through less atmosphere than they must look through when it is near the horizon.

11.8. Rotation   Tombaugh, using the 24-inch refractor of the Lowell Observatory, finds that under the best conditions fairly distinct markings can be seen on Mercury. They are dark like the "seas" on the moon and scarcely move from day to day. Other observers, principally Schiaparelli and Antoniadi, believe that Mercury does not turn at all with respect to the sun, which would mean that the planet makes one rotation (with respect to the stars) every 88 days, its period of revolution.

11.9. Librations of Mercury   Although the period of rotation of Mercury equals its period of revolution, it is wrong to say that the planet *always* keeps the *same side* turned toward the sun, as is so often stated. For this would mean that the planet turns on its axis at a steady rate so that it completes one rotation in 88 days. It is true that the planet revolves around the sun in 88 days, but it does not do so at a steady rate. The orbit of Mercury is so eccentric that its velocity ranges from 36 miles a second at perihelion to 24 miles a second at aphelion. As a result, the angular rate at which the planet is *rotating* with respect to the sun is

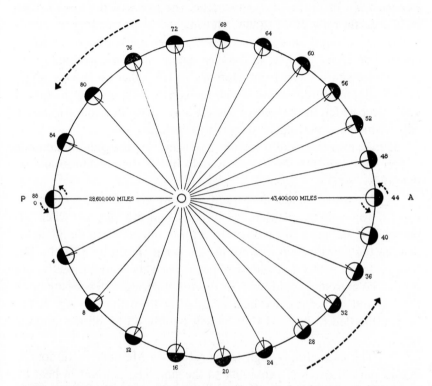

Fig. 11.2. The librations of Mercury. At perihelion, *P*, the planet is revolving at a faster angular rate than it is rotating on its axis. Starting at perihelion an observer at the position of the black line would see the sun on his meridian. The sun would then swing to his left until after 20 days it was 23.5° east of his meridian. As the planet approaches aphelion, *A*, the angular rate of rotation exceeds its rate of revolution and the sun begins to swing toward the west until it is on his meridian again at the aphelion point. After passing aphelion, the sun would swing about 23.5° to the west of his meridian and back again at *P*.

sometimes slower and sometimes faster than the angular rate at which it is *revolving* with respect to the sun.

The situation is shown in Figure 11.2, where the axis of rotation has been made perpendicular to the plane of the orbit, as is believed to be the case by some observers. To an observer on the illuminated side of Mercury the sun would appear to swing back and forth in the sky from east to west to east again in the course of a year. This swinging back and forth of the planet relative to the sun is the LIBRATION of Mercury, a formidable looking word referring to the tilting of a scales or balance. The libration amounts to 23½° on either side of the mean position. At the equator of Mercury at the mid-point of the eastern zone of libration, for example, the sun would rise as it does on the earth, only more slowly. But instead of proceeding on across the sky and setting in the west, it would turn back after reaching an altitude of 23½° and set in the east again. Since the average diameter of the sun as seen from Mercury is 1.5°, there is a zone about 134° wide on Mercury over which the sun never quite sets, a zone of 131° over which the sun never shines, and a zone of about 47° at the edges which are alternately in light and darkness.

If men ever succeed in traveling to Mercury, the only inhabitable region would seem to be a narrow strip in the zone of libration near the poles.

11.10. Temperature of Mercury

Measures made at Mount Wilson give a temperature of 644° F for a point on Mercury directly beneath the sun when the planet is at its mean distance of 36 million miles. When the planet is nearest the sun the temperature at this point would be 779° F. The temperature on the dark side has never been measured directly, but it must be extremely cold, with its exact temperature depending upon the amount of radioactive heat emanating from the surface. It has been estimated to be −414° F, which is only 45° F above absolute zero.

11.11. Reason for high temperature

The exceedingly high temperature on Mercury is, of course, due in part to its close proximity to the sun. The amount of heat increases, not simply in proportion as we come nearer the source of heat but inversely proportional to the *square* of this distance. The squares of the earth's distance (1 unit) and that of Mercury (0.38 astronomical units) from the sun are in the ratio of about 7 to 1, so the heat received by Mercury is about 7 times that received by the earth.

But another reason the temperature soars to such a height on the little planet is that it is unprotected by atmosphere. We are shielded during the day by our air. Without an atmosphere, day on Mercury, as on the moon, is very hot.

11.12. Reason for lack of atmosphere

The reason for the lack of atmosphere on Mercury is simply that, being a planet of small mass, it has not sufficient gravitational force to hold an atmosphere. In this way, also, Mercury is like the moon. Gas particles are always in motion, and this molecular motion causes expansion which, if unchecked, would make the gas thinner and thinner. The earth's force of gravity is capable of holding our air down against the earth so that it remains with us. But on Mercury, where the downward force is only slightly more than a fourth of what it is upon the earth, any air that might ever have been there would have escaped. Escape of the atmosphere would also be aided by the intense heat.

Spectrograms of Mercury were taken by Adams and Dunham, making use of the highest power of the 100-inch telescope. The plates covered the near infrared region of the spectrum, where most of the strong bands in the spectra of the outer planets occur and where three bands due to carbon dioxide gas occur in the spectrum of Venus (par. 11.21). The spectra of Mercury appeared to be identical with that of the sun, indicating that the light received from the planet is simply reflected sunlight with no trace of absorption by an atmosphere. No evidence could be found for the presence of carbon dioxide, oxygen, or water vapor.

In view of these facts, it is very puzzling that observers have repeatedly reported white spots or haze on Mercury covering some of the surface markings.

Venus

11.13. Visibility

Much more interesting than Mercury is the nearer, larger, and brighter planet Venus. Being so much farther in actual distance from the sun than is Mercury, its *angular* distance is nearly always great enough to make it visible. Venus for months at a time stands out in plain view as either an evening or a morning "star," the brightest in the sky. The Greeks were slow to observe that its morning and evening appearances were due to the same "star," just as they did not recognize Mercury seen in the morning as being identical with Mercury seen in the evening. Phosphorus and Hesperus were the names applied to Venus in the morning and evening, respectively.

11.14. Brightness

Though like all planets Venus is without light of its own, several things conspire to make it very bright. At times it is nearer to us than any other planet, and its angular width, mile for mile, is the greatest of all the planets. Being near the sun, also, it receives a great deal of illumination. Having an atmosphere, it reflects a larger proportion of the light falling upon it than a dull-colored solid surface such as that of the moon would do. Our air-filled sky is far brighter than the ground, especially if there are white thunder clouds in it reflecting the light.

11.15. Albedo

Venus reflects 76 per cent of the sunlight that strikes it, Mercury only 6 per cent. The moon, also, which, like Mercury, has no air, has an albedo of about 7 per cent. Measurements have been

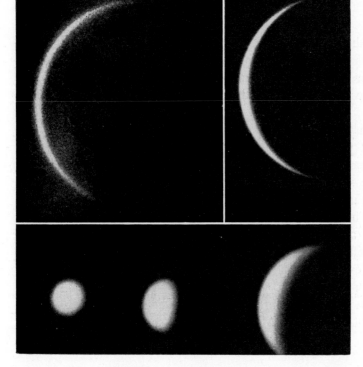

Fig. 11.3. The phases of Venus. The photograph at the upper left was taken when Venus was almost between the earth and the sun; at the lower left almost beyond the sun.

made of the light reflected from a distant cliff on the earth, and its albedo is found to be about the same as that of Mercury and the moon.

Those who have been high enough on mountains to look down on the tops of the clouds know that clouds, instead of being dark, are bright, if seen by reflected light. Even a cloudless covering of air over a planet would make it brighter than a planet without air, but not so bright as one with clouds.

11.16. Phases

The telescopic view of Venus is very interesting because of its phases. As the planet passes between us and the sun it shows a crescent, growing narrower and narrower as it approaches the line joining us with the sun. The length of the crescent increases as its width becomes less, for Venus is at its nearest when directly between us and the sun (Figs. 11.3 and 11.4).

11.17. Changes in brightness

We are accustomed to thinking of the full phase of the moon as being the time of its greatest brightness. But with Venus this is not so, for when full it is beyond the sun, at a distance more than six times as great as at the new phase. For this reason Venus is small and therefore dim at full, and larger and very brilliant when in crescent form. There is a certain stage of progress between the full, round phase and the thin but long crescent when it is at its brightest. It is then bright enough to cast a shadow during a moonless night, and it is visible to a keen eye in the daytime. This brightest phase comes

when it is the shape of the moon at five days old. It is then near enough to appear large, and the crescent is wide enough to give considerable reflecting surface. As it comes nearer the crescent lengthens but thins down to a mere streak. The times of maximum brightness occur 36 days before and after it passes between the earth and the sun (Fig. 11.1).

The time that it takes Venus to go once around the sun is 225 days. Its synodic period is 584 days, that is, about a year and seven months. This synodic period is the frequency with which it becomes the dominating feature of our western evening sky. For this reason synodic periods are of more general interest than are sidereal periods.

There are several reasons for thinking that no one has ever seen the solid surface of Venus but only the upper cloud layer (Fig. 11.5). The fact that Venus is so bright is one evidence that the light by which we see it is reflected from clouds and not from dull rock. Ordinarily Venus presents the appearance of a smooth, white, uniform disk. Surface markings have been seen visually, but only on very rare occasions.

11.18. Temperature and covering of clouds

Nicholson and Pettit, from measurements of the amount of heat radiated by Venus, obtained the surprising result that the amount of planetary radiation emitted from the bright and dark hemispheres is nearly the same. They believe the radiant energy they have measured is from high surface clouds and except by inference tells little about the actual surface temperature. They found the night temperature of Venus to be about $-26°$ F., far below the freezing point.

Fig. 11.5. Fog below as seen from Mount Wilson. Clouds on a planet would thus obscure the surface below them. (Ferdinand Ellerman, Mount Wilson Observatory.)

11.19. Markings observed by photography

Definite cloudlike markings on Venus which are always present have been photographed by F. E. Ross. The markings appear best in ultraviolet light, are weaker in blue and red light, and do not show at all on infrared plates. Bright clouds, which were presumed to be the poles, were found near the horns of the planet, while dark banded areas occur in what corresponds to the equatorial region (Fig. 11.6).

The photographs are interpreted as indicating that Venus has an outer atmospheric layer composed of a thin layer of cirrus clouds, while the inner atmosphere is exceedingly dense and yellowish. The markings on the photographs are atmospheric disturbances visible either as dark areas or as regions of enhanced brilliance. Changes in brightness of the clouds over the disk indicate that the upper surface of the cloud layer is billowy.

11.20. Rotation period

The banded structure of the atmospheric disturbances indicates that the rotation period is not so long as the orbital period of

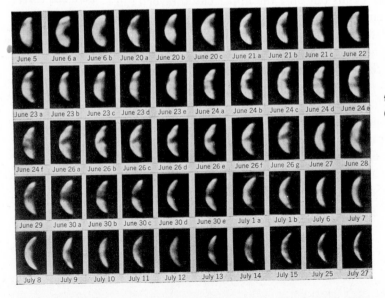

Fig. 11.6. Ultraviolet photographs of Venus, 1927. (Mount Wilson Observatory.)

revolution. The fact that the radiometric observations show little difference in the planetary temperature between the light and dark hemispheres also indicates that the planet rotates enough to keep the surface equally heated. On the other hand, repeated attempts to detect a Doppler shift of lines in the spectrum of Venus due to rotation have failed, indicating a long period. Ross concludes from a discussion of all results that a "compromise" period of around 30 days is the best solution we can obtain at present.

Careful spectroscopic observations made with the very powerful equipment at Mount Wilson have proved that there can be very little, if any, free oxygen present in the visible part of the atmosphere of Venus. Previously the evidence on this point was merely negative. Moreover, the compound carbon dioxide has been found to be an important constituent of the gases overlying the clouds from which light is reflected. This gas is heavier than oxygen, so it is probably abundant at the planet's invisible surface also. Our atmosphere contains but 3 parts of carbon dioxide in 10,000 parts of air. A large amount would suffocate animal life. The air of Venus above its clouds contains a quantity of carbon dioxide equal to a layer two miles thick at atmospheric pressure.

11.21. Atmosphere

The nature of the white cloud covering of Venus is unknown except that carbon dioxide gas must be present in great abundance. Wildt points out that the atmosphere must exert a powerful "greenhouse" effect (par. 7.10), so that the temperature at the solid surface may be as high as boiling water. He considers failure to detect water vapor in the atmosphere of Venus extremely puzzling. Evidently there are no oceans on Venus. Why a planet so similar to the earth should fail to have about the same amount of water is considered the greatest mystery in the chemistry of the solar system.

Mars

Conspicuous for its red color and great brilliance, Mars is a well-known planet. Since it is in an orbit outside that of the earth, we always see *nearly* the same side on which the sun is shining, so, unlike Venus and Mercury, it does not go through noticeable phases. It never becomes a crescent. Seen through a telescope, it appears slightly gibbous sometimes, as the moon does when two or three days from full (Fig. 7.1, p. 7.3). Only if seen from the sun would it be perfectly full at all times. More distant planets such as Jupiter and Saturn never show any phase because of the earth's proximity to the sun in proportion to the planet's very much greater distance.

11.22. Changes in appearance

11.23. Varying distance and brightness
The mean distance from the sun to Mars is 1.52 astronomical units. Thus at opposition (with the earth between the sun and Mars) Mars is at only about half the sun's distance from us and is therefore very bright. When it is in conjunction (beyond the sun) it is about two and one-half times the sun's distance, five times as far as it is at opposition. Since light decreases as the *square* of the distance increases, its brightness at conjunction, beyond the sun, should be about $\frac{1}{25}$ of that at opposition.

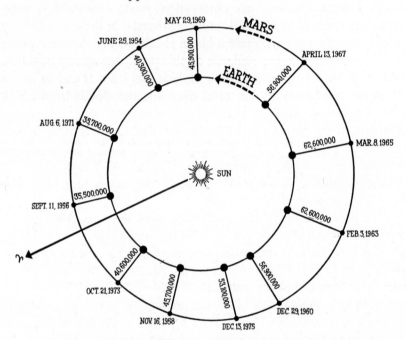

Fig. 11.7. The oppositions of Mars from 1954 to 1975. Unfavorable oppositions occur in February and March when Mars is near aphelion. Favorable oppositions always occur in August and September when Mars is near perihelion.

11.24. Favorable oppositions
Though Mars is always nearer and brighter than usual when it is opposite the sun (in the east when the sun is in the west, for example) it is not equally bright at all oppositions. When the earth passes it near its perihelion point, it is approximately 28,000,000 miles nearer to us than when we pass near its point of aphelion (Fig. 11.7). Mars is in opposition at intervals of 780 days (nearly 2 years and 2 months); this is its synodic period. But only at intervals of sometimes 15 years, sometimes 17 years, does the opposition take place near enough to the perihelion point to be spoken of as "favorable." When an opposition takes place in August or September it is a favorable one, for the earth passes the perihelion position of Mars

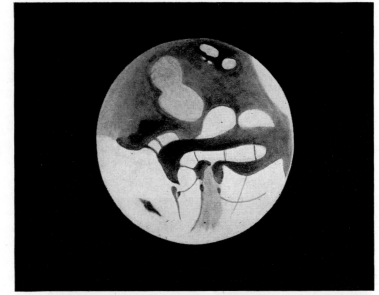

Fig. 11.8. Drawing of Mars made at the Observatoire Jarry-Desloges. Note difference in general appearance of Mars as seen by the eye and the camera (see Fig. 11.9).

near August 28 each year. Mars and the earth were closer together at the opposition of Aug. 22, 1924 than they will be again for several centuries. At the opposition of 1909, the first successful photographs of Mars were taken.

Although the average distance between the two planets at passing is 48,600,000 miles, this may be reduced to 34,600,000. No other planet except Venus comes so near us, and Venus, unfortunately, has its dark side turned toward us at the time of its nearest approach. Mars is full and in the opposite part of the sky from the sun when it is nearest the earth, and so is favorably located for observation. Its brightness at such a time (magnitude −2.8) is greater than that of any star and is greater than the brightness of any other planet except Venus.

11.25. Size and mass

Mars is much smaller than the earth. Its diameter of 4268 miles is but a little more than half the earth's diameter, and its mass little more than a tenth that of our planet (0.108). The mass can be very accurately measured, for unlike Mercury and Venus, it has satellites, which are useful for this purpose. Only Mercury, and possibly Pluto, are smaller than Mars.

11.26. Surface conditions

Mars is too far away for us to see whether or not it has mountains, such as are so easily seen on the moon. Only the large expanse of the white polar snow caps, and the bright reddish areas and dark green patches, are easily seen. To enable us to observe a feature on Mars as plainly as a similar feature a mile across on the moon, the Martian object would have to be 150 miles across; Mars, at its nearest, is about 150 times as far away as the moon (Figs. 11.8 and 11.9).

11.27. Evidences of an atmosphere
White caps near the poles, and a white strip often seen along the east side just after sunrise which is apparently a morning frost, both indicate an atmosphere from which there is precipitation, as on earth.

An atmosphere is made evident, also, by the appearance of occasional cloudiness and even dust storms, apparently, which sometimes move across the planet.

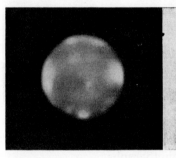 

Fig. 11.9. Mars photographed in blue light with the 200-inch Hale telescope. Blue light has little penetrating power so that it shows only the outer atmospheric shell of the planet. The polar caps are conspicuous on blue and violet photographs indicating they may be partially an atmospheric phenomenon. (*Mount Wilson and Palomar Observatories.*)

11.28. Twilight an evidence of air
An interesting proof of atmosphere is twilight. If it were not for atmosphere, the darkness of night would shut down instantly upon the earth (or upon any planet) as soon as the sun went below the horizon. The air above us catches the sun's rays after sunset and reflects them down, illuminating the ground. When Mars is in the gibbous phase some of its dark side is turned toward us. We can faintly see a twilight zone, about 8° wide, beyond the part which receives direct sunlight.

The depth of the Martian atmosphere has been estimated at 60 miles. This estimate was made by comparing photographs of Mars taken through color screens so that in one case only violet light was used, and in the other case infrared light. These colors differ in their power to penetrate an atmosphere (Fig. 11.10).

11.29. Mars an object of interest
On account of certain observations made by the Italian astronomer Schiaparelli, Mars has become one of the most widely discussed objects in the sky. About 1877, Schiaparelli discovered markings on its surface which seemed to his eye to be long straight lines. He called them "canali," which in Italian means simply channels. To English-speaking people the word sounds like "canals," which are artificial structures. They were interpreted by W. H. Pickering as strips of vegetation several miles wide, watered by an irrigation ditch down the center. Anything of less width would be hopelessly invisible. Pickering discovered small dark spots at the in-

tersections of the canals which he named *oases*. In 1893, Percival Lowell established an observatory at Flagstaff, Arizona, where Mars has been a special object of study ever since.

All astronomers admit that there is a vast amount of detailed markings on Mars, but not all have been able to see the long, fine lines on the planet depicted by Schiaparelli and Lowell. This may be due to the fact that few astronomers observe Mars as long and patiently as these two men. Visibility of the canals seems to depend primarily upon a perfectly calm state of our atmosphere rather than upon a large telescope or any particular kind of eyesight.

11.30. Nature of the canals

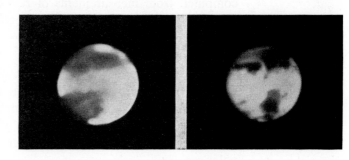

Fig. 11.10. Contrasting photographs of Mars in blue (left) and red light (right). The red light is more penetrating than blue so that it shows more surface detail. This blue photograph of Mars, however, shows more markings than are usually visible. 200-inch Hale telescope. (*Mount Wilson and Palomar Observatories.*)

Lowell believed that the canals are actual waterways constructed by highly intelligent beings for the purpose of conveying water from the melting polar caps down over the dry surface. The theory makes a strong appeal to the imagination, but in our present state of ignorance it seems too farfetched to be taken seriously. From a study of the location of the dark green areas, Tombaugh has suggested that Mars is a globe that underwent considerable shrinkage in volume after a thick crust had formed, which left the surface layers in a state of strain easily vulnerable to fracture. The round oases are interpreted as impact craters formed by collisions with asteroids, as in the case of the moon. The network of lines or "canals" radiating from the oases are fractures in the crust produced by the collisions. These long lines of fracture might provide a haven for a hardy type of vegetation similar, perhaps, to our lichens in regions otherwise unfavorable to growth. The seasonable behavior of the canals can be explained by the growth of vegetation capable of absorbing the slight moisture from the air after the polar caps melt and evaporate during each Martian year.

Instruments for measuring radiation have given data from which the planet's temperature has been calculated. Moreover the

11.31. Temperature

probable temperature of any planet can be estimated from a knowledge of the amount of heat received by it at its distance from the sun.

Mars is a little more than 1½ times as far from the sun as we are. This would give Mars slightly less than half as much heat per unit surface as is received on the earth. The temperature that this heat would produce would be far too low for comfort except under the most favorable conditions. Even at the Martian equator at noon the thermometer does not go above 50° or 60° F, at mean distance, but may reach 80° F at perihelion. Along the white, frost-covered strip at the sunrise edge a temperature as low as −121° F has been computed from measurements of radiation. This is about the temperature of "dry ice," and, taken together with higher temperatures near the center of the disk, it indicates very extreme daily fluctuations of heat and cold.

The thinness of Mars' atmosphere allows heat to escape so readily that radiation readings taken when the sun is setting show a freezing temperature. It is thought that the nights must be excessively cold, the days merely cool. Such a climate would be very unfavorable except for the hardiest forms of life, such, perhaps, as are found in our polar regions.

11.32. Atmosphere and moisture
Not only would living things on Mars have to adapt themselves to a scarcity of heat but also to a great scarcity of moisture and oxygen—perhaps no oxygen. The air is very thin, rarer apparently than the atmosphere in our lofty mountains. Moreover clouds are seldom seen, and the winter fall of snow around the poles is so light that most of it quickly melts in the spring.

From the rapid disappearance of the white caps with the coming of spring it is supposed that the snow is not deep, but perhaps more like a heavy frost. This would indicate very little water.

Some have thought that the intense cold of Mars would be sufficient to solidify carbon dioxide if that gas is in the air, making snow of it. But the snow remains on the ground when measurements of temperature show it to be higher than the vaporizing point of solid carbon dioxide (−122° F). The snow is therefore probably made from water vapor. Snow could evaporate without even rising to the melting temperature if the air were very dry. Snow and ice often disappear in dry weather on earth without melting.

11.33. An outstanding atmospheric phenomenon on Mars
It is a well-known fact that blue-light photographs of Mars usually record practically no trace of the familiar surface markings on the planet, even such intense features as the Syrtis Major, or great hourglass marking, being obliterated. During the latter part of May,

1937, however, photographs taken at the Lowell Observatory revealed that the Martian atmosphere had become so transparent as to
record not only the Syrtis Major in blue-light photographs but other
markings as well with striking distinctness. Thus the condition of the
Martian air which renders it opaque to blue and violet light had for
some unknown reason been removed temporarily to a marked degree.

Simultaneous photographs taken in yellow and red light showed
no notable changes in the dark markings, so that the changes in the
blue-light images were evidently due wholly to the suddenly increased transparency of the atmosphere alone.

Such observations indicate a sudden and great meteorological
change in the Martian atmosphere, and also that the Martian atmosphere is more opaque to blue light than our own.

Is there Life on Mars?

There is good evidence that the dark areas consist of a covering of vegetation of some sort. Kuiper notes that the colors show
regional patterns like those due to vegetation on the earth. The dark
markings change in appearance with the seasons as if they were governed by the amount of moisture in the atmosphere. It is often stated
that the dark markings are green in the spring and change to brown
in the fall. Some observers, however, believe that the *intensity* of the
markings changes rather than their color. That is, the markings are
dim in the fall and become stronger in the spring. Öpik remarks that
if the dark markings did *not* have the power to grow and regenerate
themselves they would have been covered by dust from the deserts
and obliterated long ago.

The type of vegetation which would seem to have the best chance
of existence on Mars are the lichens, of which some seventeen thousand species are known. Lichen is an interesting example of two dis-
similar organisms—a fungus and alga—living in partnership as if
for their mutual benefit. The fungus can perform certain functions
which the alga cannot, and vice versa, the result being that the two
together can flourish under conditions impossible for less hardy
plants. We find lichens growing on the Sahara desert and in regions
where the temperature is below freezing the year round. They can
exist in an atmosphere containing little or no oxygen. Lichens may
be seen growing in the form of a gray scale in the most barren places,
such as bare rock. With their seemingly unlimited adaptibility, it is
possible that lichens would survive if transplanted to Mars. (But the
reader is cautioned that this is not saying that there *are* lichens grow-

11.34. The evidence

169

ing on Mars! We do not even know that the dark areas are covered by "vegetation." Perhaps it would be better to say that they are covered by some form of "living substance.")

The possibility of the existence of animal life on Mars is much less favorable. All the evidence here is of a negative character. On such a cold, arid, oxygenless world we certainly would not anticipate a high form of animal life as we know it, at least. About all that can be said on the subject is that only lower animals with little need of oxygen (and little need and content of water) would be able to live on Mars because of the planet's low temperatures (and scarcity of water). "In short, from the standpoint of vital oxygen pressure, man and animals except those of the very lowest species can be excluded from life on Mars with certainty. Any positive arguments as to the presence of lower animals with little need of oxygen are and will remain speculations for lack of any clues." *

Lack of oxygen on Mars has been explained by assuming that the surface rocks have devoured it all, just as iron left out-of-doors combines with the oxygen of the air and crumbles to red rust. The reddish brown color of the deserts suggests that these are minerals that have undergone extensive oxidation. But Kuiper finds that the reflection spectrum of the Martian deserts does not resemble iron oxides, but closely matches a brownish igneous rock called felsite. The absence of oxygen from the atmosphere of Mars may be due to the fact that there was never much of this vital element there in the first place.

11.35. Satellites   In 1877, Asaph Hall, at the U. S. Naval Observatory, discovered two satellites of Mars (Fig. 11.11) which he named after the two mythological companions of the god of war—Phobos (fear) and Deimos (panic). It is said that Hall became so discouraged in searching for the satellites that at one time he decided to abandon the project. But his wife urged him to return to the observatory for one more look. Hall reluctantly agreed and, sure enough, found the tiny bodies just as he had hoped. Phobos is unique in that it revolves around its planet faster than the planet turns on its axis; no other such case is known in the solar system.

Pluto

11.36. Discovery   For several reasons we know less about Pluto than any of the other planets. This is partly because Pluto was discovered comparatively recently, but mainly because its small size and great dis-

* Quoted from *Physiological Considerations on the Possibility of Life Under Extraterrestrial Conditions* by Hubertus Strughold. The University of Illinois Press.

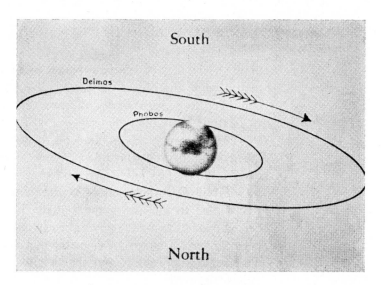

South

Deimos

Phobos

North

Fig. 11.11. Mars and the orbits of its satellites, drawn to scale.

tance make it invisible except through a telescope of at least 12-inch aperture. Even then it appears only as a point of light instead of as a disk, as do the other planets.

At the beginning of the twentieth century, a few investigators, particularly Percival Lowell, became interested in the possible existence of an unseen planet beyond Neptune. Certain small irregular motions of Uranus were interpreted by Lowell as indications of the presence of another, more distant planet. Lowell started a search at Flagstaff, Arizona, in 1906, using a small camera of 5-inch aperture to photograph stars for purposes of comparison. Since the stars are fixed, a moving body such as an asteroid can be detected by the little trail it leaves on a plate taken with an exposure of, say, an hour. Also, if two plates of the same region of the sky are compared by making the images of the stars match, a moving object can be detected by its displacement from one plate to the other. The search for the planet was continued intermittently until 1929, but without success.

In March, 1929, the program was resumed by 23-year-old Clyde Tombaugh, with much brighter prospects owing to installation at the Lowell Observatory of a new 13-inch photographic telescope having a wide field of view and especially well adapted for that type of work. It was necessary to take many plates during the course of a month at the telescope and then examine them for moving objects, a very laborious and exacting job. For example, the plates taken in the western region of the constellation of Gemini contained more than 300,000 star images each.

On the afternoon of Feb. 18, 1930, while blinking some plates centered about the star Delta Geminorum, Tombaugh suddenly came upon the images of the new planet. Announcement was delayed a month while the object was under observation. The rate of motion continued to be satisfactory and proved beyond doubt that the body was a trans-Neptunian planet.

The discovery was announced to the world on Mar. 13, 1930, the date of Lowell's birthday. A few months later the planet was named Pluto. The name was first suggested to the professor of astronomy at Oxford by an 11-year-old English girl. The suggestion was cabled to the astronomers at the Lowell Observatory and accepted out of the many names already proposed. The choice of name is particularly appropriate since the place of the planet is in the outer dark regions of space, and the first two letters are the initials of Percival Lowell.

11.37. Surface conditions on Pluto

Pluto is so far away that it never shows a disk even in the largest telescopes. From indirect observations, however, we can draw some conclusions regarding conditions on its surface.

Measures made with the 200-inch Hale telescope using a device called the disk meter give a diameter for Pluto of 3600 miles. The mass of Pluto, calculated from its gravitational attraction on Uranus and Neptune, is equal to that of the earth. With this diameter and mass, the density of Pluto would be five times that of lead, which seems impossibly high. If Pluto has the same density as the earth, then its mass would be only one-tenth that of the earth. The unreasonably high density of Pluto is a puzzle which astronomers are as yet unable to explain.

It has been suggested that Pluto has a smooth ice-covered surface which reflects light regularly like a spherical mirror, instead of diffusely like a roughened surface does. The effect of such a mirror-like surface would be to make Pluto appear smaller than it really is. But even if Pluto once had a smooth shining surface, collisions with meteorites would have roughened it long ago. Kuiper believes his observations of Pluto are consistent with a gritty-snow surface and an atmosphere less than one-tenth that of the earth.

QUESTIONS AND EXERCISES

1. In which direction is the moon moving when it eclipses the sun? In which direction is Mercury moving when it transits the sun? Explain.

2. Why is Venus brightest when at crescent phase instead of at full phase like the moon?

3. Compare the possibility of life on Venus and Mars. Which do you think is the more favorable site for some form of life?

4. Pluto looks about the same on a photograph as a faint asteroid. How could it be distinguished from an asteroid?

5. The distance of Io from Jupiter is only slightly more than the distance of the moon from the earth. Yet Io has a period of only 1.8 days compared with the period of 27.3 days for the moon. Can you explain the large difference?

6. Describe how you think the earth would look from a point in space.

7. How would the appearance of the earth differ to an observer on Mars and an observer on Venus (assuming he could see the earth through a break in the clouds)?

8. Can you think of any natural physical forces that might have produced the linelike markings on Mars besides those mentioned in the text?

9. What arguments can you think of that would be against the canals being open waterways? (*Hint:* Owing to the low atmospheric pressure on Mars, water would boil at about 79° F instead of 212° F.)

10. Could you light a match in the open on Mars? How would you have to cook on Mars?

11. Tell ways that you think photography would be superior to the eye in observing Mars and vice versa.

12. In what physical characteristic does the earth exceed all the other planets? See table on page 47.

13. How would it be helpful to astronomers if Venus had a satellite?

14. Suppose our moon revolved around Venus at the same distance as it revolves around the earth. Would its period be longer or shorter than at present?

15. We can determine the mass of a planet only from its gravitational attraction on other bodies. What type of body might be used in determining the mass of Mercury?

16. What region on the earth probably most closely resembles Mars?

17. Do you think an aircraft could fly on Mars? What condition would be favorable? What unfavorable?

12 THE LARGER PLANETS

Jupiter

FOR half of every year Jupiter is a commanding starlike object in the evening sky; only one star, Sirius, and two planets, Venus, and, very rarely, Mars, ever surpass it in brightness.

12.1. Comparison with Venus   Because of its very large orbit about the sun as compared with the orbit of the earth, Jupiter remains always in practically full phase. Moreover, Jupiter's position outside the orbit of the earth allows it to be seen not only near the sun, as with Venus and Mercury, but in any part of the zodiac from the sunrise to the sunset position. Jupiter, like other outer planets, is thus visible all night long at a time of year when it rises in the early evening. But outer planets are not usually called evening and morning stars.

The telescopic view of Jupiter, while never showing the interesting crescent phases of Venus, nevertheless displays an interesting family of satellites, lacking around Venus. The telescope also, if large enough, shows a wealth of detail in the structure of Jupiter's surface (Fig. 12.1). Venus, though very bright, is nearly featureless.

12.2. Size   Considered simply as a member of the solar system, Jupiter holds the place of eminence among the nine planets. It is not only larger than any of the others, but it is larger than all of the others together. And we may interpret the word large as referring either to volume or mass, for Jupiter is heavier and occupies more space than all of the others. The diameter of Jupiter is 11.3 times that of the earth; therefore its surface area is about 11^2, or 121, and its volume 11^3, or 1331, times the earth's.

12.3. Changing distance and brightness   According to Bode's law, Jupiter's mean distance is 5.2 astronomical units, and for Jupiter the law gives practically the true distance. Its orbit is not quite round, but it swings only half a unit

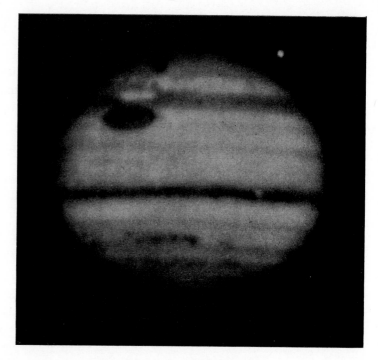

Fig. 12.1. Jupiter photographed in blue light showing large red spot and satellite Ganymede and shadow (above). 200-inch Hale telescope. (Mount Wilson and Palomar Observatories.)

farther from the sun at the long end of the elliptical orbit (aphelion) than at the short end (perihelion). Its distance from the earth varies much more than its distance from the sun, ranging from 6.45 units to 3.95 units, depending on where it and the earth are in their orbits. This change of distance makes considerable change in Jupiter's brightness, since brightness varies inversely as the *square* of the distance. It is nearest and brightest when in the opposite side of the sky from the sun. By squaring its maximum and minimum distances we may find that Jupiter is about 2.1 times as bright at opposition, when opposite the sun, as at superior conjunction, beyond the sun.

The most obvious feature of Jupiter as seen through a small telescope is a row of satellites—usually four—tiny starlike objects, perhaps two on one side of the planet and two on the other, or sometimes three or four on one side and one or none on the other (Fig. 12.2). At other times one is missing, being eclipsed or occulted by the planet, or passing over its surface, when it is not easily visible. The reason they are nearly in line is that their orbits lie almost in one plane, and we are approximately in the same plane. That is, we look at the *edges* of the orbits.

When Barnard discovered the fifth satellite in 1892, he decided not to name it but to call it merely the Fifth Satellite (Jupiter V, or J V), as he thought the numerical designations I, II, III, and IV, used by Galileo, had proven more convenient and were more commonly used than their given names of Io, Europa, Ganymede, and

*12.4. Satellites
(Fig. 12.2)*

175

Callisto. Thus, when Nicholson discovered the Ninth Satellite at the Lick Observatory in 1914, it was designated J IX ("Jix"). Nicholson discovered J X and J XI at the Mount Wilson Observatory with the 100-inch telescope photographically in 1938, and J XII in 1951 (Fig. 12.3).

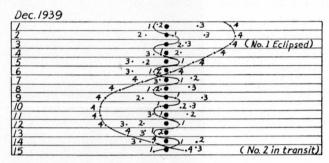

Fig. 12.2. Positions of Jupiter's four bright satellites as seen through a reversing telescope on the evenings of Dec. 1 to 15, 1939. The period of No. 1 is about 1¾ days, of No. 4, nearly 16¾ days.

The distant satellites of Jupiter fall into two groups. The members of the inner group (VI, VII, and X) move counterclockwise as seen from the north (direct) at mean distances of about 7 million miles. The members of the outer group (VIII, IX, XI, and XII) move clockwise or retrograde at mean distances of about 14 million miles. Either the satellites of Jupiter have more stable orbits at these distances or the grouping is a consequence of their origin.

12.5. Markings on the planet   Through a small telescope five or six inches in diameter the surface of Jupiter is seen to be crossed by two or three dark belts running parallel with the equator. These "belts" or "bands" lie on the surface of the planet. They do not stand out like the "rings" of Saturn. They are obviously clouds floating in the planet's atmosphere.

With a very large telescope of high power, still other narrower bands are seen, and a wealth of constantly changing detail shows that the markings are not engraved in stone as features of the moon seem to be. The darker bands are mainly in shades of red or brown; the lighter strips are of a yellowish color.

Some markings are, in their general outline, fairly constant (Fig. 12.4). One of the most talked of features a generation ago was "the great red spot," discovered in 1878. It lasted for years as a conspicuous figure some 30,000 miles long and 7000 miles wide. It can still be seen faintly but is smaller and more nearly round. The red spot, and the fact of so much turmoil in the cloudy atmosphere of the planet, gave rise to the supposition that the surface under the clouds might be hot—red hot under the "red spot." Observations made with the help of a thermocouple do not confirm this opinion but seem to indicate a temperature of about −184° F. Also, the fact

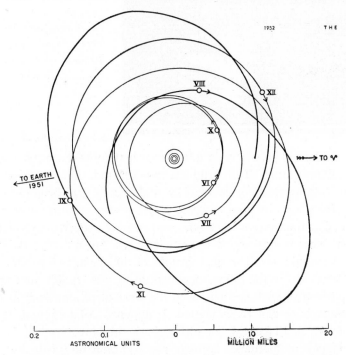

Fig. 12.3. Orbits of Jupiter's satellites. The actual paths traveled by J VIII and J IX for one revolution are shown; they are not even approximately closed ellipses. The orbits of J XI and of J XII plotted here are the paths in which those satellites were moving at the time of discovery. Because of the disturbing pull of the sun their actual paths would deviate from the indicated ellipses. The approximate positions of the satellites at the opposition of 1951 are indicated by small circles. The arrows show the direction of motion, clockwise for all the outer group, counterclockwise for the others.

that Jupiter's satellites are totally invisible while eclipsed in the shadow of the planet seems to show that they do not receive any light from the planet itself.

Even the four large satellites, when viewed with large telescopes, show surface features similar to those of the planet. These moons, with one exception, are all larger than ours, and would be

12.6. Appearance of satellites

Fig. 12.4. Jupiter. Top row: Mar. 28, 1920; Feb. 12, 1921. Bottom row: Mar. 15, 1921, the satellite Ganymede appears as white spot at upper right. Its shadow is the black spot on planet's disk. May 29, 1922. Photographed with 100-inch telescope, Mount Wilson Observatory.

visible to the naked eye on a dark night if they were not so close to the brilliant planet. The brightest one of them, if brought near enough to be placed beside Mars, would exceed it in brightness.

12.7. The planet's atmosphere

By means of photographic plates sensitive to infrared radiation, very distinct bands have been shown in the spectrum of Jupiter. Some of these bands are of unknown origin, but many of them are due to ammonia gas. The photographs of the spectra of Jupiter, and of ammonia gas in the laboratory seem to be remarkably similar. By a comparison of such spectra, even the amount of ammonia in Jupiter's atmosphere can be estimated. It appears to be equivalent to a layer of the gas 30 feet thick at atmospheric pressure.

Evidence of methane, another gas common on earth, but very rare in our atmosphere, is found in Jupiter's spectrum. This is the gas, so explosive in coal mines, referred to as *fire-damp*. Its chemical formula is CH_4.

Observations of the fluctuations in light of a star occulted by Jupiter in November, 1952, indicate that the planet's atmosphere is in a state of violent turbulence and that it is composed almost entirely of hydrogen and helium. These gases cannot be detected with the spectroscope as their absorption lines are in an unobservable region of the spectrum. The lines of methane and ammonia are in the observable region of the spectrum, but there is actually only a trace of these gases compared with the amount of hydrogen and helium present.

12.8. Temperature

From the fact that Jupiter is 5.2 times as far from the source of heat as is the earth, it can be seen that it should receive only $1/5.2^2$, or $1/27$ as much heat as does the earth, but due to its high

albedo, much of the sunlight is reflected from the planet. The temperature that a planet should have as the result of this much heat is very low—in the neighborhood of −189° F.

As a check on this method, the temperature has been found by measuring radiation from the planet. Both methods give approximately the same result.

The clouds that form the bands on Jupiter's surface can scarcely be due to water vapor, in view of the extremely low temperature. Water vapor would certainly be frozen out of the air, leaving only those gases which condense and solidify at much lower temperatures. The clouds could well be condensed ammonia and hydrocarbon gases, which the spectrum shows to be in the air. All water of the planet must be securely locked in the form of ice, too cold even to vaporize, and far too cold to melt.

12.9. Cloud bands not water vapor

Saturn

Throughout ancient and medieval astronomical history Saturn was the most distant known planet. Even in very early times there was some knowledge of the relative distances to the planets, for it was easy to observe their times of revolution. It was correctly assumed that at greater distances the planets would require longer to make the circuit. Saturn's time was 29.5 years.

Saturn is always a conspicuous object, but not so bright as Jupiter because it is nearly twice as far away, and scarcely as large. But it is brighter than the average first-magnitude star. Its brightness is more nearly constant than that of Jupiter or Mars because of its greater distance, which does not change so much, relatively, while the earth goes around the sun (Fig. 12.5).

The one thing that makes Saturn unique in the whole field of astronomy is its ring. More precisely, this feature should be called *rings*, for there are really three of them, all lying in the same plane but separated enough by spaces between them so that a fairly powerful telescope makes them appear separate.

12.10. The rings

ECS 1915

ECS 1917

1921

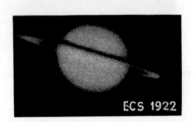
ECS 1922

Fig. 12.6. Saturn, showing changes in appearance of rings. Once in about 15 years the edge is turned toward us, as in the 1921 photograph. Then the rings are invisible because they are so thin. (*Lowell Observatory.*)

The rings lie exactly in the plane of the planet's equator. It seems rather natural that they should do so, for satellites, which they resemble, usually revolve in a plane nearly that of the planet's equator. There are also bands on the surface of Saturn that are parallel to Saturn's equator. The rings differ from bands, however, in that they are thousands of miles above the surface.

12.11. Changes in appearance The appearance of the rings differs markedly from time to time (Fig. 12.6). They go through a cycle of changes corresponding in time to the planet's period of revolution of nearly 30 years. Twice during this interval the ring stands at such an angle as to give a side view of considerable width, and twice the edge is turned toward us. In its most favorable position the ring appears as an ellipse that is nearly half as wide as it is long.

12.12. Thickness and size When the edge of the ring is turned toward us it is invisible for several days even with large telescopes. This shows that the ring is *very* thin in comparison with its width. A thickness of not more than 10 miles has been estimated. Ten miles as compared with the diameter of the outer ring, 171,000 miles, is very small. Even as compared with 10,000 miles, which is the *width* of this ring, 10 miles is small. If we should cut from the full size of a sheet of newspaper a model of the ring, the thickness of the paper would be approximately right to represent the thickness of the ring.

12.13. Nature of the rings That the rings allow light to pass through them is shown by the partial shadow they cast. Their shadow falls on the body of the planet, and a shadow also extends out into the space through which some of Saturn's satellites must pass. The astronomer Barnard once saw a satellite eclipsed by the shadow of the inner ring. While in the shadow the satellite was still visible but dim. A satellite disappears entirely from view when it goes into the shadow of the planet. Evidently the inner ring is not quite opaque. Another evidence of the discontinuous character of the material in the rings is that a star has been clearly seen through the outer one. A star seen through the middle ring was dimmed slightly but never vanished entirely, indicating that this ring is denser than the others but not actually opaque. Apparently light shining into the ring finds its way partially blocked by something before it gets through the ten miles of its thickness.

There are several lines of evidence showing that the rings are composed of meteoric particles, not of a continuous solid sheet. The first of these proofs to be discovered rested upon the mechanics of motion of the heavenly bodies. Such a strain would be put upon a continuous sheet that it would be broken to pieces.

12.14. Proofs of meteoric structure

A second evidence of the ring's meteoric structure was found in the manner in which it reflects light coming at different angles. It reflects, not as a solid sheet would be expected to do, but as if much of the light goes deep in among the particles, and is lost in the shadows.

Strongest evidence, however, was furnished by J. E. Keeler, famous for his spectroscopic work. Keeler, at Allegheny Observatory, found that the inner part of the principal ring moves at the rate of about 12 miles a second and the outer part at only 10 miles. These are the velocities with which satellites would move if at these same distances from the planet. The conclusion is that each of the millions of particles of which the rings are composed moves independently, like a tiny moon, at the velocity which is natural for it at whatever distance it is from the planet.

If Saturn were put into an ocean of water large enough to float in, it would not sink. The average density is less than three fourths that of water, whereas the average density of the earth is 5.5 times the density of water. It is, therefore, about $\frac{1}{8}$ as dense as our own rock-ribbed planet. To carry the comparison a little further, if Saturn were compressed until it had the density of the earth it would be only about $\frac{1}{2}$ its present diameter.

12.15. The planet itself

To account for the low specific gravity two theories may be advanced: one, that Saturn has enough heat to keep it in gaseous form; the other, that it has a solid core surrounded by a deep atmosphere.

12.16. Explanation of its low density

Radiometric measurements of surface temperature show $-235°$ F. There is no evidence of great internal heat. The much more probable theory is that a solid or liquid core is surrounded by a cloudy atmosphere extending far enough out to increase very greatly the planet's apparent size. It may be that half its apparent size is due to atmosphere. Whatever may explain the very low average density of Saturn will undoubtedly explain why all of the four major planets are so much lighter than the smaller ones, in proportion to their size. None of the four is as much as a third as dense as the earth.

12.17. Composition of atmosphere

Spectroscopic observations that were made at Mount Wilson and Lowell Observatories show ammonia gas and methane (marsh gas) in the atmosphere of Saturn as well as in that of Jupiter. In Jupiter ammonia predominates, in Saturn methane. Saturn, being so much farther from the sun than Jupiter, is, naturally, much colder. It is thought that nearly all of the ammonia has been frozen out of the atmosphere of Saturn. A larger proportion of methane has been left in the air because it freezes at a lower temperature. The spectroscope shows only what is in the air, not what is in solid form.

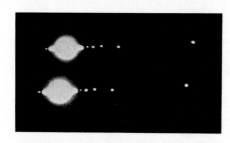

Fig. 12.7. Inner satellites of Saturn, Mar. 2, 1921. Photographed with the Lowell 24-inch refractor by E. C. Slipher. From left to right: Enceladus, Mimas, Tethys, Dione, Rhea, Titan. (Lowell Observatory.)

It is believed that the water of the four great planets—Jupiter, Saturn, Uranus, and Neptune—is all condensed out of the air and frozen to form a layer of ice at the bottom of the atmosphere.

12.18. Satellites

Saturn has a family of nine known satellites (Fig. 12.7). With one exception, the satellite called Titan, these are much smaller than our moon, though several of them are large enough to be seen with a telescope of a few inches' aperture. The very small outermost one, called Phoebe, is remarkable because of its retrograde motion around the planet. Its motion is like that of the outer three of Jupiter's satellites.

Kuiper (1944) has found a close resemblance between the spectrum of Titan, the largest satellite of Saturn, and Saturn itself, except that the methane bands on Titan are definitely weaker.

The mass of Titan is so low that its atmosphere would be quickly lost by a slight increase of temperature of only 200° F. Hence, if Titan has gone through a period of high surface temperature as is supposed to be the case for all bodies in the solar system, then evidently Titan's atmosphere must have been formed *after* that period.

The color of Titan is orange, in marked contrast to the color of

Saturn and Jupiter and their satellites. Kuiper attributes the difference to the action of the atmosphere, such as the oxidation assumed to be responsible for the reddish color of Mars.

Uranus

Uranus was the first planet to be discovered with a telescope. *12.19. Discovery* Two more major planets have been found since which were not known from antiquity. In each of the three cases the discovery became headline news of the time.

The discovery of Uranus was made in 1781 by the greatest astronomer of that period, William Herschel. In a sense Herschel's work was an accident. He noticed the planet late one night while examining some faint stars in Gemini, where it happened to be at that time. He observed slight apparent differences between this object and an ordinary star, differences that might not have been noticed by a less practiced eye. Herschel was regularly sweeping the heavens (with a telescope made by himself) to learn all he could about every object within sight. Though justly acclaimed as the discoverer, Herschel was not the first to *see* Uranus. One other astronomer, in preparing star charts, had seen this planet twelve times, and recorded its position, never guessing that it was anything but a star.

It was the size of the disk, only 4″ in diameter, but wider than the image of a star, that first excited Herschel's suspicions. For several weeks, as he watched it, he thought that it was a comet. But within the year it had moved far enough so that a mathematical astronomer, using Herschel's observations, computed its orbit and found it to be a planet. As in the cases of both Neptune and Pluto, observations made of the positions of the planet before its real discovery were very helpful in computing its orbit.

Herschel naturally (and perhaps prudentially), named the new planet Georgium Sidus, in honor of his king, George III. The king knighted Herschel and appointed him his private astronomer, thus making it possible for him to carry on his work more extensively, and to build larger telescopes. Other European astronomers called the planet "Herschel," but finally the name Uranus, suggested by Bode, director of the Berlin Observatory, became permanent.

Although Uranus is four times as large as the earth, and *12.20. Distance,* therefore a little more than four times as large as the bright "evening *size, and ap-* star" Venus, it is just visible to the unaided eye on a dark night. *pearance* Sixth-magnitude stars are the dimmest we can see without a telescope, and Uranus's magnitude is 5.7. The two main reasons for its dimness are, first, that it is so far away from us; and second, that it is too far from the sun to be brilliantly illuminated. Its mean distance from the sun being a little more than 19 times ours, it receives only $1/19^2$ or $1/361$ as much light and heat per unit of surface as the earth does. It must be intensely cold unless it possesses heat of its own, and there is no evidence that it does.

Like all four of the "major" planets it doubtless looks larger than it is. Its mass has been found with great exactness, for it has satellites, which are useful in making this measurement. Since its mass and its apparent size are known, its average density can be calculated. It is very light, being less than $\frac{1}{4}$ as dense as the earth. This leads to the belief that the planet is surrounded with a covering of cloudy atmosphere, which adds to its apparent diameter.

12.21. Motions   Uranus is too far away to show much detail of surface markings such as are so noticeable on Jupiter, and to a less degree on Saturn. It is therefore necessary to use the spectroscopic method of finding the direction and rate of rotation on its axis. Like the rotation of Jupiter and Saturn, that of Uranus is very rapid, the period being only about 10¾ hours.

There is one very peculiar thing about the rotation of Uranus and the motion also of its five satellites, whose orbits lie nearly in the plane of the planet's equator. The plane of its equator is almost at right angles to the plane of its orbit around the sun. The satellites, being in orbits which are in the plane of the equator of the planet, also move at nearly right angles to the direction of the planet's motion.

12.22. Seasons   The plane of the earth's equator is tipped 23½° from the plane of the earth's orbit. It is this inclination of equator to orbit that gives us our seasons. If the plane of the equator, instead of being tipped 23½° could be still further inclined to 90°, or to a plane perpendicular to the orbit, then our seasons would be much more marked. The vertical rays of the sun would come not only to the tropics but to the poles.

The equator of Uranus, if it ever was in the plane of its orbit, has in some unexplained way been tilted not only 90 but 98°, so that the direction of the planet's axial rotation is *backwards* with respect to the orbit. If the inclination of our equator were similarly increased (from 23½ to more than 90°) the earth would turn backward with respect to our motion around the sun.

The same cause that originally gave Uranus a retrograde rotation, or changed its direction from direct to retrograde, has evidently acted similarly upon its satellites, for they also move in the same retrograde fashion.

Neptune

Neptune, like Uranus, is chiefly of interest because of the way it was discovered. From observations of Uranus made after its discovery, astronomers soon found an approximate orbit for the planet which enabled them to calculate its path in the past as well as in the future. Calculations a century back revealed that Uranus had been observed and recorded as a star. These pre-discovery observations should have enabled astronomers to get a very good orbit for Uranus. On the contrary, the old observations indicated that Uranus was considerably off its predicted path. As time went on Uranus departed farther and farther from its predicted course until astronomers felt virtually sure that there must be another planet beyond Uranus pulling it from its path.

12.23. The work of Adams and Leverrier

Two young mathematicians unknown to each other, one in England and the other in France, took up the problem of calculating where an outside, unknown planet would have to be to cause the observed disturbance in the motion of Uranus. Adams, the Englishman, completed his work first, laid it before the Astronomer-Royal of the Greenwich Observatory. Having no star chart for the part of the heavens where he was asked to look for a planet, and knowing nothing of the young man from whom the request came, the astronomer delayed the matter. When the search was finally started the work was slow for lack of a star chart.

In the meantime Leverrier, of France, finished his work and wrote to an assistant observer in the Berlin Observatory named Galle, asking him to look in a certain place for a planet. This was almost the exact spot selected by Adams. That night the planet was found within a few minutes after the telescope was turned to the spot given by Leverrier.

12.24. Physical conditions

Like the earth and Venus, the more distant pair, Uranus and Neptune, are twin planets. Little is known of the surface features of either of them. Neptune especially is apparently featureless. However, their sizes and masses and densities are quite similar. This strongly suggests similarity in their physical composition as well. Probably Neptune, like the others, owes much of its apparent size to clouds of great depth, for its average density is low.

12.25. Satellites

One satellite, called Triton, can be seen encircling Neptune in retrograde fashion, as mentioned above. The direction of the other satellite, called Nereid, is still uncertain.

12.26. Effects of position

It requires nearly 165 years for Neptune to make a revolution around the sun. Its year, therefore, is that long. But a year on so distant a planet must mean very little as far as seasons are concerned. Being 30 times the earth's distance from the sun it must receive only 1/900 as much heat as we do, and from this its resulting mean temperature has been calculated to be −359° F, provided the planet is a good absorber of heat. Summers on such a planet would be of negligible consequence. The winters could not be appreciably colder than the summers.

From Neptune the sun would look like a star, but intensely bright. It would be too small to show any noticeable disk to the unaided eye. At 30 times as far it would have only $\frac{1}{30}$ as great an angular diameter.

The absence of visible markings on the face of Neptune makes it impossible to observe its period of rotation directly.

Measures with the spectroscope give about 15.8 hours as the length of Neptune's day.

QUESTIONS AND EXERCISES

1. Which of the larger planets has the most equable seasons? Which the most extreme?

2. What type of activity on the surface might conceivably account for the rapid changes in the appearance of the cloud belts of Jupiter?

3. Saturn is 95 times as massive as the earth. Yet you would weigh little more on Saturn than on the earth. Explain.

4. Surface gravity on Jupiter is 2.65 times as much as on the earth. Think of all the effects such high surface gravity would produce, such as falling, jumping, running, etc.

5. Notice in Fig. 12.4 that part of the ring on the upper left hand side of Saturn appears to be missing. Why? What are the dark markings near the outer edges of the ring?

COMETS 13

Comets

MANY people grow to adult life without ever having seen a comet. The only conspicuous one whose period of return is within the span of a lifetime came in 1910 and will not be seen again until 1986. This was a brilliant and beautiful object. But the same year in which this regular but infrequent visitor, known as Halley's comet, appeared, an unexpected one still more luminous was discovered, not by astronomers, but by a group of workmen on a railroad in South Africa. It was so bright that it could be seen in the daytime. A few days later it moved so as to be visible in the northern hemisphere.

No one knows when a new, unannounced comet may sweep across the sky. Though astronomers with the telescope discover several each year, most of them are wholly invisible to the naked eye. No one with unaided vision need expect to see more than eight or ten, at most, in a lifetime, and, judging from the records of past experience, only two or three of these will be of great size and brilliance.

For the benefit of those who have never seen a comet it should be said that there is a great difference between a comet and a meteor in nature and appearance. A comet has no evident motion; it shines in the sky all night as calmly as the moon. It is a distant and vastly large object, always larger than the earth, and sometimes as large as the sun, that is, more than 100 times the diameter of the earth. The average diameter of a comet is about ten times the diameter of the earth. A meteor, often called a shooting star, is in the earth's atmosphere, and very small, usually no larger than a tiny bit of gravel, according to estimates. A comet stays in view for hours, days or weeks. The shooting star flashes across the sky in an instant,

13.1. Infrequency of comets

13.2. Difference between comets and meteors

187

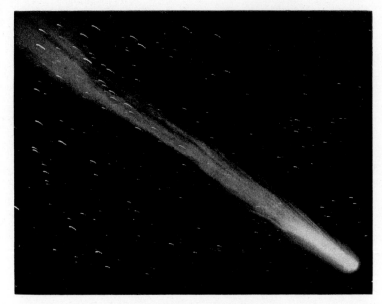

Fig. 13.1. Brooks' comet, Oct. 23, 1911. This is the comet that in 1886 passed closer to Jupiter than any of the planet's eleven satellites and had its orbit changed from 29 years to 7 years. It came within a distance of less than Jupiter's diameter from the surface of the planet. (*E. E. Barnard, Yerkes Observatory.*)

and is gone, unless it leaves a luminous trail which may persist for a few seconds or minutes.

13.3. Fireballs

It should be added, however, that the meteor may sometimes be of the variety known as a fireball, in which case it may brightly illuminate the night sky for a few moments. If discovered later on the ground, it may be found to weigh several pounds or several hundred pounds. The tiny shooting star, visible any night, and the great fireball are thought to be of the same nature, differing only in size.

13.4. Meteors derived from comets

The reason for so closely associating comets and meteors in our minds and in the textbooks is that meteors—many of them at least—seem to originate from comets. We receive an unusually large number of meteors on those nights when the earth is known to be passing the point of intersection of its own orbit with that of certain comets. Such an increase in the number seen constitutes what is known as a shower of meteors.

13.5. Structure of a comet

The head of a comet, which is more or less globular, is supposed to be made up mainly of meteoric matter, that is, of solid particles of a great variety of sizes. The particles are widely spaced from each other (Fig. 13.1).

A comet is more than a mere swarm of meteorites, for the spectroscope shows that among the solid particles there are gases which are responsible for a part of its light. There is also very fine dust mingled with the gas. This material is held together by mutual attraction of all the parts.

13.6. Parts of the comet

The HEAD of a comet consists of a large, nebulous body called the COMA, near the center of which there may be a small, bright NUCLEUS. The word *coma* is from a Latin word meaning hair.

From the coma streams the long filmy TAIL. The tail is dimmer than the coma, but it is difficult to tell just where one gradually merges into the other.

Some comets have no visible nucleus, and some are without a tail; they have only the coma. The most voluminous portion of the ordinary comet is its tail, which may be many millions of miles long. But the tail contains exceedingly little material. It is supposed that the greater part of the comet's mass is in its nucleus, although this is far smaller than either the coma or the tail. Even if the bright nucleus has any measurable diameter it is not often even a tenth part the

Fig. 13.2. The comet's tail usually stands out from the sun, and bends back. It is longest when near the sun, and is probably absent altogether when very far away.

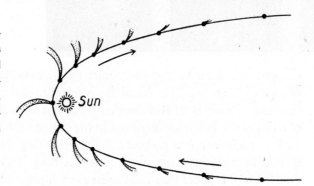

diameter of the entire head. Measurements of 500 to 900 miles have been made for the nuclei of various comets, but the heads of comets are seldom less than 15,000 miles in diameter.

13.7. The tail

Whenever a comet comes near the sun it develops a tail unless, perhaps, it may be devoid of tail-making material. The tail is made from the gas and fine dust expelled from the heat and driven by some force, as smoke issuing from a chimney is driven by the wind (Fig. 13.2).

The nature of the initial force that expels the finely divided tail-making material out of the head is not known. It seems to be an entirely different force from that which sweeps it back from the sun after it has left the head, for this material often starts toward the sun and then is turned back in the opposite direction.

The force exerted by the sun upon the comet's tail after it has freed itself from the heavier material of the head is one of repulsion, for nearly always the tail stands out away from the sun as if repelled by electrical or magnetic force. Similar charges of electricity repel each other, as we often demonstrate while using a comb on a dry day. The comb gives all of the hairs the same kind of electric charge, and the hairs all stand out away from each other. It was formerly

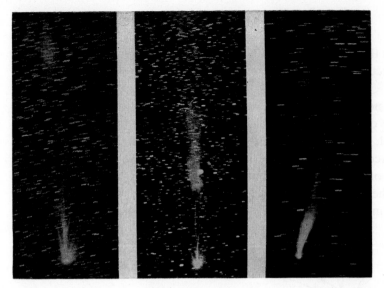

Fig. 13.3. Morehouse's comet taken at intervals of one day, showing material in the tail drifting back. (Yerkes Observatory.)

thought that the sun and the comet might both have the same kind of charge. This would account for repulsion, and perhaps it does account for a part of it. But another force has been discovered capable of causing the behavior observed in the comet's tail.

13.8. Light pressure

Light exerts a pressure. Before this fact was actually demonstrated in the laboratory, as it now has been, theoretical consideration led to the belief that light must exert a pressure. It is small or we should feel it. The full force of the pressure of sunlight on one square mile of surface at the distance of the earth from the sun is only 2 pounds, or a pressure equal to the weight of a scrap of very thin paper half the size of one's fingernail per square yard.

So small a force has no appreciable effect on heavy objects, but upon fine dust particles the sun's light-repelling pressure is greater than the sun's gravitational attracting force. This probably accounts for the tail's pointing away from the sun. The value of light pressure upon a gas atom is more difficult to calculate. Whether or not it is greater than the attractive force of the sun's gravitation upon the atom is not known.

13.9. Motion within the tail

The tail of a comet it not a permanent appendage. Like smoke from a locomotive, it is continually flowing outward, and would be lost entirely but for the new material being supplied from the head. Since the flow of matter from the head is not quite steady but sometimes comes in puffs, it is possible to follow the movement of knots or other irregularities by photographing them from hour to hour or from day to day (Fig. 13.3).

In the tail of Halley's comet, in 1910, such irregularities were found to move 0.6 miles per second while still near the head. Farther out, the velocity was found to have increased to 57 miles per second.

Like the velocity of a falling body, it increases owing to the effect of a continual force.

As the comet goes around the sun, the tail usually bends back in the direction from which the comet came. This is as naturally would be expected, for the part thrown to the outside of its orbit must fall behind, having a larger circuit in which to travel. Sometimes the tail splits into two or more parts curving back at different angles. This seems to be due to the various materials of which the tail is made. The lighter material would be forced back from the sun with greater velocity, and therefore would curve less than the heavier, slower moving constituents.

13.10. Shape of the tail

Although comets emit light, they are not, strictly speaking, self-luminous in the sense that they shine by their own radiation as the sun and stars do. A comet is such a flimsy, tenuous thing that it could not possibly generate enough heat to shine "by itself." The conclusion seems inescapable that the comet shines by some process due to the action of sunlight falling upon it. This action consists of absorption of certain rays from sunlight by the cometary molecules and their emission almost immediately afterward. The process by which an atom or molecule absorbs certain radiation and then emits it in the form of perhaps several different rays of longer wave length is called FLUORESCENCE. When the ray emitted is the same as the one absorbed the process is called RESONANCE-FLUORESCENCE. It is now believed that resonance-fluorescence is the process that produces the bright bands in the spectra of comets.

13.11. The light of comets

Comets generally increase in size and luminosity as they approach the sun, but they also exhibit sudden irregular changes in brightness which are extremely puzzling. The most remarkable comet known in this respect is 1925 II (Schwassmann-Wachmann 1). Everything about this comet is unusual. It revolves in a nearly circular path 590 million miles from the sun between the orbits of Jupiter and Saturn. The comet may appear surrounded by a faint nebulosity, but at other times its image on a photographic plate is as sharp as that of a star. Usually it is about magnitude 16 to 17, but it may increase in brightness a hundredfold in a few days. Its most spectacular outburst occurred sometime between Dec. 7, 1945 and Jan. 26, 1946, when it increased 2700 times in brightness from about magnitude 18 to 9.4. Halley's comet is considered a large, bright object, but it is only about magnitude 16 to 17 when half the distance from the sun of 1925 II, and is too faint to be observed when at the distance of Jupiter.

13.12. Fluctuations in the brightness of comets

The cause of these extraordinary fluctuations is unknown. Attempts to connect the outbursts with sunspot activity have not been particularly convincing, but observations of the comet are incomplete and the question is still open.

Orbits of Comets

In ancient and medieval times comets were regarded with superstitious dread. They were thought to be harbingers of war, pestilence, or famine. Knowledge often dispels fantastic fears. So after Edmund Halley, some 250 years ago, had applied Newton's laws of gravitation to the motion of comets, and had predicted the return of several of them, including the one since known by his name, it became

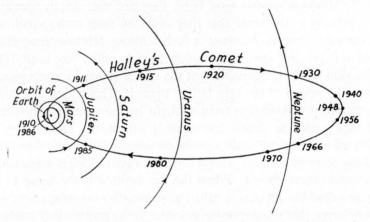

Fig. 13.4. Orbit of Halley's comet. Note the decrease in velocity as the comet leaves the sun, and the increase as it returns.

evident that comets are as law-abiding as planets. They come into view when nature's laws bring them, not when some catastrophe impends (Fig. 13.4).

13.13. Halley's comet   Halley, who was a contemporary and friend of Sir Isaac Newton, noticed that the comet which he was observing in 1682 was moving in much the same path as that followed by comets which had been observed 75 years and 151 years earlier. He assumed these to be different appearances of the same comet and predicted its return early in 1759. Though he did not live to see his prediction verified, the comet came April 13, 1759, and has made two other appearances on schedule since then. This comet was the first whose return was definitely predicted and is the only very noticeable comet whose period is within the span of a lifetime. Search of ancient and medieval manuscripts of Europe, China, and Japan have enabled the returns of Halley's comet to be traced with fair certainty back to

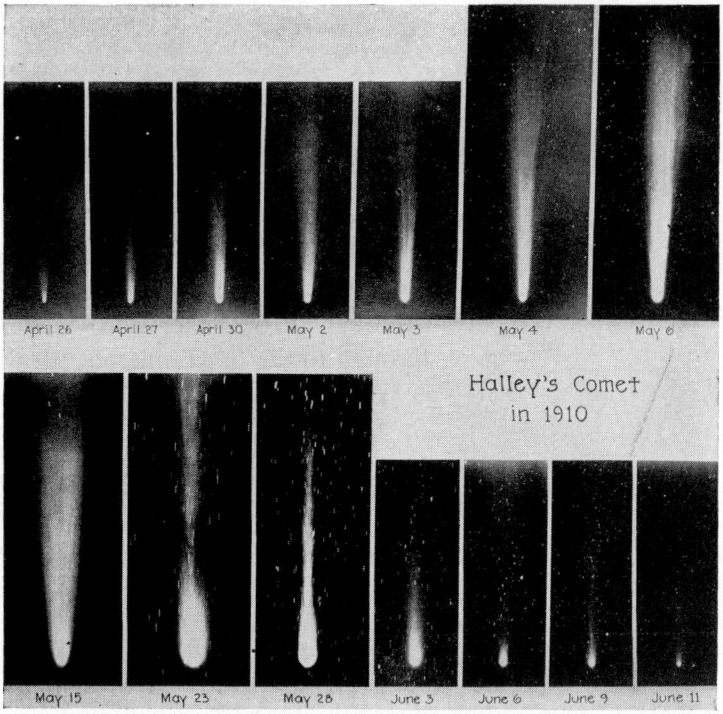

Fig. 13.5. Successive views of Halley's comet from April 26 to June 11, 1910. (Mount Wilson Observatory.)

April 26 April 27 April 30 May 2 May 3 May 4 May 6

Halley's Comet in 1910

May 15 May 23 May 28 June 3 June 6 June 9 June 11

87 B.C. and with some degree of probability back to 240 B.C. (Figs. 13.5 and 13.6).

13.14. Kinds of orbits possible

Orbits in which comets travel are usually ellipses of high eccentricity, that is, orbits very much longer than they are wide. Planets, also, travel in ellipses, but the orbits of the earth and most of the other planets are of such small eccentricity that the eye could not distinguish a correctly drawn diagram of one of these orbits from a true circle.

There are five kinds of orbits in which it would be *possible* for a comet (or other heavenly body) to travel. These are the straight line, the circle, the ellipse, the parabola, and the hyperbola. These

Fig. 13.6. Head of Halley's comet, June 5, 1910. Exposure 9 minutes, 60-inch reflector. (Mount Wilson Observatory.)

are all called conic sections because they can all be made by sectioning (cutting) a cone (Fig. 13.7).

If, from a point in one side of a cone, a cut is made straight through the cone perpendicular to the axis, a circle is formed. Any other cut going all the way through the cone (or the cone extended) gives an ellipse. A cut that is parallel to the other side (so that it does not go through to the other side) makes a parabola. Cuts neither going through to the other side nor parallel to it give hyperbolas of

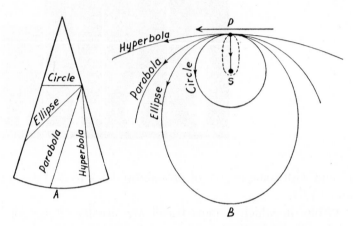

Fig. 13.7. Conic sections, the possible orbits of heavenly bodies.

various shapes. A plane that just touches that side gives a straight line. All parabolas, like all circles, are the same shape, though they may be of various sizes, but ellipses and hyperbolas may be more or less eccentric, that is, broad or narrow.

13.15. Why bodies follow different orbits   *S* in Figure 13.7 represents the sun, and a body of small mass at *p* is moving in a direction perpendicular to the line connecting it with the sun. The orbit it will follow is determined by its speed. Depending upon its distance from the attracting central body, and the force of that attraction, there is a certain velocity at which it would go in a circle. At velocities a little less or greater it would follow an ellipse of some sort. If the velocity were the square root of 2 (about 1.41) times the circular velocity, it would go in a parabola. At a still greater speed it would have a hyperbolic path. Parabolic or hyperbolic speeds would carry the object clear beyond the sun's power to bring it back, and it would never return. The outer ends of parabolic or hyperbolic orbits never come together, as the two sides of an ellipse do.

Comets depend upon the sun for their light energy, and hence become too faint to be seen at a distance of more than about 5 astronomical units. The orbits they follow are so nearly parabolic that in most cases it is difficult or impossible to tell whether they are moving in long, narrow ellipses and will eventually return or in parabolic paths that will take them permanently away from the sun. More and more the belief is growing that comets are, and always have been, members of the solar system.

13.16. Do comets travel in elliptical or parabolic orbits?

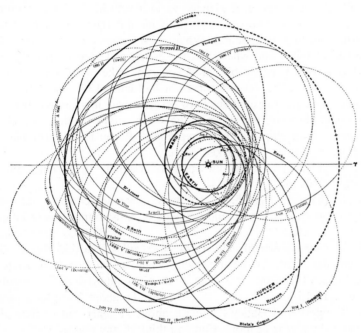

Fig. 13.8. Jupiter's family of comets. (*Popular Astronomy.*)

If a comet has come in from a practically infinite distance and passes close by the sun, it travels at tremendous speed at perihelion, the place nearest the sun. At a distance of the earth's orbit from the sun, such a comet would be moving at the rate of 26 miles per second. Several comets have been observed to go through the outer corona of the sun traveling at the rate of 300 miles a second. If one should hit the sun it would do so with a speed of 386 miles a second.

13.17. Velocity of comets

There are about thirty dim comets which have elliptical orbits of fairly low eccentricity, so low that they are not much beyond the orbit of Jupiter at their most distant point from the sun (Fig. 13.8). These comets are supposed to have been deflected at some time in

13.18. Jupiter's family of comets

195

the past by going too close to Jupiter, so that their orbits were changed from very long ellipses to short ones. Now their periods of revolution are only from 3.3 years, for Encke's comet, with the shortest of all known orbits, to about 8 years. From their probable history they are known as Jupiter's family of comets.

QUESTIONS AND EXERCISES

1. Using Figure 13.4, describe Halley's comet with respect to shape of orbit relative to those of planets, various velocities, why it cannot be seen very far away (two reasons), probable difference in comet at times of perihelion, and at aphelion. Where is the comet now? When will it come again? When and where was the comet first seen by Halley?

2. If a cone is accessible, or if you can make one from stiff paper, mark on it where the various curves in *B,* Figure 13.7 would fit against the cone. Which of these curves *must* be just where it is and nowhere else? How would changing the slope of the other curves on the cone change the shapes of the ellipse and the hyperbola? If you have a wooden cone saw through it along the marked curves.

3. What effect has the sun upon the visibility of a comet and the formation of its tail?

4. If the earth weighs 5.4×10^{21} tons, how many comets, each weighing a million million tons, could be made of an account of material equal to that in the earth?   *Ans.* 5,400,000,000 comets.

5. The earth's orbital velocity of 18½ miles a second give it an almost circular orbit. To what velocity would its motion have to be increased to send it off on a parabola, so that it could leave the solar system? (See par. 13.15.)   *Ans.* To about 26 miles a second.

6. The period of Halley's comet is about 77 years, but its time of return varies by a year or more. Can you think of any reason why?

METEORS 14

A *METEOR* is what we see as a bright streak across the sky, lasting for an estimated average time of about half a second. It is caused by a *meteorite,* which is a solid particle. The meteorite may be the size of a grain of sand or a large boulder. These particles become heated by friction with the air when within some 70 miles of the surface of the earth, where the air becomes dense enough to resist their motion materially. Practically all meteors are simply the result of collisions between these tiny bodies and the earth. Very few are produced by the gravitational attraction of the earth.

14.1. Meteors and meteorites

It is natural to suppose that we see hot meteorites just as we see sparks, for sparks are hot particles flying upward from a bonfire. But the very justifiable question is asked, "How can a particle the size of a sand grain, at a distance of 50 miles or more, give so much light?"

14.2. Cause of a meteor's light

THE SPECTROSCOPE HELPS TO SOLVE THE PROBLEM. It shows very little background of continuous light in the spectrum of a meteor, such as would come from a hot solid. Rather, it shows a line spectrum, as from an ionized gas. Moreover, the lines in the spectrum show that the gaseous atoms that give them are far more highly ionized (broken apart) than moderate heat could possibly cause. Hence it is believed that the whole trail of the meteor through the atmosphere is ionized by the meteorite. It is this great cylinder of air that we see, made luminous by the re-combination of the atoms as they fall together again after being ionized. The light is somewhat of the nature of that from neon gas in a neon advertising sign, which is ionized electrically and is not very hot. The meteor's light may also be compared with the aurora borealis. We must not think that *heat* is the only form of energy that can be transformed into light.

On any clear, moonless night several meteors may be seen in the course of an hour's careful watching. But on certain nights in each year many more than the average number are visible; sometimes one or two appear per minute. On a few very special occasions many thousands fall in a single night.

One of the most remarkable of these "meteoric showers" came after midnight on Nov. 12, 1833. The meteors were said to "fall like snowflakes"; as many as "200,000 within a few hours' time" being visible at some places. Since all the meteors seemed to originate at a certain point in the sky (in the constellation Leo), and to stream out in all directions from that point, they "made the sky look like an umbrella."

Thirty-four years earlier, in 1799, a similar shower had been seen. Also, 33 years later, in 1866, they fell again, but not in such great numbers. On the two occasions since that time when the shower was expected the display was disappointing. It is believed that the perturbing influence of Jupiter, Saturn, and Uranus has drawn the swarm so far to one side of the previous track that only the outlying particles collide with the earth's atmosphere. The orbit of the meteoric material no longer makes an intersection with the orbit of the earth. As H. N. Russell, Director of the Princeton Observatory, picturesquely put it, "an overpass has been substituted for the grade crossing."

In one case, that of Biela's comet, the head was seen to have divided into two parts, each with a nucleus and a tail, since its last previous appearance. Biela's comet has now disappeared, but annually, about November 25, when we cross its orbit, we see unusually large numbers of meteors that have been traveling along the comet's track (Fig. 14.1). When we are crossing the track of any comet, we may expect to see more than the usual number of meteors. Bits of meteoric matter are often found to be scattered all along the comet's orbit, so that when we cross it each year the whole earth is showered with meteors.

Groups of meteors that originated from comets, although they seem to be held together by weak gravitational attraction, are scattered both sideways and along the length of the comet's orbit. At least eight clouds of meteoric material are known to be traveling along the paths of vanished comets. The distribution along the orbit makes a meteor shower certain each year when the earth crosses the orbit (Fig. 14.2). The scattering of the material into a strip several thousand miles wide gives a shower that lasts for several nights (and days).

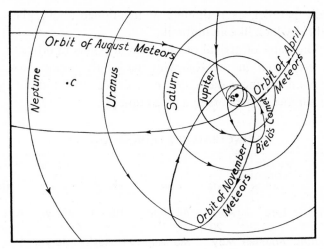

Fig. 14.1. Orbits of April meteors (Lyrids); August meteors (Perseids); November 15 meteors (Leonids); and November 23 meteors (Andromids). (*Adolpho Stahl Lectures. Stanford University Press.*)

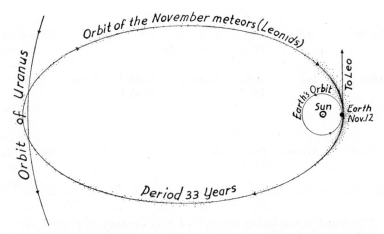

Fig. 14.2. Illustration of the reason for periodic showers of meteors. The shoal of particles may take more than one year to pass the point of intersection with the earth's orbit. Some meteors may be distributed all along the orbit.

14.5. The radiant point of showers

If you stand between the rails of a train track, the two rails seem to diverge from practically the same point in the far distance. Two, or many, meteors, traveling in parallel lines toward us, seem to come out of the same far-off point in the sky. Meteor showers are named for the constellation out of which they seem to come (Fig. 14.3). However much their paths seem to diverge, their travel is practically parallel, even though, as mentioned above, the Leonids "made the sky look like an umbrella."

14.6. Some of the principal showers

The dates of arrival of the earth at points in orbits of meteor swarms are given in the following table. By looking toward the radiant point on these dates one may expect to see more than the average number of meteors in a given time.

PRINCIPAL METEOR SHOWERS

METEOR SHOWERS	RADIANT IN CONSTEL- LATION	DATE	TIME	COMET	PERIOD OF COMET	REMARKS
Lyrids	Lyra	Apr. 20	All night	1861–I	415 yr.	A few every year
May Aquarids (or Eta Aquarids)	Aquarius	May 2–6	Morning	Halley's	76 yr.	Seen in some numbers every year
Perseids	Perseus	Aug. 9–13	Best after midnight	Swift's 1862–III	120 yr.	Many every year. Lasts several nights
Orionids	Orion	Oct. 19–23	Best after midnight			Dependable and numerous
Leonids	Leo	Nov. 14–17	Morning	Tempel's 1866–I	33 yr.	Last for 3 years Stream shifted since 1866
Geminids	Gemini	Dec. 10–13	All night			Dependable and numerous

The most remarkable shower of this century appeared, as had been predicted, on the evening of Oct. 9, 1946 and was visible throughout North America. It continued in noticeable intensity for only a few hours. A frequency as high as one a second was reported. Evidently the swarm of particles is concentrated in a comparatively small space at a point in the orbit behind the Giocobini-Zinner comet, from which it came. The meteors were seen in northern Europe 13 years earlier, when the earth crossed the comet's orbit, but the shower did not last long enough for the rotating earth to bring North America around into it. Presumably in 1959 the earth will again cross the orbit when the comet and its shoal are there.

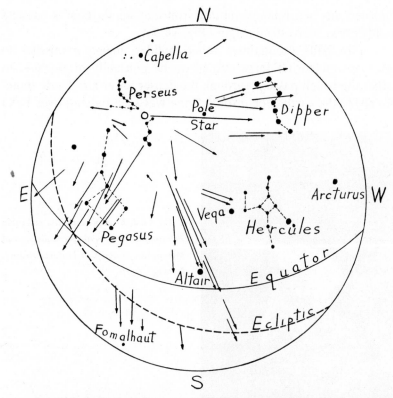

Fig. 14.3. Trails of meteors recorded by Dr. and Mrs. Edison Pettit from 10 to 12 P.M. on a hazy night, August 11. Note that, within reasonable limits of error, nearly all lines seem to come from a region marked with a circle, near Perseus. The few other lines represent stray meteors.

Meteorites

Opportunities of seeing *meteorites* (the flying objects that cause the meteors) are almost as rare as are opportunities of seeing ancient Egyptian mummies. They are hardly ever seen out of museums. But many museums do possess specimens of iron and stone meteorites (Figs. 14.4 and 14.5). Stone specimens usually are glazed with a black coating of melted rock and pitted with shallow holes from which the stone has been melted in their passage through the air (Fig. 14.4).

When an iron meteorite is cut open and its freshly exposed surface polished and etched with dilute nitric acid, a remarkable system of crystallization formations, called, in honor of their discoverer, "Widmanstätten figures," frequently appears. As these Widmanstätten figures are peculiar exclusively to the predominant type of iron meteorites, any specimen of natural iron that shows them is unquestionably of extraterrestrial origin (Fig. 14.5).

14.7. Fire balls

Fire balls (sometimes called bolides, meaning missiles to throw) are meteorites large enough to be unusually bright, and to weather the rough passage through the denser lower air. These sometimes strike the earth. For instance, one was seen passing over Iowa

Fig. 14.4. A stone meteorite weighing 749 pounds. (The Nininger Collection of Meteorites, Museum of Natural History, Denver.)

in 1877 in daytime, appearing as a red streak. After a sound like an explosion, great numbers of pieces fell. When the dry grass had burned off the next spring, 744 pounds of the fragments were collected, the largest weighing 431 pounds. The nickel-steel pieces of which the meteorite was composed were still untarnished after the winter snows and rain, for the metal is rather like "stainless steel."

The meteorite that scooped out the 600-foot-deep "meteor crater" of Arizona occurred at a time that was pre-historic for that part of the world. It must have been a marvelous sight if any saw it fall—and were far enough away to survive the occasion. Ten tons of fragments have been picked up in the neighborhood of the crater, and are now preserved in museums.

14.8. Radio study of meteors

A vast improvement in the study of meteors has recently been introduced by radio scientists in America and England. They have used radar, and especially the Doppler radar known as the "whistling meteor" technique. A radio with a loudspeaker can be used to give a

Fig. 14.5. An iron meteorite polished to show the Widmanstätten figures. (Yerkes Observatory.)

sound like a whistle whenever a meteor shoots across the sky, day or night, clear or cloudy. The whistle, properly interpreted, gives a measure of the velocity with which the meteor travels, and with other radio measurements, will also give its position, direction of travel, and altitude above the earth.

The meteor's "whistle" is not the result of any sound coming from the meteor or made by the meteor. It results from electric waves sent out by radio and reflected from the meteor. These electric waves come as silently through the air as the waves bearing our radio broadcast programs. The sound is made in the receiver.

The observing scientist sends out electric waves from a transmitter that is usually several miles from his receiver. Some of these waves go to the approaching meteor and are reflected back to the receiver; some come directly to the receiver. The frequency of the reflected waves is a little greater than it was when they were sent out because of the motion of the oncoming meteor. The reflected waves and the direct waves (both silent) work together in such a way as to cause a *sound* in the receiver. The pitch of the sound shows the speed of the meteor. The effect of motion of a body upon the frequency of waves, whether sound, light, or electric waves, is known as the Doppler effect. Astronomers measure the speed of a star by a technique with the spectroscope employing this same Doppler effect.

14.9. Some results from the radio method of study

At Stanford University the method has been made so sensitive that a meteor can be registered every few seconds. The number is highest in the morning, when the observer is riding on the front side of the earth as it goes around the sun. The front side of the earth is continually scooping up many millions of meteoric particles.

14.10. Do meteors come from among the stars?

This rapid radio method has been used to measure the velocities of a great many meteors, and it has proved that few if any of them come in from among the stars. At the National Research Council of Canada, the velocities of about 11,000 meteors were found.

Only 32 of them seemed to have the speed that would have been reached if they had come from clear out of our system, and even these were only a little too fast for elliptical orbits. The conclusion must be that all, or nearly all, meteors are part of our solar system and travel in elliptical paths until at last they strike the earth or some other large body of the solar system.

QUESTIONS AND EXERCISES

1. What does the spectrum of a meteor show about the cause of its light? Why could we usually not see the meteorite itself?

2. What is the reason for a shower of meteors? How is it related to a comet? Why do showers come annually? Why is there also a longer period of return in greater abundance?

3. How is radio used in the study of meteors? How does measurement of velocity of meteors help in the determination of their origin and orbits?

4. What apparently became of Biela's comet that disappeared, and what was left in its place?

5. Through how many cubic miles of space does the earth move per day? If it sweeps up 80,000,000 meteorites a day, what is the average amount of space for each meteorite? How great would be the average distance between them?

Approximate answers: 80,000,000,000,000 cu. mi.

1,000,000 cu. mi.

100 mi.

6. How is the loss of the 33-year-period shower of Leonids accounted for? Why is it so much more difficult to be sure where a comet will be in the distant future than it is to compute the orbit of a planet a long time in the future or the past?

7. What evidence is there in the United States that a large meteorite or comet once struck the earth?

8. Twice as many meteorites are observed from midnight to dawn as from evening to midnight. Also, on the average, the velocity of meteorites in the morning is higher than in the evening. Can you think of an explanation? (Consider the rotation and revolution of the earth in encounters with meteors.)

STAR DISTANCES 15

Comparisons and Illustrations of Distances

IN OUR study of the planets we saw that they are starlike in appearance; in all other respects planets are very different from stars. Stars are hot and self-luminous; planets have no light of their own, but shine, as the moon does, by reflected sunlight. The stars are far away from the sun; they are not controlled by its gravitational force; stars do not go around the sun as planets do. The sun is a star of intermediate size; most stars are very many times larger than even the largest planets.

The stars are essentially like the sun. That stars differ in appearance from the sun is due to their greater distance from us. If we could view the sun from a star we should see it as a point of light. As seen from the earth it is apparently larger and hotter than stars simply because we are closer to it. If we were as near to any other star of average size and temperature we should call the star a sun, and our climate would be much as it now is under the influence of the sun.

15.1. Similarity of stars and sun

Sir Isaac Newton was the first scientist to point out the enormous distances to the stars. His argument was that for them to be uninfluenced by the sun's attraction so as to avoid going around the sun, they must be hundreds of times as far away as Saturn, the farthest known planet of Newton's time.

15.2. An early estimate of star distances

Furthermore, Newton reasoned, the sun would have to be at least 100,000 times as far away as it is, in order for it to be as dim as a star. Assuming, as he did, that the stars are suns, like ours, he estimated that they must be at least 100,000 times as far as the sun is from us. We now know that the nearest star is 270,000 times the sun's distance from the earth.

Stellar distances are so much greater than any of those distances which come within the range of our travel and personal experience that our minds find great difficulty in comprehending them.

15.3. Aids to the imagination

Comparisons, models, diagrams, and other such devices are therefore necessary aids to any clear mental picture of the stellar system. In geography we find ourselves largely dependent upon maps for a knowledge of the great expanses of the earth; in astronomy we are many times more dependent upon such devices when we try to comprehend the greater expanses of the sky.

15.4. A model made to scale

Let us think of the earth as being represented by a point 1 foot from another point standing for the sun. Then on the same scale Pluto, the most distant planet in the sun's system, would be 40 feet away from the sun. The whole model or diagram could be in one large room. The nearest star on the same scale could be shown by a point 50 miles away. Other stars in a map or model made on such a scale would have to be placed hundreds or thousands of miles from the point standing for the sun. To embrace *all* of the stars in the stellar system we should have to extend our model approximately a million miles in some directions, and roughly a tenth of that distance in other directions. When we remember that 1 foot represented the distance of the earth from the sun, and that all distances from 50 miles to 1,000,000 miles give the places for various stars in the model, we get some conception of the vastness of the stellar system.

But the space in which the stars of our system, called the galaxy, are located is *not infinite* in extent. Observations made with the aid of large telescopes reach beyond the outskirts of our main Milky Way system into a region where stars are very sparsely distributed. This region extends far into intergalactic space until another galaxy is encountered. It appears now that there is no truly "empty" space. All space seems to be dotted here and there with more or less compact stellar systems, separated from each other by average distances of some ten or twenty times their diameters.

Our stellar system is often referred to as the GALAXY. Stellar systems beyond our galaxy are referred to as EXTERNAL GALAXIES, or EXTRAGALACTIC NEBULAE. The latter term is imperfect since the word *nebula* properly means a cloud. Although these extragalactic objects resemble clouds in appearance, they are now known to consist of stars too distant, except in a few cases, to show on photographs taken with the largest telescopes.

Stellar Parallaxes

15.5. A base line for measurement of star parallaxes

The stars are too far away to be measured by using a base line as short as that used for the moon (see paragraph 7.2 and Fig. 7.3). The earth is sufficiently large to contain a base line long enough for the measurement of the moon's distance and that of some of the nearer planets. But even an 8000-mile line is too short a base for stellar distances. The much greater lengths from one point in the earth's *orbit* to another are none too great to serve as base lines in getting the parallax of a star. Even the great distance of nearly 186,000,000 miles between the two points at opposite sides of the earth's orbit, which are occupied by the earth at intervals of six months, makes too short a base line for measurement of any except a few thousand of the nearer stars. Most of the stars are so far away that their direction is not perceptibly different as seen from opposite sides of the earth's orbit, even with the most powerful telescopes.

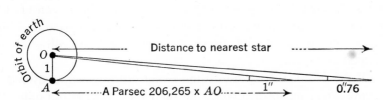

Fig. 15.1. Length of a parsec compared with the distance to the nearest star.

We said that to measure a distance of about 10 miles across the Grand Canyon a surveyor would probably want a base line of a mile. But even the nearest star is so far away that trying to measure its distance with a base line of 186,000,000 miles is like trying to measure the width of the Grand Canyon with a base line of—not a mile—but 2.5 inches in length!

15.6. Radius of orbit as a base line

Since the parallax of any star differs with the particular length of base line that happens to be used in finding it, the astronomer calculates the value that it would have had if a distance equal to the mean *radius* of the earth's orbit had been used as the base line. The radius is, by common consent, used as the standard length, just as the radius of the earth is used as the standard base line to which all parallaxes of points within the solar system are referred.

The definition, therefore, of the parallax of a star is the *difference in direction* to the star as seen from the sun and the earth, when the line from earth to sun is at right angles to the line joining the sun with the star. Or, it may be defined as the *angle at the star* made by the two lines of sight from earth and sun. As seen from Figure 15.1, the base line is one side of a triangle, equal to about 93,000,000 miles, whose other two sides reach to the star. Considered differently, the parallax of a star is the maximum angular separation of earth and sun as seen from the star.

History of Parallax Work

15.7. Ancient astronomers looked in vain for annual parallax

Very early in the history of astronomy observers supposing that perhaps the earth goes around the sun, watched carefully to see if any of the brighter stars, which they assumed to be nearer ones, showed any movement from side to side during the year. Before the invention of the telescope it was manifestly impossible to observe such small parallaxes. Largely for the reason that no parallax could be seen, ancient astronomers concluded that the earth did not go around the sun, but that it stood still, while the sun went around *it*.

15.8. Recent progress in measurements

Among thousands of millions of stars in our far-flung stellar system, distances to only about 6000 have, as yet, been measured by observation of an annual shift of the star from side to side. Many more are within the possible limits of measurement and will gradually be added to this list.

Of the 6000 stars whose distances have now been measured by the only *direct* means available, the surveyor's method of finding the trigonometric parallax, only 600 are near enough so that their light reaches us within less than 65 years after it starts from the star. These 600 stars are less than 65 light years distant.

15.9. Photography in modern parallax work

Parallaxes of stars are now found almost exclusively by photography. Instead of the tedious process of visual observation in the measurement of the position of stars, pictures are taken from time to time; then these are examined and measured under a special form of microscope to find the slight changes in position from one time of year to another. Most of the star images in the pictures will retain almost exactly their same relative position with respect to each other. But if one is near enough so that the change in the earth's position as it goes from one side of its orbit to the other is great enough to make any perceptible difference in direction of the two lines of sight to the nearer star, it will seem to shift with reference to the more distant stars. Knowing the base line, which is the distance between the two points of view, and the slight shift of the star's image in the photograph, which is its parallax, we can calculate its distance.

15.10. Correcting for motion

During the interval between the pictures the star itself may have moved considerably, and the solar system has moved, carrying the observer with it. It is therefore necesssary to take several pairs of pictures at six-month intervals in order to eliminate the effect of the star's own motion and ours. It is evident that if two pictures are taken just a year apart the star being measured should be in exactly the same place in both pictures with reference to the practically unchangeable background of stars, if neither the star being measured

nor the solar system had moved during the year. Any change in these two pictures is therefore due to motion. Knowing the change of direction due to motion, we can allow for it in order to find the change in direction due to seeing the star from opposite sides of the earth's orbit, which is the parallax.

Units for Measuring Stellar Distances

The distance to the nearest star, Alpha Centauri, is 25,000,000,000,-000 miles. So large a number is utterly beyond our power to comprehend. Even if we could comprehend it in some degree, it would be awkward just to write it. The figure takes up too much space and we could never remember how many zeros there should be. In expressing the distances to the stars we need new units that will yield figures of convenient size that will convey some meaning to us.

One of the most convenient units of stellar distance is the *light year*. A light year is the distance that a beam of light moving with a speed of 186,300 miles per second would travel in a year. Expressed in this unit the distance to Alpha Centauri is 4.3 light years. When you look at Alpha Centauri you see the star not as it is now but as it was 4.3 years ago. Alpha Centauri happens to be a star that closely resembles the sun. By looking at Alpha Centauri you know how the sun would look if it were 4.3 light years away.

15.11. The light year and the parsec

Another unit of stellar distance favored by astronomers is the *parsec*. The parsec is the reciprocal of the parallax of a star; in other words, its parallax turned upside down, or divided into 1. A star with a parallax of 0″.5 would be at a distance of 2 parsecs. A parsec is equal to 3.26 light years. The distance to Alpha Centauri in this unit is 1.3 parsecs. Even these units begin to fail in expressing the distances of the external galaxies, which are hundreds of millions of light years distant.

Measuring the parallax of a star is a long, painstaking process which requires a good deal of patience and attention to detail. An astronomer would not think of publishing the parallax of a star unless he had about twenty plates of it distributed over two or more years. He does not go to all this effort merely because he is curious to find the distance of some star from the earth. For example, Sirius, the brightest star in the sky, appears to be four times as bright as Alpha Centauri. But maybe Alpha Centauri is really brighter and only appears to be fainter than Sirius because it is farther away. We cannot tell until we know the distance of the two stars. It turns out that Sirius is 8.7 light years away, twice as far as Alpha Centauri. Thus Sirius is actually 17 times as bright as Alpha Centauri. This is a com-

15.12. Why astronomers measure the distances to the stars

parative small difference in luminosity. We know of other stars that are thousands of times brighter than Alpha Centauri. Why is there such a big difference in the luminosity of the stars? Is it because they are bigger or hotter or what? Thus a knowledge of the distances of the stars is only a means in gaining a knowledge of something much more important—a knowledge of the constitution of the stars themselves.

THE TWENTY BRIGHTEST STARS
(Compiled by Peter van de Kamp, 1953)

NAME OF STAR	RIGHT ASCENSION 1900	DECLI-NATION 1900	APPARENT MAGNI-TUDE	SPEC-TRUM	PARAL-LAX	ABSOLUTE MAGNI-TUDE	LUMI-NOSITY (SUN = 1)	LIGHT YEARS
Sirius *	6ʰ41ᵐ	−16°35′	−1.6	A0	0.″375	+1.3	23	8.7
Canopus	6 22	−52 38	−0.9	F0	.018	−4.6	5200	180
α Cen-tauri †	14 33	−60 25	+0.3	G0	.760	+4.7	1	4.29
Vega	18 34	+38 41	0.1	A0	.123	+0.5	48	26.5
Capella †	5 09	+45 54	0.2	G0	.073	−0.5	120	45
Arcturus	14 11	+19 42	0.2	K0	.090	0.0	76	36
Rigel	5 10	− 8 19	0.3	B8p	.005	−6.2	23,000	650
Procyon *	7 34	+ 5 29	0.5	F5	.288	+2.8	6	11.3
Achernar	1 34	−57 45	0.6	B5	.023	−2.6	800	140
β Centauri	13 57	−59 53	0.9	B1	.016	−3.1	1300	200
Altair	19 46	+ 8 36	0.9	A5	.198	+2.4	8	16.5
Betelgeuse	5 50	+ 7 23	0.9	M2	.005	−5.6	13,000	650
α Crucis *	12 21	−62 33	1.4	B1	.015	−2.7	900	220
Aldeba-ran *	4 30	+16 19	1.1	K5	.048	−0.5	120	68
Pollux	7 39	+28 16	1.2	K0	.093	+1.0	30	35
Spica	13 20	−10 38	1.2	B2	.021	−2.2	600	160
Antares *	16 23	−26 13	1.2	M1	.019	−2.4	700	170
Fomalhaut	22 52	−30 09	1.3	A3	.144	+2.1	11	23
Deneb	20 38	+44 55	1.3	A2p	.006	−4.8	6000	540
Regulus †	10 03	+12 27	1.3	B8	0.039	−0.7	140	84

* Double star.
† Triple star.

15.13. Brightest stars in order of total radiation reaching the solar system

It is of interest to compare the ten stars that appear brightest to our eyes with the ten stars that send the most radiation to the solar system. The latter group are the stars that would appear the brightest to an observer with supersensitive vision able to see *all* kinds of radiation; that is, not only visual light, but also the infrared and ultraviolet radiation which our eyes cannot see. To such an observer Sirius would still be the brightest star in the sky, but Betelgeuse and Antares would now be second and third in brightness instead of twelfth and seventeenth on the list of visual stars. The feeble intensity of starlight may be judged from the fact that the radiation from Sirius actually is only 0.000000000075 as much as that reaching us from the sun.

THE TEN BRIGHTEST STARS IN ORDER OF TOTAL RADIATION REACHING THE SOLAR SYSTEM

THE TEN BRIGHTEST STARS AS THEY APPEAR TO THE EYE			THE TEN BRIGHTEST STARS IN ORDER OF TOTAL RADIATION REACHING THE SOLAR SYSTEM		
NAME OF STAR	SPECTRUM	APPARENT MAGNITUDE	NAME OF STAR	SPECTRUM	RATIO OF BRIGHTNESS (SIRIUS = 1)
Sirius	A0	−1.6	Sirius	A0	1.00
Canopus	F0	−0.9	Betelgeuse	M2	0.91
α Centauri	G0	0.3	Antares	M1	0.65
Vega	A0	0.1	β Centauri	B1	0.57
Capella	G0	0.2	Canopus	F0	0.53
Arcturus	K0	0.2	γ Crucis	M3	0.48
Rigel	B8p	0.3	Arcturus	K0	0.44
Procyon	F5	0.5	Achernar	B5	0.35
Achernar	B5	0.6	Rigel	B8p	0.35
β Centauri	B1	0.9	Spica	B2	0.33

QUESTIONS AND EXERCISES

1. Can we ever have a knowledge of anything in the universe as it is now? Do we ever have a knowledge of anything except as it was in the past?

2. The southernmost part of the United States on the continent of North America is in about latitude 25° N. How many of the twenty brightest stars may be seen from there during the course of the year? How many from 40° N.?

3. Do you think there may be stars nearer than Alpha Centauri as yet undiscovered? If so, how do these stars probably compare in luminosity with the sun?

4. Suppose that the twenty brightest stars were suddenly extinguished. Which would be the first to disappear? Which one the last? Which ones would still appear to be shining after 80 years?

5. The sun is about an average star, indicating that there must be many others like it. If this is true, why is there only one other star like the sun in the table in par. 15.12?

6. Might stars invisible to us appear bright to an observer able to perceive all kinds of radiant energy? Describe the general characteristics of such stars.

16 THE MOTIONS OF THE STARS

WE HAVE seen that the celestial sphere has several apparent motions which the stars share as a whole. There is the daily westward motion of the celestial sphere caused by the eastward rotation of the earth upon its axis which causes the stars to rise and set. The stars rise earlier each evening as if they were moving westward to meet the sun, when in reality the sun is moving eastward to meet the stars due to the revolution of the earth around it. But no matter how carefully you watched with your naked eye you never could detect the slightest motion of the stars *relative to one another*. The stars seem as truly fixed upon the celestial sphere as if they were light bulbs set in its surface.

Yet the stars do move. They have motions which cause them to change position relative to one another over long periods of time, a discovery made by Edmund Halley more than 200 years ago. By comparing the positions of stars in catalogues made 2000 years earlier with those in his day, Halley found that Sirius, Aldebaran, and Arcturus had apparently moved by amounts too large to be due to errors of observation. If this were true, it was an important discovery indeed—the first indication of motion in the hitherto "fixed" stars. Yet Halley brought the matter to the attention of astronomers almost apologetically as being "not unworthy of the Royal Society's attention."

Today we know that nothing in the universe can be considered stable. All the stars are moving, but their change in position only becomes perceptible to the unaided eye after many centuries. If we could see the Big Dipper every 200,000 years we would find this constellation has changed so much we would scarcely be able to recognize it from one era to the next (Fig. 16.1). A few stars are known, however, that are moving so rapidly that with modern instruments their change in position can be detected—not after many years—but in a matter of weeks or even days.

The angular distance by which a star changes its position upon the celestial sphere in a year is its *proper motion*. In Figure 16.2 let S_1 be the position of a star at some date and S_2 its position one year later. During the year the star has moved the distance S_1S_2 along the arrow S. As seen from the earth, however, we only know

16.1. *Proper motions and radial velocities of the stars*

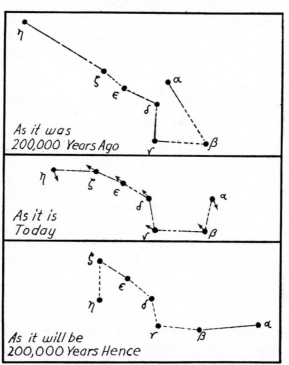

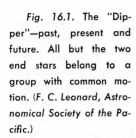

Fig. 16.1. The "Dipper"—past, present and future. All but the two end stars belong to a group with common motion. (F. C. Leonard, Astronomical Society of the Pacific.)

As it was
200,000 Years Ago

As it is
Today

As it will be
200,000 Years Hence

that it has shifted position in the sky by the angular distance μ, which is its proper motion. If we knew the star's proper motion *and* its parallax, then we could find the distance in miles that it has moved across our line of sight, or its cross motion T. If we had a photograph of the star's spectrum, we could also determine its motion toward or away from us, or its radial velocity R. Finally, if we knew the star's cross motion and its radial velocity, we could find its space motion S, or the actual velocity of the star relative to the earth.

Due to the fact that most of the stars that can be seen with a telescope are so far away, relatively few of them show any proper motion at all, even in photographs taken several years apart. One ob-

16.2. *Picking out stars of large proper motion*

server has examined more than a thousand pairs of photographic plates of the same regions, taken at intervals of 30 years. On these plates, covering a large proportion of the entire sky, there is a total of about 25,000,000 star images. Of these only 80,000 gave any observable evidence of motion during the 30-year interval.

The seemingly impossible task of examining so great a number of stars was accomplished by means of a "blink microscope." Stars that

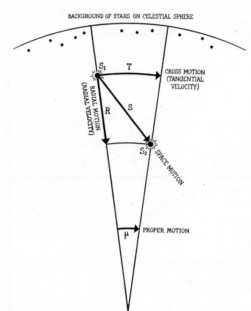

BACKGROUND OF STARS ON CELESTIAL SPHERE

Fig. 16.2. Proper motion is the angle, μ, through which the star appears to move against the background of stars on the celestial sphere. *T* is the linear distance through which it appears to move. This is called tangential velocity or cross motion. The radial motion is measured with the spectrograph. *S* is the star's space motion, which corresponds to its real direction and velocity. The star's distance must be known to find the linear distances.

had moved as much as 0″.2 a year jumped back and forth while the others remained steady. No stars in the list were found to have any greater proper motion than that of stars already known. The maximum velocity detected among all these stars was only 4″ annually.

Selecting the stars of large proper motion in this way is equivalent to selecting the nearer stars. Though any individual star *may* have a large angular motion on account of the favorable direction and exceptionally high velocity of its motion, nevertheless, the *average* distance to a large number of stars is proportional to their average proper motion.

The star with the largest known proper motion is the one called "Barnard's" star after its discoverer (Fig. 16.3). This star, 6 light years away, is moving so fast that it would cover an angular distance equal to the width of the moon in 180 years. As might be expected,

Fig. 16.3. "Barnard's runaway star" (shown by arrow), giving change of position in 22 years. The pictures are about 1¼° wide from top to bottom. Estimate the star's present position. (E. E. Barnard, Yerkes Observatory.)

large proper motion is an excellent way of picking out stars close to the earth. Proper motion is a much better indication of nearness than brightness. The average distance of the twenty stars with the largest proper motions is 15 light years. But the average distance of the twenty stars of greatest apparent brightness in the sky is 101 light years.

Only 200 stars are known with a proper motion even a tenth as much as Bernard's star. The average proper motion of the stars visible to the unaided eye is about one-hundredth as much as Barnard's star. No wonder that during our lifetime the constellations appear as fixed landmarks in the sky.

The Motion of the Sun

Think of yourself walking through a forest. The trees that lie ahead of you in your path appear to be opening out, or moving farther apart. The trees behind you appear to be closing up, or approaching one another. Those to your right and left appear to be moving backward, but have scarcely any motion toward or away from you.

If we consider the stars to be motionless and the sun moving among them, we should expect to observe some effects similar to those observed by a man walking in a forest. Stars that lie ahead of the sun in its path should appear to be moving toward us and separating in the sky. Stars behind us should appear to be receding and coming together. Halfway between, the stars should appear to be drifting backward but should show scarcely any motion toward or away from us (Fig. 16.4).

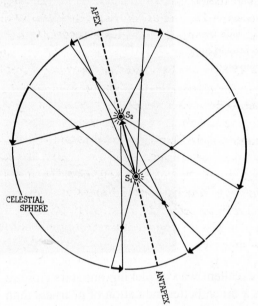

Fig. 16.4. The stars seem to be moving away from the point on the celestial sphere toward which the sun is moving (apex), and closing in on the opposite point (antapex).

16.3. The motion of the sun in space, or the "sun's way"

In 1783 Sir William Herschel found from the proper motions of thirteen stars that the sun is moving toward the star λ Herculis. The stars in that part of the sky appeared to be separating and the others moving in accordance with the idea that the sun was headed in that direction. Herschel reasoned that their common behavior could be well accounted for by assuming a motion of the solar system rather than that thirteen stars were moving so as to produce a particular effect with respect to the sun.

From the proper motions of the thirteen stars, Herschel could only estimate the direction of the sun's motion in space. He had no way of finding the velocity of the sun. The rate at which the sun is moving could not be determined until much later when the radial velocities of the stars became known. Not until 1900 was a concerted effort made to determine the solar motion from radial velocities.

Today after an immense amount of investigation we can answer the question, "In what direction and how fast is the sun moving with respect to the naked-eye stars?"

A study of the motions of 8000 close stars shows that the sun is moving with a speed of 12 miles a second toward a point in the constellation of Hercules at right ascension 18 hours, declination 30° N. —within 7° of the star λ Herculis that Herschel found from his thirteen stars!

We have made the problem much too simple by supposing that the stars are motionless and that the sun is doing all the moving. Actually the sun is moving and so are all the stars around it as well. When we say that the sun is moving at 12 miles a second toward Hercules what we really mean is that this is the motion of the sun *relative to the 8000 stars close around it*. If we had used a different group of stars we would have arrived at a different solar motion. When you drive along the highway you generally proceed at about the same average rate as the rest of the traffic. Suppose that the average speed of the cars around you is 50 miles per hour and that you are doing 53 miles an hour. You will be moving a little faster than the bulk of the traffic, although some cars will pass you. But if your motion were referred to some heavy trucks doing 33 miles an hour you would fly past them at a relative speed of 20 miles an hour. But you would be moving slowly relative to a man on a motorcycle who shoots past you at 73 miles an hour.

16.4. The local cluster of stars

Galactic Rotation

Now suppose that instead of comparing our motion relative to the cloud of stars moving along with us through space, we make a comparison with stars far outside the local cloud. How fast are we moving with respect to them? Can such studies tell us anything about the rotation of the galaxy as a whole?

For a long time we have been familiar with the idea, first firmly established by Copernicus, that the planets revolve around the sun. We know also that systems of satellites, such as that of Jupiter revolve around their central planet. That all of the stars in the galaxy revolve around some common center of gravity has long been considered a probability, but now it is being proved.

Several methods have been employed by various astronomers in arriving at results which have so far been accomplished in solving this very difficult problem of galactic rotation (Fig. 16.5). First, Shapley succeeded in locating the *center* of the stellar system. He studied the distribution of the great globular clusters, those brightest and most distantly seen members of the galactic system. Much more than half of these clusters, which number more than a hundred in all, are in one half of the sky. They are within 90° of the dense star

16.5. Locating the center of the stellar system

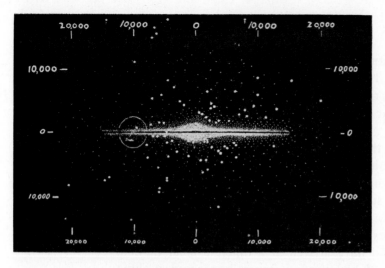

Fig. 16.5. Diagram of the stellar system by Oort. The solar system is at the center of the circle at the left. The circle is drawn with a radius of 2000 parsecs (6500 light years). Beyond this distance only the brightest objects of the galaxy can be investigated. Distances to stars beyond the circle can be estimated only by very special, indirect means.

The large dots, which extend far above and below the galactic plane, are the globular star clusters, about a hundred in number. Interspersed among them are a few outlying stars. The globular clusters occupy a nearly spherical space, while most of the stars of the galaxy lie near the plane of the Milky Way.

Distances in parsecs each way from the axes through the center are shown by the figures around the edge. (To change to light years multiply by 3.26.) (*Dominion Astrophysical Observatory.*)

clouds of the constellation Sagittarius. The compact arrangement of stars and nebulosity in that part of the heavens goes far toward proving that this region is not only the center of the globular cluster system but the center of the whole stellar system as well.

16.6. Varying velocity of stars   Motion around the center of the stellar system cannot be studied by observing only the stars of our own local star cloud, for they and the sun are all moving more or less in common. The very distant stars, either nearer the center than the sun or farther from the center, are the ones which may be expected to travel either faster or slower than we do, and therefore to show *relative* motion. Outer planets travel more slowly than those near the sun; Pluto has only about $\frac{1}{11}$ the linear velocity of Mercury.

If stars were equally distributed throughout all parts of the stellar system the whole system would turn as a wheel does, or as any solid, like the earth, turns. If this were the case all stars would have the same angular velocity and we should be unable to know whether the system is turning or not—unless we should become conscious of our motion by observing some extra-galactic objects.

If there is concentration of mass toward the center of the system the inner stars will move faster than the outer ones. The difference in motion at different distances from the center will not be so great as if nearly all of the mass were compressed into one great central body as is the case with the solar system. There is no mammoth star around which other stars revolve, but there is sufficient difference in the velocity of rotation at different distances from the center to show that the stars must be much more densely congregated there than elsewhere.

Figure 16.6 shows the motions of stars along circles drawn at

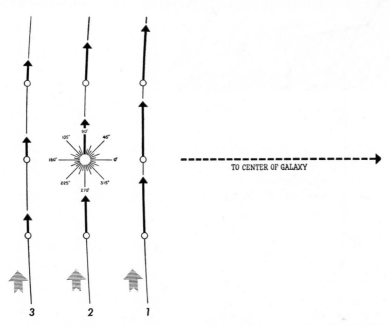

TO CENTER OF GALAXY

3   2   1

Fig. 16.6. Stars move faster the less their distance to the center of the galaxy. Stars at three different distances are shown moving at different speeds like cars in different lines of traffic. Sun is shown in lane 2 in center.

different distances from the center of the galaxy. All stars at the same distance are supposed to be moving with the same velocity. Thus stars at the same distance as the sun on line 2 are all moving with a velocity equal to the length and direction of the arrows on that line. Stars on line 1, closer to the center, are moving more rapidly than those on line 2. Stars farther from the center of the galaxy, on line 3, are moving more slowly than those on line 2.

Now let us find how these stars appear to be moving relative to the sun alone. We find these motions by applying a velocity to each of the stars equal in amount and opposite in direction to the velocity of the sun. The result is shown in Figure 16.7. The sun seems motionless and only the stars are moving around it. (Think of yourself again as being in an automobile surrounded by rapidly moving traffic. You

219

are driving in the center lane in line 2. The traffic in line 1 on the average is moving faster than you are. The traffic in line 3 is moving more slowly.) The stars in line 2 directly ahead of us and behind us show no motion whatever, neither radial velocity nor proper motion. Stars straight toward the direction of the center of the galaxy seem to be drifting ahead of us, but show no motion in our direction. Stars directly beyond us with respect to the center seem to be drifting back-

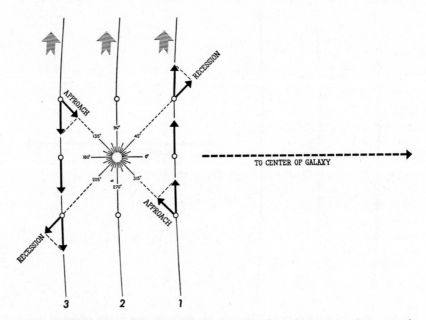

Fig. 16.7. How the stars appear to move as seen from the sun. A velocity equal and opposite to the velocity of the sun has been applied to the stars in Fig. 16.6. Stars directly ahead and behind the sun show no motion due to galactic rotation. Stars in lanes 1 and 3 show velocities of approach or recession depending upon their position relative to the sun.

ward, but also show no motion in our direction. But stars at 45° from these directions show both a proper motion and a radial velocity. They are either increasing or decreasing their distance from us, depending upon how we see them with respect to the direction of the galactic center.

16.7. Results summarized   The conclusions reached in this still very incompletely covered field of astronomical research is that the solar system is located some 33,000 light years from the center of the galaxy, which is in the direction of the constellation of Sagittarius. Our position is about two-thirds of the distance from the center to the circumference. With respect to the local cluster of stars in our vicinity—the stars that you see at night in the sky—the sun is moving with a speed of 12 miles per second toward the constellation of Hercules (Fig. 16.8). But the sun together with the local cluster of stars is moving with a speed of 180 miles a second toward the constellation of Cygnus, which is about 40° to the northeast of the sun's path toward Hercules. We might express it by saying that the sun and the stars around it are on a grand tour toward Cygnus but that the sun is taking a private

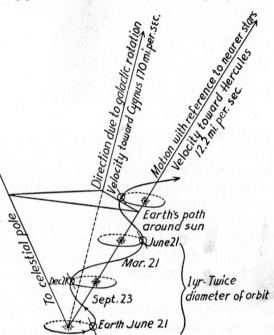

Fig. 16.8. Motions of the earth and sun. Revolution around the sun, coupled with solar motion, gives the earth a spiral path. At the same time rotation of the galactic system gives the solar system and the stars near us a much faster motion toward Cygnus.

side trip toward Hercules. At the rate the sun is moving around the center, it should take about 220 million years to complete the circuit. During the 2000 million years which is the estimated age of the earth since geologic history began, there has been time for nine revolutions of the solar system around the whole circuit of the galaxy.

QUESTIONS AND EXERCISES

1. Give some examples from ordinary experience which show how large proper motion indicates nearness.

2. What common property would show that stars that may appear far apart are actually related?

3. Is a star with large proper motion necessarily moving more rapidly than one with small proper motion?

4. Give factors that would produce a large proper motion.

5. How is proper motion distinguished from radial velocity? Would nearness increase the radial velocity of a star?

17 KINDS OF STARS AND GROUPS OF STARS

The Brightness of the Stars

17.1. The meaning of magnitudes

THE most obvious way stars differ from one another is in their apparent brightness. They range all the way from Sirius, sparkling like a blue-white diamond, down to stars so faint they are barely on the limit of visibility. It is not surprising, therefore, that the earliest attempts to classify the stars were made on this basis. In A.D. 138, Ptolemy made a catalogue of 1038 stars, which he divided into six classes of brightness or magnitude. The fifteen brightest stars in the sky he called first magnitude, and the stars that he could just see he called sixth magnitude. Other stars were put in intervening magnitudes. The seven stars that form the outline of the Big Dipper were magnitude 2. The four brightest stars in the Pleiades were of the 4th magnitude, etc.

Whether a star is called magnitude 1, 2, or 3, however, fails to tell us how they really compare in relative brightness. It only tells us that Ptolemy thought a star of magnitude 2, for example, looked fainter to him than a star of magnitude 1 and brighter than a star of magnitude 3. But *how much* fainter or brighter? It is somewhat like taking 1000 men and dividing them into six classes according to their income. The men with the most income we put in class 1, and those who barely make enough to live on we put in class 6. We now know that a man in class 1 makes more money than a man in class 2 and vastly more than one in class 6. But exactly how much more? That is the information we really want.

Not until 2000 years after Ptolemy did astronomers finally get around to deciding how much brighter a star of one magnitude is than another. In 1850, a scale of magnitudes was proposed such that a difference of 1 magnitude between two stars meant that one is 2.5

(exactly 2.512) times as bright as the other. The number 2.512 was selected because it makes a first-magnitude star exactly 100 times as bright as a sixth-magnitude star.

Ptolemy's original scale was too limited, however, for there are some objects in the sky brighter than a first-magnitude star and with the telescope we can see myriads of stars that are fainter than the sixth magnitude. The magnitude scale can be readily extended in both directions to include such objects. A star 2.5 times as bright as a first-magnitude star is of magnitude 0. A star 2.5 times as bright as a star of magnitude 0 is of magnitude −1. In the other direction, the scale has been extended in practice down to magnitude 22.5, which is about the faintest star that can be photographed with the 200-inch Hale telescope.

The apparent brightness of the stars differs enormously—much more than the artificial lights of a city. Sirius, the star that appears brightest to us, has a magnitude of −1.6 and is 4000 million times as bright as the faintest star we can photograph. The sun appears to us as 10,000 million times brighter than Sirius.

Although the sun appears to be millions of times brighter than the other stars, it is also much closer than these stars. If the sun could be moved off to the distance of the stars perhaps it would look as faint as they do. Simply by looking at the stars we have no sure way of telling whether one is actually brighter than another. If the stars were all removed to the same distance, however, we could tell which are really the brighter at a glance. In some cases nature has done this for us. There are clusters and clouds of stars so distant that we can regard the individual stars in them as being at all the same distance, in the same way that a man in San Francisco can consider all the people in New York as being at the same distance from him. But this still is of no help in comparing the actual brightness of the sun with the brightness of the stars in the cluster. What we would like to know is what the brightness of any star would be as seen from some standard distance.

17.2. The absolute magnitude of the stars

Now we know that the brightness of a star varies inversely as the square of its distance from us. Therefore if we know the distance of a star and have measured its apparent magnitude, we can calculate what its magnitude would be at any other distance. Astronomers have agreed that the magnitude a star would have if seen from a distance of 10 parsecs (32.6 light years) shall be called its ABSOLUTE MAGNITUDE. Only by comparing absolute magnitudes can we tell the real relative brightness of the stars.

17.3. Giant and dwarf stars

Technical terms are usually hard to grasp on first acquaintance, but astronomers have adopted some picturesque expressions for stars of different luminosity that are very descriptive. Stars with an absolute magnitude brighter than +1 are called GIANTS. (Remember that the smaller the magnitude of a star the brighter it is. Think of magnitude as being like a man's golf score. The smaller his score the better player he is.) Stars of absolute magnitude fainter than +1 are called DWARFS. A few very luminous stars are called SUPERGIANTS. The brightest star known is S Doradus in the Large Magellanic Cloud, with an absolute magnitude of −9, which makes it 400,000 times as luminous as the sun, which has an absolute magnitude of 4.73. The least luminous star is the companion of one known by its catalogue number of BD +4° 4048. This star has an absolute magnitude of about +20. This means that the sun is 1,000,000 times brighter than this star. Thus the brightest star in our galaxy is 28,000 million times more luminous than the faintest star known to us. (There may be still fainter stars that we are unable to see.)

17.4. The color or temperature of the stars

Some of the brightest stars show differences in color. Antares and Betelgeuse are red, Aldebaran and Arcturus are orange, Capella is yellow, and Rigel and Sirius are white. Glowing bodies may differ in color because of the chemicals in them. In a fireworks display we see glowing balls of red, green, and blue because they contain chemicals which emit these spectrum rays strongly. On the other hand, a glowing body may also appear red, orange, yellow, or white, depending upon its temperature.

Astronomers are convinced from a study of the spectra of stars that their differences in color are due entirely to temperature. Antares looks red because its temperature is much lower than that of a white star like Rigel. There are deep-red stars with a surface temperature as low as 3200° F, and white stars with a temperature possibly as high as 90,000° F.

17.5. The spectra of the stars

Visitors to an observatory often ask, "What do astronomers do?" Most of them spend a large part of their time examining photographs of the spectra of the stars. The spectral lines in a star can be made to tell us what is going on in its atmosphere. These lines can be compared to a message written in a cipher code. We can read the message as soon as we know the key to the code. Similarly, we can get a vast amount of information about the atmosphere of a star if we know how to analyze its spectrum.

The spectra of the stars differ widely in appearance (Fig. 17.1). White stars such as Rigel and Sirius show only a few lines, produced by atoms of hydrogen and helium. (An atom is the smallest possible

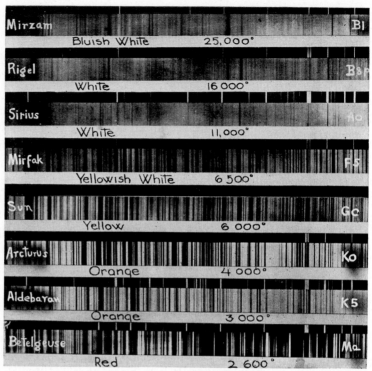

Fig. 17.1. Types of stellar spectra. The gradually decreasing temperatures from top to bottom are chiefly responsible for the spectral differences. (Only the blue region is shown.) (Yerkes Observatory.)

particle that can exist as an element such as hydrogen or helium.) In yellow stars like Capella, the helium lines have vanished and the hydrogen lines are not so prominent, although there are many other lines due to atoms of metals such as iron, calcium, and titanium. In orange stars such as Arcturus and Aldebaran, the metallic lines are increasingly prominent. In red stars such as Antares and Betelgeuse, whole portions of the spectrum are blotted out by closely packed series of lines or bands due to the molecule titanium oxide. (A molecule is the smallest possible particle that can exist in the form of a compound.)

Why do we find helium in the hot white stars and not in the cool red stars? Why do we find titanium oxide in the red stars and not in the white stars? Is it because there is no helium in the red stars and no titanium oxide in the white stars? Such an explanation seems too simple. It is like saying that the Sahara desert is dry because there is no water there. But we might flood the Sahara desert if conditions over the earth could be changed radically. It is conceivable that we might get helium lines in the spectrum of Betelgeuse and bands of titanium oxide in the spectrum of Rigel if conditions in their atmospheres changed radically. The main condition that determines what lines are produced in the atmosphere of a star is *temperature*. We do not see lines of helium in Betelgeuse because its temperature is too low to produce them. We fail to find bands of titanium oxide in Rigel because its temperature is too high for this compound to exist there.

There are some stars which have about the same temperature, yet their spectra are quite different. Here the only explanation seems to be that there is a difference in the chemical abundance of certain elements in the stars. On the whole, however, the chemical composition of the stars in the part of space that we can observe is remarkably uniform.

17.6. Classifying stars by their spectrum lines

Since astronomers spend so much of their time examining the spectra of stars, it is not surprising that they have arranged stars into various spectral types. Investigations of stellar spectra began about 1882 and have continued with increasing fervor up to the present day. Originally the stars were classified as *A, B, C,* etc., down to the letter *P,* but in the course of time some letters were dropped and a few more added until today we have the present rather illogical-looking system of alphabetical classification shown in the accompanying table. Perhaps the most surprising feature is that the spectra of hundreds of thousands of stars can be classified into a dozen or so main groups. It is to be emphasized that the progression in spectral types *O, B, A, F, G, K, M,* etc., represents a series of stars of decreasing temperature which is closely related to their color.

MAIN CHARACTERISTICS OF SPECTRAL TYPES

TYPE	TYPICAL STARS	TEMP.	COLOR	SPECTRUM
O	Zeta Puppis	60,000° F	Blue-white	Helium lines
B	Rigel, Spica	40,000	Blue-white	Helium lines
A	Sirius, Vega	20,000	White	Hydrogen lines; metals appear
F	Canopus, Procyon	14,000	Yellowish-white	Metals stronger
G	Sun, Capella	11,000	Yellow	Many metallic lines
K	Aldebaran, Arcturus	8,000	Orange	Calcium lines very strong
M	Betelgeuse, Antares			Titanium oxide
R	U Cygni	4,000 to	Red	Carbon compounds
N	Y Canum Venaticorum	6,000		Carbon compounds
S	R Andromadae			Zirconium oxide

An Over-all View of the Stars

Herschel, the first astronomer to take up a serious study of the nature of stars and their behavior, suggested that the heavens are like a garden in which we may find plants in all stages of development. By observing your plants, those more mature and those nearly dead, we could in a few minutes reconstruct the life history of the plant. The length of human life or, indeed, the length of time that man has been on earth, is shorter in comparison with the life history of a star than is the time of a brief visit to a garden in proportion to the whole life of a plant. Our only hope, therefore, of learning the course of a star's development is by observing the various stages through which it has passed as exemplified in the present condition of many varying types of stars.

A method of arranging the stars so that we can get some notion of their relationship to one another is shown in Figure 17.2. In this diagram, the stars are classified according to their *luminosity* and color, or *spectral type*. Such a diagram was first made by H. N. Russell in 1913 and is called a RUSSELL DIAGRAM. Each dot upon the diagram represents a star. The luminosity scale on the left increases from the lower part of the diagram upward, so that very faint stars would be plotted near the bottom of the diagram, those of moderate brightness near the middle, and the very luminous stars near the top. The position of a star from left to right on the horizontal scale depends upon its spectral type. The hot, white stars of spectral classes *O, B,* and *A* would be on the left; the yellowish stars of moderate surface temperature of classes *F, G,* and *K* would be near the center; and the cool red stars of class *M* on the right.

17.7. The Russell diagram

In order to plot a star upon the diagram, its distance (parallax) must be known with reasonable accuracy, for otherwise we have no way of knowing its true luminosity or absolute magnitude. If we went only according to appearances, Sirius *looks* considerably brighter than the pole star, and on this basis would be plotted higher on the diagram. But when we make allowance for the greater distance of Polaris we find that actually it is fifty times more luminous than Sirius. When Russell made the first diagram only about 300 stars were available with well-determined parallaxes. Today fairly reliable parallaxes are known for several thousand stars. These additional stars have not essentially changed the form of Russell's first diagram, but several new features have been revealed that were not originally evident.

Later, when we have become better acquainted with stars of different types, we shall give another diagram which shows the locations of these stars in more detail (Fig. 21.5).

Think of the Russell diagram as a map showing the countries occupied by people (stars) of different nationalities. In the upper left-hand corner are the blue-white supergiants, the brightest stars in our galaxy. To the right and lower are the red giants, huge stars of low

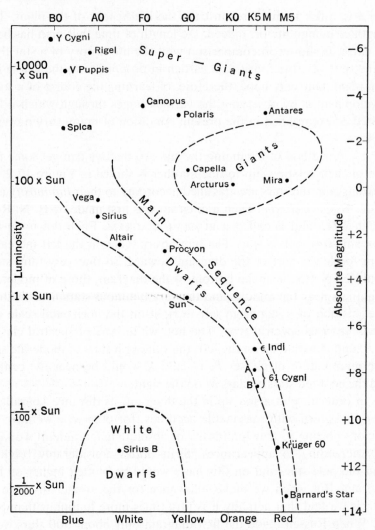

Fig. 17.2. The Russell diagram for stars near the sun. Broken lines roughly define the regions in which these stars occur in greatest abundance. The positions of a few representative stars are shown. Notice the "Hertzsprung gap" between the giants and the beginning of the main sequence, and the absence of red stars of moderate brightness.

density and low surface temperature. Running crosswise from a little above the middle of the diagram down to the lower right are the stars of the main sequence. Notice that there is a gap between the red giants and the white stars of the main sequence. Stars of the main sequence are similar to the sun. They range from white stars of moderate luminosity down to faint red dwarfs. In the lower left-hand cor-

228

ner is a curious group of white stars of low luminosity called "white dwarfs." Their color indicates that their surface temperature is as high as 20,000° F, so their low luminosity must be due to their extremely small size. We shall have more to say later about the white dwarfs (Pars. 17.10 to 17.12).

The amount of radiation given out by a fire depends upon how big it is and what you are burning. Obviously you will get more radiation from a big fire than a little one. But some substances burn with a much hotter flame than others. Gasoline burns with a hotter flame than wood. You can get more than twice as much heat by burning a pound of gasoline than by burning a pound of wood.

17.8. Size of stars from their temperature and absolute magnitude

By analogy, the amount of radiation emitted from a star must depend upon its size and its temperature. A large hot star must emit more radiation than a small cool star. But it is also possible that a small intensely hot star might emit more radiation than a large cool star. A cool star, if large enough, however, might emit more radiation than a very hot small star. It seems reasonable to expect, therefore, that the absolute magnitude of a star will depend upon both the star's size and surface temperature.

We can see at once that some stars must be much larger than the sun and others considerably smaller. Consider, for example, a supergiant star such as Betelgeuse, which has an absolute magnitude of −3.9, but whose surface temperature is only 6000° F as compared to the surface temperature of the sun of 10,300° F. A square foot of surface on the sun emits 16 times as much radiation as a square foot of surface on Betelgeuse. The high luminosity of Betelgeuse *must* be due to its enormous size. Betelgeuse is a big bonfire but not a very hot one. Conversely, red stars of low absolute luminosity *must* be smaller than the sun. They are small bonfires that burn feebly. The situation is not so clear when we come to the white stars of high luminosity. Is their high absolute luminosity due to their high temperature or large size or both?

In the case of Betelgeuse and other red giants, it is possible to get a direct check on their size with an optical device designed by A. A. Michelson called the *interferometer*. We cannot explain here the principle upon which the interferometer is based or how the measures on the stars were made. It must suffice to say that with an interferometer attached to the 100-inch telescope the angular diameter of Betelgeuse was measured in 1920. The angular diameter of Betelgeuse combined with a knowledge of its parallax, showed this star to be 500 times the size of the sun. The sun could be put in the center of Betelgeuse and there would be plenty of room for the earth and Mars to revolve in their present orbits. All the giant red and orange stars selected for measurement with the interferometer have diameters from 10 to 100 times that of the sun (Fig. 17.3).

The white stars are too small to measure their diameters directly with the interferometer. Their size has to be calculated theoretically from their temperatures and absolute magnitudes. They range from about two to ten times the diameter of the sun for the blue-white

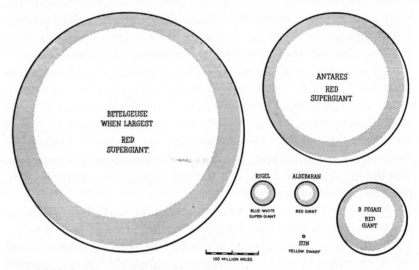

Fig. 17.3. Relative dimensions of some supergiant, giant, and dwarf stars.

supergiants. The white dwarfs are less than 2 per cent the size of the sun—no bigger than the planets of the solar system.

Masses from Double Stars

17.9. Masses of the stars   We have seen that there is a vast range in the size and luminosity of the stars. Do they also differ as widely in mass, or the quantity of matter they contain?

Our sole means of finding the mass of a body—what we ordinarily call its "weight"—is by its gravitational attraction upon other bodies. We cannot hope to determine by any direct measurements the mass of a star isolated in space far from all other bodies. The star must be close enough to another one to affect it visibly by its gravitational attraction.

Two stars form what is called a BINARY SYSTEM when they form a pair revolving around their common center of gravity. When both stars can be seen in the telescope, the system is known as a VISUAL BINARY. These stars move in accordance with the law of gravitation just as the planets do. We saw that according to Kepler's third law the time required for a planet to revolve around the sun depends upon its distance from the sun and the combined mass of the sun and planet (Par. 6.14). Kepler's law can also be applied to double stars. We can observe the period required for one star to revolve around the other. We can measure their angular distance apart. If we know the parallaxes of the stars, we can change their angular distance apart to their actual distance apart in miles. Knowing these three quantities —period, distance, and parallax—we can then find the sum of the masses of the two stars.

Out of the thousands of double stars known, there are only a few hundred for which we can determine their masses. Even in these cases we can only determine the *sum* of the masses for the two stars forming a binary system. Still, this gives us information that is very helpful. In a few cases we can get the absolute orbits of the two stars in the system about their center of gravity (Fig. 17.4). This can only be done when the positions of the stars can be measured relative to faint distant stars in the background. When the absolute orbits are known, then the mass of the individual stars in the system can be found.

Such evidence as we can derive from visual binary systems and a few other sources show that the range in mass of the stars is rather small. There are stars that are probably less than one-tenth as massive as the sun, and there are others that are 100 times as massive. The extreme range in mass appears to be about 6000 to 1. This seems quite moderate compared with the range in the size and luminosity of the stars.

White Dwarfs

17.10. White dwarf stars

The white dwarf stars down in the lower left-hand corner of the Russell diagram are among the strangest—if not *the* strangest— bodies that astronomers have so far encountered in space. When their properties first became known, in about 1922, some scientists hesitated to believe that matter could exist in such a state. The white dwarfs are not only prize curiosities in themselves but may be of great significance in furnishing us with a clue to the course of stellar evolution.

17.11. The first discovered white dwarf star

A star known as the "Companion of Sirius," or "Sirius B," gives only 1/400 as much light and heat as the sun. It is difficult to see this star, for its light is almost drowned out by that of its very luminous companion, the Dog Star. The two stars mutually attract one another so that each goes around a common center of gravity between the two. From the distance separating the two stars and the length of time required for them to make the revolution, a calculation based on Kepler's harmonic law shows their combined mass to be 3½ times the mass of the sun. Their *relative* masses are found from the position of their center of gravity. The small companion star is thus found to be about the mass of the sun (Fig. 17.4).

Determination of the size of this interesting star shows it to be of about the size of the planet Uranus, or $\frac{1}{30}$ the diameter of the sun. This value is derived from the star's absolute magnitude and temperature. The star's spectrum reveals its temperature. If the star were of the same density as the sun, its mass would be $(\frac{1}{30})^3$, or $1/27,000$ that of the sun. To be as heavy as the sun it must therefore be 27,000 times as dense, or about 40,000 times as dense as water. A pint of water weighs a pound; a pint of the material of which this star is made would weigh 40,000 pounds, or 20 tons.

17.12. Accounting for a white dwarf's density

Without an explanation such a statement as that just given would be wholly incredible. The heaviest metals we know are but little more than 20 times the weight of water. Their density cannot be much increased by pressure. In this star we have all its material, from surface to center, compressed to an *average* density of 40,000. Doubtless at the center the density far exceeds this figure.

We can easily understand the almost infinite compressibility of matter if we think of the atoms of which it is composed as Niels Bohr pictured them. He assumed that each atom consists of a central nucleus, *very* small, around which revolve electrons, like planets around the sun. The nucleus contains *nearly* all the mass of the atom. It is at least 1800 times as heavy as an electron, and in most atoms many times this. Both electrons and nuclei are exceedingly small in comparison with the space included within the orbits of the electrons.

It is further assumed that atoms that make up the star cannot come close enough together so that the orbits of their electrons overlap or interlock. The atoms may be illustrated by men each whirling around himself a weight attached to a long cord. The men could not approach near one another. But if the cords should break and the weights fly away the men could crowd close together, so that in a given small space a great weight of men could congregate.

The diameters of most white dwarfs range between those of the earth and Uranus. None are so small as the moon. The smallest one known appears to be Ross 627, which is about the same size as Mercury. If its mass is equal to that of the sun, its average density is about 20 million times that of water.

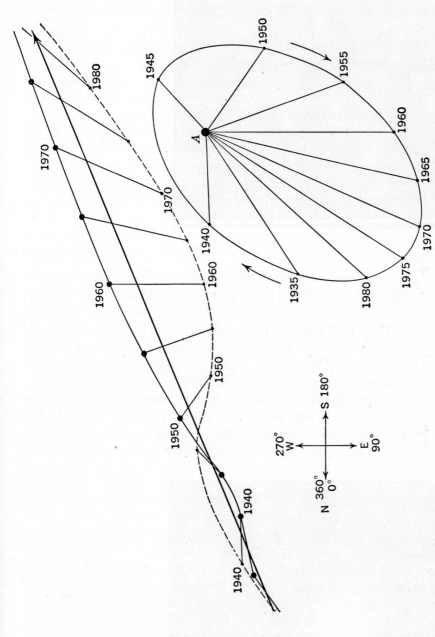

Fig. 17.4. Motions of Sirius and its companion. The ellipse shows the motion of the companion relative to Sirius. The heavy curved line is the path of Sirius. The dotted line is the path of its companion star. The long, straight line is the path of the center of gravity of the pair. The period of Sirius is 50 years.

Fig. 17.5. A photograph of NGC 6553 taken in blue light with an exposure of 45 minutes. (*Walter Baade, Mount Wilson Observatory.*)

Star Clusters

After such simple organizations as binary and multiple stars, involving only a single pair or a group of three or four stars, or possibly five or six, comes the CLUSTER, of hundreds or thousands of associated stars (Figs. 17.5 and 17.6). If, perhaps, the double star owes its origin to the division of a single star too large to hold itself together while rotating on its axis, the cluster is probably a disintegrated nebula, which was large enough to break up into many stars.

Whatever the origin of the cluster, the material of which the stars are made seems to have possessed a motion which has been inherited by all of the stars in common. They move at the same rate through space and all in the same direction. If they had not done so during

Fig. 17.6. A photograph of the star cluster NGC 6553 taken in red light with an exposure of 75 minutes. (*Walter Baade, Mount Wilson Observatory.*)

Fig. 17.7. The Pleiades ("Seven Sisters"). Time exposures show diffuse nebulae associated with the stars. (Mount Wilson Observatory.)

the many millions of years which we may suppose to have been the life history of these stars they would by now have been widely dispersed. The only sure way to determine which stars belong to a cluster, and which are merely in the same field of view, perhaps nearer or farther than the cluster, is to observe each star's motion.

17.13. Kinds of clusters

Two kinds of clusters are recognized. The Pleiades is a group of close to 500 stars, seven of which, the "Seven Sisters," can be seen with the unaided eye if the night is dark. They cover an area somewhat larger than the angular size of the moon. This is a good example of an "open cluster" (Fig. 17.7). The aggregation of stars seen in Figure 17.6 is an example of a globular cluster. The great cluster in Hercules shown in Figure 1.7 is one of the finest examples in the sky. It is faintly visible to the unaided eye.

More than 300 open clusters are known, and there are probably many more whose common motion has not yet been noticed. But there are only 93 globular clusters in our whole stellar system. Few, if any, more are likely to be discovered, for existing telescopes can reach to the farthest limits of the stellar system. Globular clusters are intrinsically very bright because they are composed of so many stars. Nearly all that are now known were observed by the Herschels more than a hundred years ago, while they were "sweeping the sky" for any object of unusual appearance.

17.14. Stars passing through a cluster

The stars of an open cluster are so far apart that the cluster may move through a region where there are other stars going in other directions. Or other stars may move through a cluster without seriously disturbing either it or them.

One most notable example of a cluster occupying the same region (temporarily) that other stars inhabit is the Ursa Major cluster. All but two of the Dipper stars are a part of the Ursa Major group and are about 80 light years from us. Fully 90° from the Dipper, in the southern sky, is Sirius, the Dog Star, which is a member of the same cluster. Its similarity of direction and rate of motion proves its kinship to the Dipper.

17.15. Another name for open clusters
The name GALACTIC CLUSTERS is often applied to groups of loose structure, for they are nearly always found in or near the Milky Way. This name distinguishes them from globular clusters, which shun the Milky Way.

17.16. Globular clusters
Globular clusters are quite distinct from open groups in several respects. Each globular cluster has many thousands of stars; the clusters are more compact toward their centers; they lie outside of the Milky Way; they are the most distant class of bodies in the stellar system (Fig. 17.6).

The globular clusters are believed to be a part of our stellar system, not extra-galactic as are the spiral nebulae. But they seem to form a sort of border or frame around the system of stars. None of them is seen in the plane of the Milky Way, but this is doubtless because those in this plane are at so great a distance as to be obscured from view by the clouds of dark nebulous matter which lie along the plane of the Milky Way.

17.17. Arrangement of globular clusters
According to estimates made by Shapley, who was first to recognize the great distances to the clusters, the nearest one is 18,000 light years away and the most distant one 184,000 light years. In one direction from the sun, toward the dense star clouds in the constellation Sagittarius, the clusters are much more numerous and more distant than on the opposite side. The whole system of clusters occupies not exactly a sphere but a slightly flattened spheroid. The stars of the galaxy occupy this same region, but the system of stars is flattened to a thinner disk along the plane of the Milky Way than is the system of globular clusters. The solar system is near to one side of the system of clusters. Hence, only four clusters are in that half of the sky away from the center. More than 80 are in the half toward Sagittarius.

Star Clouds

Not only are stars grouped as *doubles, triples,* or *quadruples* and as *star clusters* of the open galactic type or the globular type, but there are *star clouds,* containing not hundreds or thousands of stars but millions. The stars of the galaxy are not arranged with an equidistant distribution. Their appearance does not resemble the uninterrupted nimbus clouds of a rainy day but is more like a broken mackerel sky or a sky filled with cumulus clouds.

If we could go outside the galaxy and look back at it from a distance we should probably be able to see the star clouds to better ad-

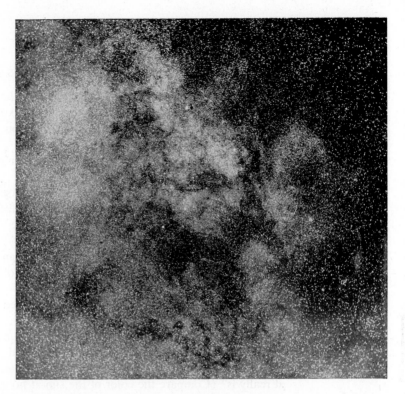

Fig. 17.8. Star clouds and dark obscuring matter in Sagittarius toward the center of the stellar system. Exposure 4½ hours. (Yerkes Observatory.)

vantage. They would perhaps look like the knots of condensation in the spiral nebulae such as appear, for instance, in NGC 2841, shown in Figure 21.6.

17.18. Clouds in Sagittarius

Figure 17.8 shows an immense star cloud in the constellation Sagittarius. It is known that in this part of the sky lies the center of the galaxy, and here the greatest concentration of stars is found. It seems to be a region such as is shown at the center of Figure 17.8.

17.19. The local star cloud

Since the time of John Herschel, more than a hundred years ago, it has been recognized that we are within one of the clouds, which is known as the local star cloud. Most of the stars visible to the naked eye belong to this local cloud. It, like the whole galaxy, is a flattened affair, and it lies at a slight angle (about 12°) to the plane of the Milky Way. Its size is not definitely known, but has been estimated to be about 700 light years thick and 2000 light years wide.

17.20. The Magellanic Clouds

Far off to one side of the Milky Way two star clouds are found, visible in the southern hemisphere. As seen from the Straits of Magellan they pass not far from the zenith, and so are called the Clouds of Magellan or the Magellanic Clouds. They are now known to be members of a local cluster of galaxies. They are about 27,000 light years in diameter and about 150,000 light years distant (see table in par. 21.6).

QUESTIONS AND EXERCISES

1. Can you think how the revolution of the earth around the sun could be demonstrated by the spectrograph? Explain.

2. From a study of Fig. 17.2, what can you say about the absolute magnitudes of red stars?

3. In the table of twenty brightest stars in par. 15.12, how many are white, yellow, orange, red?

4. Why would you not expect to get a correct idea of stars as a whole from a study of those visible to the unaided eye?

5. Do you think we have probably observed all the supergiant stars in our galaxy?

6. If you knew the apparent magnitude of an A-type star, could you make an estimate of its distance with the help of the diagram shown in Fig. 17.2?

7. Discuss the differences between the red giants and the white dwarfs.

8. The mass of Betelgeuse is equal to 15 suns. The mass of Sirius B to 1 sun. On which star do you think you would weigh the more? Why?

9. Can you think of any reason why a star might appear redder than it really is? (Compare the color of the sun at noon and at sunset.)

10. Discuss the effects of temperature, size, and distance on the apparent brightness of a star.

11. If a star were approaching the earth rapidly would its absolute magnitude gradually decrease?

12. How can we be sure that Sirius B is such a very faint star?

13. The parallax of Betelgeuse is rather uncertain. Why are we sure that it is a red supergiant? Why not a red dwarf?

VARIABLE STARS 18

Stars Whose Light Varies

IF THERE is one object in our lives upon which it would seem that we can always depend, it is the sun. The sun shines so steadily year after year that unconsciously we assume all the other stars do the same. "The eternal stars" is a familiar expression.

Yet there are thousands of stars known whose light does vary. In some cases the variation is so slight that it can only be detected by extremely sensitive measuring instruments. In other cases a star flares up from invisibility until it rivals Sirius in brightness. Few variable stars behave in such a spectacular manner, however. Usually they are discovered by systematically comparing photographs of the same field of stars taken at different times under the same conditions. If one star has changed brightness, it is as conspicuous as a man in full evening dress at a barbecue dinner.

18.1. Types of variable stars

There are so many different types of variables that the experts differ as to how to classify them. The most important main types are the following:

1. Cepheids
    Type I
    Type II
2. RR Lyrae stars
3. Long-period variables
4. Irregular variables

18.2. Cepheid variables

It is a question whether one manifestation of nature can be considered more important than another, but to astronomers the cepheid variables are certainly of prime importance for reasons which will soon appear. They derive their name from Delta Cephei, a third-magnitude star in the northern constellation of Cepheus, which was the first star studied of this type.

18.3. Cepheids
in the Lesser
Magellanic
Cloud

About 1905, Miss Henrietta Leavitt, of the Harvard College Observatory, began a study of a series of photographs of the Lesser Magellanic Cloud. The Great and Small Magellanic Clouds, named after the famous Portuguese navigator, are two faint patches of light about 20° from the south pole, and hence invisible from the United States. To the eye they appear like luminous clouds that have strayed from the Milky Way, but actually they are stellar systems 150,000 light years outside our own galaxy. Miss Leavitt's work on the Lesser Magellanic Cloud turned out to be so important that we shall discuss it in some detail.

When Miss Leavitt began her investigation she had no idea of the distance of the cloud except that it must be very far away. She found many stars on the photographs whose light increased and decreased regularly in the same way as the cepheid variable stars in the galaxy. The time required for a cepheid to change from minimum light to maximum and back to minimum is its *period of variation*. There were cepheids in the cloud with periods ranging from about a day up to 127 days.

The Lesser Magellanic Cloud is so far away that all the stars in it are at practically the same distance from us. Thus Miss Leavitt could tell the relative brightness of the stars simply from the difference in their apparent magnitudes. A star of magnitude 12 was 16 times as bright as one of magnitude 15. That is, if a star looked brighter than another then she knew it really was brighter. (This is not true of the cepheids in our galaxy which are at widely different distances.) She noticed that the cepheids with the shortest periods were the faintest, and those with the longest periods the brightest. This relationship was so definite that when the periods were plotted against apparent magnitudes the points lay along a fairly smooth curve, which came to be called the *period-luminosity curve*.

If Miss Leavitt had known the distance of the cloud she could have converted the apparent magnitudes of the cepheids into absolute magnitudes. She would then have been able to say how their luminosity compared with the luminosity of other stars. For example, she would have known whether the cepheids are very luminous objects like Canopus, or only moderately luminous like Sirius, or rather faint like the sun.

A little thought will show that the period-luminosity curve has tremendous possibilities as a yardstick for measuring great distances in space. Let us suppose that this curve holds good for cepheids—not only in the Lesser Magellanic Cloud—but anywhere in the universe.

Suppose also that the absolute magnitudes of the cepheids composing this curve were known. Then we can determine the distance of any object that contains a cepheid. All we need to do is to observe its period. Reference to the period-luminosity curve would give its absolute magnitude. The absolute magnitude together with the apparent magnitude would give its distance. It seemed almost too good to be true.

First, however, there was the little matter of converting the apparent magnitudes of the cepheids in the cloud into absolute magnitudes. Miss Leavitt died in 1921, but she lived long enough to see this portion of her work carried through by Harlow Shapley, from observations made at Mount Wilson.

If the distance and hence the absolute magnitude of a single cepheid in our galaxy had been accurately known, then the absolute magnitudes of all the cepheids in the cloud could have been determined by comparison with it. But in our whole galaxy there was not a single cepheid close enough so that astronomers could get a reliable measurement of its parallax by the direct trigonometric method.

But astronomers are not easily discouraged. It is possible to get the average distance of a group of stars from an analysis of their motions. An analysis of the motions of 11 bright cepheids in our galaxy gave an average absolute magnitude of -2.4 for a cepheid with a period of 6 days. The period-luminosity curve showed that cepheids in the cloud with a period of 6 days had an apparent magnitude of $+14$. Therefore, a cepheid in the cloud of apparent magnitude $+15$ has an absolute magnitude of -1.4, and one of apparent magnitude $+13$ has an absolute magnitude of -3.4. In this way, the apparent magnitudes of all the cepheids on the period-luminosity curve were converted into absolute magnitudes. Now at last astronomers had a means of finding the distance of any object however remote provided it contained a cepheid whose period could be observed.

There was one possible source of error in this method of determining distances which originally was not thought to be very dangerous. It had been assumed that all cepheids behave in the same way. In other words, that all cepheids with the *same period* have the *same absolute magnitude*.

It now appears that there are two distinctly different types of cepheids, which give different period-luminosity curves (Fig. 18.1). The two types of cepheids are called I and II. Cepheids of Type I are 1.5 magnitudes brighter than those of Type II. Their periods range from 1.5 to 40 days. They brighten rapidly, then gradually grow

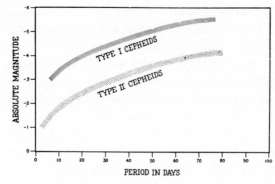

Fig. 18.1. Period-luminosity curves for cepheids of Types I and II. The cepheids of Type I are four times brighter (1.5 magnitudes smaller) than cepheids of Type II with the period.

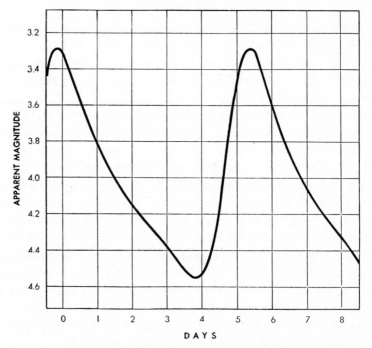

Fig. 18.2. Light curve of Delta Cephei shows the character of its pulsation. In a period of 5 days and 8 hours its apparent brightness gradually decreases more than a full magnitude and then quickly increases again. This star is a cepheid of Type I.

fainter (Fig. 18.2). Cepheids of Type II have periods of from 12 to 25 days. They brighten, become slightly fainter, then level off before dropping to minimum light (Fig. 18.3).

The existence of two types of cepheids was not clearly recognized until about 1952. This naturally led to considerable confusion over the distances of different objects, which only recently has been straightened out. To do so it was necessary to double the size of the universe outside the Milky Way, as we shall see in Chapter 21, Galaxies.

Variables of this type were formerly regarded as cepheids of very short period, but now are considered as probably a separate group. They take their name from RR Lyrae, a seventh-magnitude star, which is the prototype of the group. The RR Lyrae variables

18.4. RR Lyrae variables

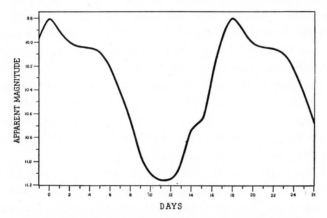

Fig. 18.3. Light curve of W Virginis. In a period of 11 days its brightness decreases by about the same amount as Delta Cephei. This star is a cepheid of Type II.

were formerly called "cluster type variables" because they were first discovered in globular star clusters. Now, however, they are known to occur in all parts of the sky.

The way in which the RR Lyrae variables change brightness is similar to that of the cepheids, except that they do so much more rapidly. The average period of the RR Lyrae stars is only half a day. The shortest known is CY Aquarii, which runs through its light cycle in 88 minutes. Periods longer than 20 hours are rare. The longest known is 29 hours. Whereas the cepheids have a wide range in luminosty from absolute magnitude of −1 to −5 (250 to 10,000 times the luminosity of the sun), the RR Lyrae variables all have the same median absolute magnitude of 0 (86 times the luminosity of the sun). Many of the stars of this class vary with such clocklike regularity that their periods are known to a hundredth of a second.

Although the RR Lyrae variables were once classed as cepheids, there are important differences between them that indicate they are distinct groups of stars. The cepheids are all situated close to the Milky Way, and their motions are very small. The RR Lyrae stars

243

are widely scattered over the sky, and they have the highest known velocities of any group of stars in our stellar system.

18.5. Long-period variables The long-period variables are giant red stars with periods of from 100 to 700 days. Their light changes are only roughly periodic, however, so that their brightness cannot be predicted with high precision. The most famous long-period variable is Omicron Ceti, whose variability was discovered in 1596. Its brightness changes in such an extraordinary manner that about 300 years ago it was named Mira, the "Wonderful." Mira is such a characteristic example of stars of this type that the long-period variables are often referred to simply as "Miras." At maximum, Mira is usually about magnitude 3.5, although it has been known to reach 1.5, when it outshines all other stars in that part of the sky. At minimum, it sinks below naked-eye visibility to about magnitude 9. The average period of Mira is 330 days, but may vary by 30 days or more either way. Mira is attended by a small white companion so faint that it can only be discerned when the red giant is near minimum light.

18.6. Irregular variables These stars are red giants like the long-period variables, but their behavior is much more erratic. Their variation is also much smaller, being less than two magnitudes in most cases. Betelgeuse is one of these fluctuating stars. Measures with the interferometer indicate that the diameter of Betelgeuse has varied from 186 million to 280 million miles, or from about 200 to 300 times the diameter of the sun.

18.7. Cause of the light variation Lines in the spectra of cepheids show a regular shift to the red and violet, as if these stars had a backward and forward motion superposed upon their steady velocity through space. Now it seems incredible that a body alone in space could be moving in this manner, speeding up and slowing down, like a man running back and forth on top of a moving flat car. The most reasonable explanation is that a cepheid moves steadily as a whole but *pulsates*. The star's temperature rises, it expands, and reaches maximum light when expanding the fastest. As the star contracts it grows fainter, and reaches minimum light when contracting the fastest. The pulsations of the cepheids and RR Lyrae stars have been compared to the expansion and contraction of a balloon as air is forced in and out. This crude picture is probably much too simple, yet it does give a fairly good description of the observations.

It is believed that the long-period variables and irregular variables also pulsate, but that they do so erratically in contrast to the steady rhythmical pulsations of the cepheids and RR Lyrae stars.

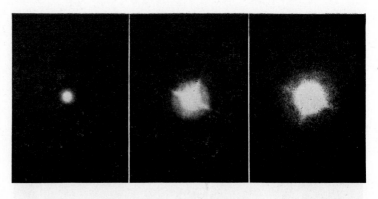

Fig. 18.4. Expanding nebulosity around Nova Aquilae, Nov. 3, 1918. Left, July 20, 1922; center, Sept. 3, 1926; right, Aug. 14, 1931. (Mount Wilson Observatory.)

18.8. New stars or novae

In contrast to the regular brightening and fading of the RR Lyrae stars and even the irregular changes in the long-period variables, occasionally a star will suddenly flare up from obscurity to great brilliance and then sink slowly back into the obscurity from which it came. Such spectacular objects are called NOVAE or NEW STARS, or sometimes TEMPORARY STARS. The name is somewhat misleading, since it erroneously implies that a star has spontaneously originated where none existed before. Actually, it is believed that a nova is one of the myriads of faint stars which for some reason has undergone a catastrophe that caused its light to increase by some hundred thousand fold in a day or two.

The appearance of a bright nova is the signal for astronomers to drop their regular work and turn their telescopes on the newcomer. Study of the spectra of novae reveals that shells of gas are blown from the star with a velocity of a thousand miles a second or more. The star literally "blows its top," as only the surface layers are affected. Months or years after the outburst an expanding luminous shell of gas may be found surrounding the star (Fig. 18.4).

Three stars are known that have suddenly flared up in brightness like a nova two, three, and four times. They have been named RECURRENT novae. There are also a few other stars known as PERMANENT novae, which have streams of gas pouring from their surface continually as if they were always in a state of eruption.

18.9. "Flare" stars

These are faint red dwarf stars that have been observed to increase as much as 100 times in brightness in a few minutes or even seconds. The observations suggest that for some reason a brilliant "hot spot" suddenly develops on the star's surface. It is tempting to identify these hot spots with the flares (par. 10.27 and Fig. 10.22) observed on the sun, but only a few of the very largest flares on our sun would be capable of producing the increase in light that has been observed in these faint red stars.

18.10. Supernovae

In 1885 a star appeared near the nucleus of the Andromeda nebula which reached apparent magnitude 7.2 and became about a

Fig. 18.5. The Crab Nebula in Taurus, Messier 1. Photographed in red light. Remains of an old supernova observed by the Chinese in A.D. 1054. 200-inch Hale telescope. (*Mount Wilson and Palomar Observatories.*)

tenth as bright as the whole nebulae. Its light changes followed the typical pattern of other novae but the spectrum as observed visually was not typical. The outburst aroused widespread interest, since the nature and distances of the spiral nebulae were then unknown so that the actual brightness of the object was a matter of speculation.

Later investigation revealed other novae in the Andromeda nebula as well as other spirals. They seemed to fall into two distinct groups: those that attained a luminosity comparable with the nebula in which they appeared, and much fainter novae that appeared more frequently in single nebulae.

When the distance to the Andromeda nebula was finally determined from a study of variable stars within the spiral, the maximum brightness of the faint novae was found to be about the same as the common novae within our own galaxy. The star of 1885, however, was of another order of brightness, for at maximum it had attained a brightness equivalent to that of 100 million suns. By 1933 the difference between normal novae and the exceptional objects such as that of 1885 was so well recognized that they are generally distinguished by the title of SUPERNOVAE.

A systematic search for supernovae indicates that they occur at the rate of about one outburst per nebula every 300 years.

Three supernovae are believed to have occurred in our own galaxy in the last 900 years. The first was in A.D. 1054, and is still visible as the mass of expanding luminous gas called the Crab Nebula (Figs. 18.6). The second occurred in the constellation of Cassiopeia in 1572. This nova, which was visible in full daylight, turned Tycho

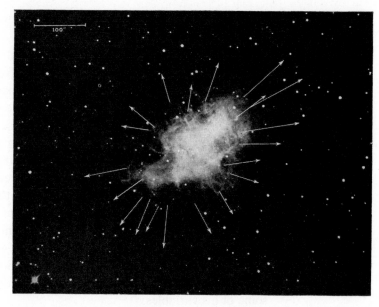

Fig. 18.6. Expansion of the Crab Nebula. The arrows indicate the motion of twenty nebulous points in 500 years. Projected backward they suggest and outburst occurring about 900 years ago. Measures and diagram by John Charles Duncan.

Brahe's attention to astronomy. The third, in 1604, was studied by Kepler.

If a supernova should appear at the distance of the nearest star in our galaxy, Alpha Centauri, it would be about 2000 times as bright as the full moon.

18.11. The cause of novae

Years ago astronomers felt there was no mystery about the cause of novae. The outburst was simply due to a collision between two stars. Such a catastrophe would certainly produce a spectacular burst of light, but it fails utterly to account for the high frequency with which novae occur. The stars are so far apart that a collision would only occur on the average around once in hundreds of thousands of years, whereas there have been thirteen bright novae observed since 1900, and doubtless many faint ones that passed unobserved.

It seems more reasonable to suppose that for some reason the outer layers of a star become unstable, causing them to be blown off with explosive violence. There is evidence that novae occur among stars with less hydrogen than others. If this is the case, then we need not fear that our sun is likely to turn into a nova and vaporize us, as our star appears to be well-supplied with hydrogen.

Stars That Eclipse Each Other

The only star whose light varied that was known to the ancients was Beta Persei, a second-magnitude star which the Arabs called Algol, meaning "changing spirit." From this the name *Demon Star* was derived. No systematic observations of Algol seem to have been made until John Goodricke studied it in 1782. Although Goodricke was a

deaf-mute from birth, he was a brilliant scholar with a special apti-
tude for mathematics and astronomy. Far from being the usual poor
struggling young student, he was heir to a baronetcy and received an
excellent education. When 18 years old he became interested in variable stars and began observing Algol, whose light changes had been
described a century earlier. By comparing the brightness of Algol
with nearby stars, Goodricke found that its period was 2 days 20
hours and 49 minutes, in almost exact agreement with the best modern determinations. Goodricke conjectured that the cause of the variation "could hardly be accounted for otherwise than either by the
interposition of a large body revolving around Algol or by spots upon
its surface." For this discovery Goodricke was awarded the Copley
medal, the highest honor that the Royal Society of England could
bestow. He died in 1786 from exposure brought on while observing
some of his variables.

18.12. Eclipsing double stars

Stars like Algol show regular changes in brightness somewhat
like that of a cepheid, but they are not truly variable stars. As Goodricke surmised, their changes in brightness are due to the eclipse of
the brighter star of the system by its fainter companion. They are
simply double stars revolving around their center of gravity like the
visual double stars. But whereas the two stars in a visual binary system are dozens or thousands of astronomical units apart, the two
stars in an eclipsing system are usually only a small fraction of an
astronomical unit apart. In some cases, it is believed they are so close
together that their surfaces are actually in contact.

Since we cannot observe the two stars in an eclipsing system, how
do we know that the variations in light are due to eclipses and not to
real changes in the luminosity of a single star?

The answer is that we cannot always be *sure*. Trying to explain
all the peculiarities in the light changes is often extremely difficult.
But for many stars the evidence for eclipses is so overwhelming that
there can be no doubt in the matter. This evidence is of two kinds.

1. The changes in light are exactly of the kind we would expect
if one star is regularly eclipsed by another.

2. The changes in radial velocity indicated by the spectroscope
are exactly of the right kind to produce eclipses at the times the light
is faintest.

Figure 18.7 shows what happens in an eclipsing system similar to
that of Algol. Two stars are revolving in circles around their common
center of gravity at *C*. The smaller and brighter star is twice as massive as its larger but fainter companion. It follows from the law of
gravitation that the fainter star must revolve in an orbit that is twice

the size of the orbit of the brighter star. The two stars keep on opposite sides of the point C as if they were at the ends of a rigid rod piv-
oted there.

We will suppose for simplicity that the larger star is so faint that
its light cannot be detected by our instruments and that during eclipse
it blots out the bright star completely. Therefore, the spectroscope

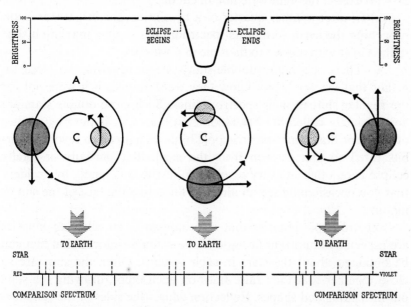

Fig. 18.7. Change in brightness and shift in spectral lines in an eclipsing binary
system. Only the light of the smaller bright component is observed. Large dark star
moves in orbit twice the size of bright star that is twice as massive. At A the bright star
is moving away from the Earth and its spectrum lines are shifted to the red relative to
their stationary position. At B the dark star eclipses the brighter one so that the light of
the system is cut off briefly. Since the motion is across the line of sight, the spectrum
lines show no shift. At C the brightness has risen to normal and the lines are shifted to
the violet since the bright star is now approaching.

will show only the shift in the lines of the bright star. In the diagram
the direction of motion is shown by the arrows.

At A the bright star is moving directly away from the earth so
that the lines in its spectrum will be shifted to the red of their mean
position by their maximum amount. Since the bright star is unob-
scured, its light will be steady and up to its full value, which we call
100 per cent.

The light remains steady at 100 per cent until a little less than a
quarter of a revolution later, when the faint star begins to cut out the
light of the bright one at the point marked "Eclipse begins." The

light falls rapidly and is completely extinguished slightly before the eclipse becomes central at *B*. After passing the mid-point *B*, the bright star begins to emerge from behind the faint one; the light increases rapidly and reaches 100 per cent again at the point marked "Eclipse ends." It will be noticed that at *B* the motion of both stars is directly across the line of sight so that the spectrum lines would show no shift even if the light were not all cut off.

At *C*, after another quarter of a revolution, the bright star is approaching the earth so that its spectrum lines show a maximum shift to the violet with respect to their mean position.

18.13. Importance of eclipsing binary stars
There are many double-star systems revolving so close together that we would not know they were doubles if it were not for the regular shift in their spectrum lines. Such close double stars are appropriately called SPECTROSCOPIC BINARIES. It is purely a matter of accident that some spectroscopic binaries happen to revolve in orbits tilted so that as seen from the earth they partially or totally eclipse each other at every revolution, just as it is purely by accident that you occasionally see an airplane flit across the face of the sun or moon.

Spectroscopic binaries that also happen to be eclipsing binaries are especially important because of the valuable information that can be obtained about the stars in such systems. Often the stars are so close together that they raise tides on each other, drawing the stars out into elongated shapes. Reflection causes the sides of the stars facing each other to be brighter than the sides turned away. Systems are known in which the stars are ejecting streams of gas at each other. From a detailed study of certain eclipsing binaries, we can get the masses of the two stars, their densities, dimensions, temperatures, and a knowledge of conditions in their atmospheres.

18.14. RW Tauri: A star with a luminous ring
An excellent example of the seemingly incredible amount of information that can be obtained regarding an eclipsing binary system from observations of its light curve and line displacements is that of RW Tauri. One component of this pair is a brilliant white star. The other component is a fainter yellow star about twice its diameter. Once every 2.77 days the large yellow star eclipses the bright white one, totality lasting for 84 minutes (Fig. 18.8).

In 1941, A. H. Joy found that at the beginning of an eclipse the bright hydrogen lines in the spectrum of this binary system were displaced to the red of their normal positions. At the middle of the eclipse the bright hydrogen lines vanished. At the end of the eclipse the bright hydrogen lines reappeared but now were displaced to the violet of their normal positions.

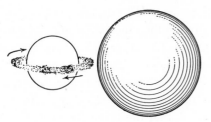

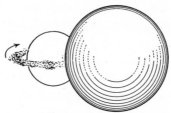

a. Large, faint *K0*-type star about to eclipse smaller, more brilliant *B9* star with luminous ring of hydrogen gas surrounding it. Spectroscopic analysis of light shows only presence of bright *B9* star.

b. The *B9* star, although partially eclipsed, still so far outshines the *K0* star that spectroscope reveals only usual *B9* spectral characteristics.

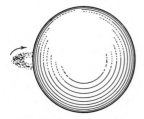

c. At moment when *B9* star is completely blocked out, brilliant bright lines of hydrogen gas flash out. These bright lines show Doppler shift to *red* side of normal position, indicating velocity *away from* observer of 210 miles per second.

d. The *B9* star and its ring are both totally eclipsed for thirty minutes. During this phase spectroscope shows only very faint solarlike spectrum of the *K0* star.

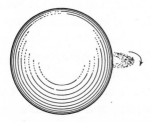

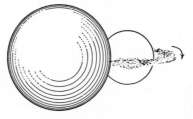

e. At third contact, ring on other side is revealed and spectroscope now shows bright hydrogen lines again, but this time shifted to the *violet* by an amount indicating velocity of 210 miles per second *toward* the observer.

f. Spectrum is now same as that in *a*, a typical hot *B9* star only. Entire process repeated in 2 days 18 hours.

Fig. 18.8.

He interprets these observations as indicating the presence of a flaming ring of hydrogen gas surrounding the white star which is slightly smaller than the diameter of the larger yellow companion. The displacements of the bright hydrogen lines are produced as the yellow star covers up one end of the ring at the beginning of the eclipse and the opposite end at the finish of the eclipse. At mid-eclipse the ring is entirely covered so that the bright hydrogen emission disappears.

From the observed displacements of the bright hydrogen lines Joy deduces that the gas is rotating in the ring at the rate of 217 miles per second with a rotation period of 14 hours, and that the diameter of the ring is four times that of our sun. The intensity of the bright lines vary, indicating that the ring is thicker in some parts than in others.

18.15. Rotation of the stars Since all stars remain mere points of light no matter how much we magnify them, it may seem strange that we can detect their rotation. Yet not only has the rotation of many stars been detected, but their speed as well. The method is spectroscopic and resembles in principle the method used to measure the rotation of the sun. In the case of the sun the image is so large that we can point the spectroscope first to the approaching edge of the sun and then to the receding edge. At the approaching edge the spectral lines will be shifted to the violet and at the receding edge to the red. By measuring the amount the lines are shifted, the speed of rotation of the sun can be found.

Star images are so small that we cannot think of pointing the spectroscope at the approaching and receding edges. But if the star is spinning rapidly, its spectral lines will still be shifted in opposite directions so that they appear greatly widened. White stars rotate with a speed of about 30 miles a second on the average—about 30 times as fast as the sun. No star is known with a rotational velocity greater than 160 miles per second. If a star rotated much faster than this the surface layers would become unstable and fly off into space. A white star twice the size of the sun spinning at 160 miles per second would have a period of rotation of 9½ hours, as compared with 25 days for the sun at the equator.

Some white stars show no velocity of rotation. This is because their axes of rotation must be pointed nearly straight toward the earth. The spectral lines are not widened because opposite edges of the star are neither approaching nor receding from us, and hence show no shift to the red or violet.

The magnetic field in sunspots was discovered by the splitting of the lines in their spectra. Evidence for a magnetic field in the stars has been found by the same method. Only rapidly rotating white stars show magnetic fields. In some cases these are about twice as strong as those in the largest sunspots. In most stars examined, the magnetic field is variable. In one star, the magnetic field was found to reverse itself from north to south polarity regularly every 4½ days.

18.16. The magnetic field in stars

QUESTIONS AND EXERCISES

1. Goodricke found that Algol varied in a regular period by comparing its brightness with stars around it. What is a possible source of error in such a method?

2. From Figure 18.1 find what is the absolute magnitude of Type I and Type II cepheids with periods of 10 days, 15 days, and 40 days.

3. The absolute magnitude of a Type I cepheid with a period of 16 days is −3.8. What is the period of a Type II cepheid of the same absolute magnitude?

4. How much difference is there in the period of a Type I cepheid with an absolute magnitude of −4 and a Type II cepheid of magnitude −4?

5. From Figure 18.2 how many days are there from minimum to maximum? From maximum to minimum?

6. What is the apparent magnitude of Delta Cephei at maximum and minimum (Fig. 18.2)? What is its median apparent magnitude (the mean of its magnitudes at maximum and minimum)?

7. Would the cepheids we observe in the Andromeda nebula probably be mostly of short or long period? Why?

8. Why would a "flare" such as those observed on the sun be capable of producing an observable increase in brightness only in red dwarfs?

9. The explosion which produced the cloud of gas called the Crab Nebula occurred about 900 years ago. These gases are found to be still expanding. Why did the expansion not cease long ago?

10. Do you think that the variations in brightness of the cepheids might be produced by giant sunspots? Discuss arguments for and against.

19 WHAT KEEPS THE STARS SHINING?

THE most obvious feature about the stars is the one which astronomers have always found the hardest to explain—the fact that they *shine*. What is the source of energy which keeps the stars shining year after year without noticeable diminution in brightness? In their search for an answer, astronomers have eagerly seized upon each discovery in physics that might help them in solving their own problems.

19.1. The contraction theory   About a century ago astronomers believed they had the answer at last. The great German physicist, Helmholtz, in a popular lecture delivered in 1854, showed that if the sun contracts it must release heat. This contraction is equivalent to the fall of particles by different amounts depending upon their distances from the center of the sun. Making the most unfavorable assumptions Helmholtz found that a shrinkage of 250 feet per year would be ample to supply the sun with its annual output of energy. At this rate, the decrease in size of the sun would be so slow that it could not be detected for ten thousand years.

Astronomers soon became so convinced of the truth of the contraction theory that they arbitrarily informed the geologists that the greatest possible age for the earth was about 25 million years and that their time scale should be adjusted accordingly. This the geologists flatly refused to do, as they had excellent reasons for believing that the age of the earth is much greater—more than 100 million years, at least.

Although contraction is still believed to be an important source of energy during certain periods in a star's career, it is far from being the main source, as was once supposed. Toward the close of the nineteenth century, the discovery of radium led to the uneasy suspicion among astronomers that internal friction might not be the only source of solar energy. They could watch radium release enough energy every hour to melt more than its own weight of ice, knowing that it could continue to do so for another thousand years. Application to the sun, however, was little more than a hopeful possibility. No spectrum lines of radioactive chemicals had been found in the solar atmosphere. Besides, nobody had the faintest idea from whence radium derived its energy.

Then, in 1905, Einstein published a little paper that changed the whole situation. He showed that as a result of his theory of relativity there is an equivalence between mass and radiant energy. We know that if we burn a pound of coal it will give us a certain amount of radiant energy in the form of light and heat. After burning, the chemicals composing the coal have not been destroyed. During the process of burning they are turned into other chemical forms, most of which go up the chimney as a gas. What Einstein asserted was that if we could *annihilate* a pound of coal (or any other substance) so that it did not exist as matter any more, we would also get energy— about a billion times as much as we would get by burning the coal! Here might be the source of energy that kept the stars shining. But how do you go about annihilating matter?

19.2. Energy from within the atom

By 1925, scientists felt sure the sun must get its energy from some sort of atomic annihilation process. The one that seemed most likely was the instantaneous collision of four hydrogen atoms to produce a helium atom. The weight of a helium atom is not quite equal to the weight of four hydrogen atoms. Presumably the hydrogen atoms lost a little mass in the collision which was transformed into radiant energy. We may compare it to a collision between four automobiles. The impact causes some water to leak from their radiators so that the cars do not weigh so much after the smashup as they did before.

Now it is possible that in the millions of years that the sun has been shining there have been occasions when four hydrogen atoms have combined to form one helium atom with the release of some energy. But such collisions would be so extremely rare that they could never produce enough energy to have kept the sun shining at its present rate. We must have a collision which happens much oftener between only two bodies. (Collisions between two cars are all too common. But how many times have you seen four cars come together at the same instant?) In fact, even a two-body collision is not enough. An investigation shows that there must be a *series* of collisions to produce energy at the rate needed.

In 1939, a physicist at Cornell University, H. A. Bethe, announced a series of atomic collisions, or reactions, which seemed to

19.3. The carbon cycle

be capable of producing energy in the sun at just about the right rate. The series involves collisions of carbon and hydrogen, the end result being that four hydrogen atoms are transformed into a helium atom, the carbon atom emerges unscathed in its original form, and a little mass has been converted into energy. Because the series of atomic reactions begins and ends with carbon, it is usually referred to as the "carbon cycle."

It must not be supposed, however, that atoms in the sun go through these steps in an orderly manner like automobiles coming off the assembly line. If we could see the reactions in the sun at any instant, we would find all stages of the cycle going on at once. To complete a cycle requires on the average 6½ million years, and since the lifetime of the sun is estimated at 10 billion years, the carbon atoms will have been transformed into other substances and regenerated many times in their role of converting hydrogen into helium with the evolution of energy.

19.4. The "proton-proton" reaction
Just about the time astronomers had decided that the question of energy generation in the sun was pretty well settled, another reaction was proposed which may be of more importance than the carbon cycle in the sun and red dwarfs. The nucleus of a hydrogen atom is called a *proton*. Occasionally two protons will collide to produce an atom of double the weight of ordinary hydrogen called "heavy hydrogen." If an atom of heavy hydrogen picks up another proton an unusual light form of helium atom is produced. Two of these light helium atoms may in turn unite to form one atom of ordinary helium with two protons left over. Nothing but hydrogen has been used in making the heavy hydrogen, light helium, and ordinary helium. Again hydrogen has been converted into helium with a loss of mass which appears as radiant energy.

It would seem inevitable that there will come a time when the supply of hydrogen will run low and the star will be compelled to make some radical readjustment in its mode of energy generation if it intends to keep on shining. Just how a star meets this difficult situation is still uncertain. It may start to contract thus releasing gravitational energy, which raises the temperature of the star sufficiently so that new nuclear processes are set in operation. There are theoretical reasons for believing that when a star has exhausted virtually every source of energy available it becomes a white dwarf. If this is true then a white dwarf represents the last stage of stellar evolution. But the reader is warned that this is a field in which our ideas are changing almost from day-to-day, and there is no theory that has won general acceptance as yet.

Model Stars

From inspection of the outside of a building, and a knowledge of its total size, weight, and cost, an experienced contractor could probably make a fairly good estimate of how the building is constructed within. Astronomers are confronted by a similar problem with the sun. From their knowledge of the outside of the sun, and its total mass, size, and output of energy, they attempt to reconstruct a model of the inside of the sun.

What do astronomers have to guide them in this task?

They know the total mass of the sun. It is 2000 trillion trillion tons—2 followed by 27 zeros. This is the amount of building material available.

They know that the distance from the center of the sun to the surface is 432,000 miles, which tells them the size of the globe in which they have to put their building material.

They know that each square inch of the sun's surface shines with a light equal to 300,000 standard candles. This is the rate that the sun is pouring radiant energy into space.

They also know that the temperature of the sun at the surface is 10,300° F and that the density at its surface is about 1 per cent of that of the air at sea level.

In proceeding to build a star with the same specifications as the sun, they have several general conditions to guide them. They feel sure that the temperature and density of the sun must increase as they proceed from the surface toward the center. But how fast do they increase? If they make the density increase too rapidly, they will be in danger of running out of building material before the star is finished. If they make the temperature rise too fast, the star may get so hot inside it will blow up. Or if it does not rise fast enough, it will be so cool inside that the star will collapse. The sun is a stable star that shines with a steady light, and so our model star must be one that is subject to no violent upheavals or other changes in luminosity. The forces acting on every bit of matter from center to surface must balance exactly.

It would take too long to describe the difficulties that astronomers have encountered and the progress that they have made in their struggle with this problem. We shall limit ourself therefore simply to a bare statement of our present ideas about conditions within the sun as far as it is possible to do so.

The temperature of the sun rises from 10,300° F. at the surface to 34,000,000° F. near the center. The central temperature may be several million degrees lower, depending upon how effective the proton-proton reaction is in generating energy, a factor that is still uncertain. The flow of heat from the center of the star to the surface is almost wholly by radiation—the same way that heat reaches you across space from an electric stove. Flow of heat by conduction, as from the hot end of a poker to the cool end, is much too sluggish to be of importance. Also, transfer of heat by circulating currents, as in a hot-air heating system, would not be nearly lively enough to transport heat through the star at the required rate.

The density of the outer atmosphere of the sun is much less than that of the air you breathe, but at the center it is 100 times as dense as water, or 10 times denser than platinum. Yet the sun is gaseous throughout. This is because at the high temperature near the center of the sun the outer superstructure of the atoms is torn away so that there is plenty of room left for the particles to circulate with comparative freedom as they do in a gas.

The sun is now believed to be composed almost entirely of hydrogen and helium. In some model suns the percentage of hydrogen is 65 per cent; in others the hydrogen is as high as 82 per cent. Hydrogen and helium together probably constitute more than 95 per cent of the sun's mass. It has been said that the stars are mainly hydrogen and helium, with an impurity of carbon, nitrogen, and oxygen, and only "traces" of the other elements.

The Mass-Luminosity Law

19.7. The mass-luminosity relation among the stars

The fact that we can so-to-speak draw up a blueprint of a star closely resembling the sun in size, mass, and luminosity indicates that our theory of stellar interiors must be generally correct. Nevertheless, it would be reassuring to have some entirely independent check on the theory. The fact that one family can live on a particular budget does not mean it would necessarily work for others.

Such a check is found in the relation that exists between the mass and the luminosity of a star. We have seen that the masses of the two components in a few double stars are known from their gravitational attraction upon each other. When the masses of these stars are plotted against their absolute magnitudes, the points instead of being scattered at random, fall along a curve shown by the line in Fig. 19.1. Evidently there is a relation between the masses of the stars and their luminosity (absolute magnitude) such that the greater the mass the greater the light-giving power. We see that a star 5 times as massive as the sun would be a giant 100 times as luminous as the sun. But a star one-fifth as massive as the sun would be only 1/2000 as luminous, so faint we would be unable to see it unless it was quite close to the earth. This important relation, called the "mass-luminosity law," was discovered in 1924 by A. S. Eddington, a theoretical astronomer at the University of Cambridge, England.

It can be shown from purely theoretical reasoning that the luminosity of stars made of the same chemical elements depends only upon their mass. In fact, we can derive a mass-luminosity law purely from theory that agrees closely with the curve obtained from the actual masses and luminosities of double stars. Although the agreement is not perfect, it is close enough to show that we must at least be on the right track.

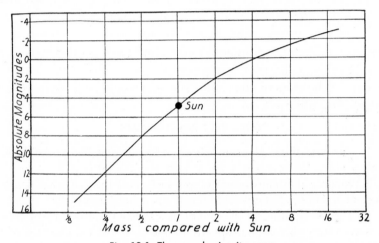

Fig. 19.1. The mass-luminosity curve.

The theoretical results help us to see why the extreme range in stellar mass is comparatively small—probably only about 6000 to 1. A star one-hundredth as massive as the sun would be so faint that it could scarcely be termed a star at all, but would be more in the nature of a glowing planet. On the other hand, a star a hundred times as massive as the sun would be so distended by the powerful blast of radiation streaming through it that it would be in danger of blowing up. Therefore, the stars of which we have any knowledge are confined somewhere between these extremes.

As we have seen, the only direct method of determining the mass of a star is from its gravitational attraction on another body, as in a double-star system. But out of the 30,000 known double-star systems of various kinds there are only a few score for which we are able to obtain reliable masses. The mass-luminosity law is thus of great practical value to astronomers in that it enables them to obtain

19.8. Mass of a star from the mass-luminosity law

the mass of a star if its luminosity, or absolute magnitude, is known. Of course, strictly speaking we cannot determine a star's absolute magnitude unless we first know its parallax, and its parallax is about as hard to determine as its mass. But fortunately astronomers have several shoestring methods of estimating a star's absolute magnitude without measuring its parallax. For example, from the appearance of certain lines in the spectrum of a star an experienced observer can not only tell the spectral class of the star but whether it is a giant or a dwarf. Suppose the observer decides that a star is a red giant of class M. Reference to the Russell diagram (Fig. 17.2) shows that red giants have an average absolute magnitude of −1. (Some observers even claim they can tell whether a star is a red giant or a red dwarf simply by its appearance in the telescope, without bothering about its spectrum!). With this value of the absolute magnitude the observer then goes to the mass-luminosity curve and reads off the mass of the star. Thus from the mass-luminosity law it is possible to obtain an estimate of the mass of an isolated star that would be quite impossible to determine otherwise.

QUESTIONS AND EXERCISES

1. Can you think of some reasons why the sun has probably been shining essentially as it is now for at least about 3000 years?

2. Suppose the temperature of the surface of the sun were doubled. How much more radiation would reach our upper atmosphere?

3. The temperature of the umbra of a sunspot is about two-thirds of the temperature of the photosphere around it. If the temperature of the whole sun were reduced to that of the sunspot umbra, how would its rate of radiation be changed? See par. 10.6.

4. The lifetime of a star is probably measured in hundreds of millions of years. Astronomers would like to know the changes a star undergoes in the course of its life. How can they hope to learn anything about such changes in the brief time they can study them?

5. Can you think of reasons for believing some stars are probably older than others, from comparisons of their size, temperature, luminosity, etc? Give your arguments. Do you think the red giants are probably younger or older than the white dwarfs? Why?

6. Do you think that stars change slowly or that their evolution may proceed rapidly at times? How do novae fit into the scheme of evolution? (Nobody knows the answers to questions 5 and 6 but you can learn a good deal by discussing them.)

7. Scientists a century ago believed the sun was kept shining by the meteorites falling into it. Discuss the theory pro and con.

8. If the sun suddenly blew up like a nova how long would it be before we knew about it on the earth?

GALACTIC NEBULAE AND OTHER INTERSTELLAR MATERIAL **20**

Our Stellar System and other Systems

OUR system of stars is called the galaxy, a name derived from the Greek word, *gala,* meaning milk. Galaxy and Milky Way are often used synonymously to mean our entire system of stars, though Milky Way usually refers to the white pathway across the heavens which is due to the fact that the stars along that zone are more numerous than in other parts of the sky. We do not usually consider the stars at each side of the light-colored strip as belonging to the Milky Way, but *all* the stars that we can see belong to the Milky Way *system,* called the GALAXY, or GALACTIC SYSTEM.

On account of the flattened shape of the stellar system, and our position near its central plane, we see more stars out along this plane than in other directions. The milky appearance is due to the greater number of stars. The whole stellar galaxy of some 30,000,-000,000 stars and a great many gaseous clouds called nebulae, constitute a lens-shaped figure, whose greatest diameter is somewhere around 100,000 light years and whose thickness may be as little as one tenth of its width. (For the probable appearance of the stellar system see pictures of spiral nebulae.) Our system is surrounded by a vast region very sparsely strewn with stars which separates our galaxy from other systems.

A hundred and fifty years ago William Herschel, the father of modern astronomy, did pioneer work in observing with a keen eye and an inquiring mind all the different kinds of stars and other objects he could see in the whole sky. He saw some stars that were double, some that were in clusters, and many white patches against the sky that he thought were gaseous clouds. But he could not be certain of this. Some star clusters which with a small telescope appeared

20.1. Isolation of of the stellar system

20.2. Distinguishing between gas clouds and star clouds

261

merely as a blur of light were separable into individual stars when viewed with a larger telescope. He had no means of knowing whether or not all of the cosmic clouds, which he called nebulae, were really clouds of finely divided matter or whether they were dense and distant star clusters (Figs. 20.1 and 20.2).

Spectrographs attached to large, modern telescopes, show that *some* of the nebulae seen by Herschel are actually clouds of gaseous matter, mingled with dust particles. These clouds are within the stellar system. Other similar-appearing clouds are shown to be systems of stars far outside of our own galaxy. Thus there are two kinds of "nebulae," as they are still called. The typical cloud *within* the galaxy gives a *bright-line* spectrum, showing that it is composed, at least partly, of a gas under low pressure. The extragalactic nebula gives a

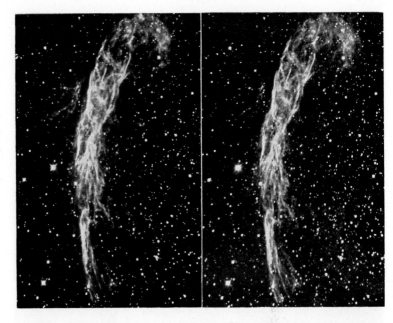

spectrum such as we should get if we could go far outside of our system of stars and point the telescope at the whole galaxy. It is a continuous spectrum, crossed by a multitude of dark lines such as stars like the sun would give. In some cases the spectra of these extragalactic systems have a few *bright* lines, indicating that gaseous nebulae are found in them along with the stars, just as there are gaseous nebulae, which give bright lines, in our own stellar system. The gas clouds in some of the distant systems can be shown to be localized in certain parts of the nebula.

Diffuse and Planetary Nebulae

Two terms are used in describing the general *forms* which cosmic clouds of the galaxy assume. The DIFFUSE, or "irregular," nebula is a formless mass spreading over an angle in the sky about as large as that apparently covered by the moon. The PLANETARY nebula is round, or nearly so, and smaller, and requires stronger magnification to show its disk shape. Many of the more distant ones appear so very little larger than ordinary stars that they would probably have remained unnoticed but for their bright-line spectra, which make them conspicuous.

One of the most beautiful examples of the diffuse type is the cloud in Orion. The middle star of the sword of the giant is seen, even with the naked eye, to be slightly fuzzy. The telescope brings out details of the luminous cloud that fills a widely extended space among the stars seen in the surrounding region (Fig. 20.3).

Planetary nebulae, of which there are more than a hundred, re-

Fig. 20.3. The great nebula in Orion. Exposure 3 hours with the 100-inch telescope. The central portion has been reduced in intensity in order to show the dimmer outlying parts and still keep detail in the brighter portion. (*Mount Wilson Observatory.*)

semble planets only in that they are approximately round (Fig. 20.4). They are much larger than the space occupied by the sun and all the planets. Calculated from their angular diameters, and the distances to more than twenty of them, the linear diameters of planetary nebulae are found to be several thousand times that of the entire solar system.

In many cases, and perhaps in all, if we could see them, there is a very bright, white-hot star at the center of the nebula. This star seems to impart light to the whole nebula, not as the sun illumines the earth, for the nebula is much brighter than it could be if shining by reflected light, but by some process not so well understood as reflection. Either the star's ultraviolet light or emissions of electrons from the star sets the surrounding gases shining, somewhat as Arctic atmosphere is made luminous (probably by electrons from the sun), producing the Aurora Borealis. Or, perhaps the process of illumination is more like that by which a certain kind of paint shines at night after absorbing sunshine during the day. The central stars of planetary nebulae are of the *O* type, and are the bluest of all known stars. Temperatures as high as 100,000° F have been estimated for them.

Some of the planetary nebulae appear as a ring (Fig. 20.4), probably because they are spherical *shells*. The sides of a shell would

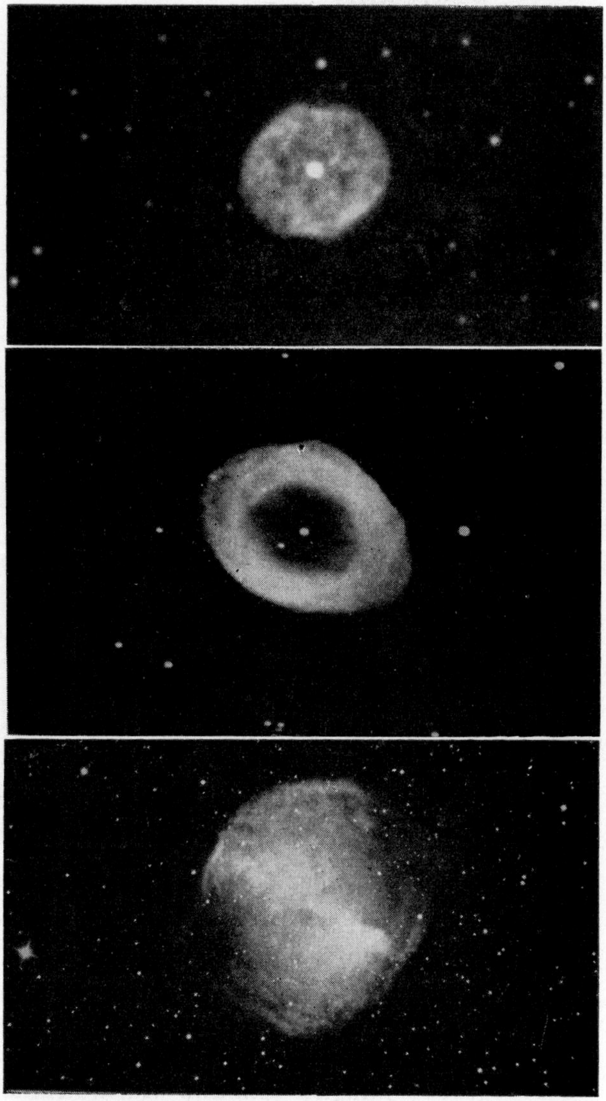

Fig. 20.4. Three planetary nebulae. Top, NGC 1501, shows central star; exposure 2 hours, 60-inch telescope. Middle, NGC 6720, Ring Nebula in Lyra, 100-inch telescope. Bottom, NGC 6853, Dumbbell, 2 hours 40 minutes, 100-inch telescope. (Mount Wilson Observatory.)

show most plainly because of the greater depth through which we are looking.

From a study of the light and spectra of diffuse nebulae it is found that they, too, owe their luminescence to neighboring stars. In some cases, where there are no very hot stars near enough, the nebulae are dark; they make their presence known only by their obscuring power, which hides the stars beyond (Fig. 20.5).

20.3. The light of diffuse nebulae

On the evening of Aug. 29, 1864, William Huggins, a pioneer in the application of the spectroscope to the study of the heavenly bodies, for the first time directed his telescope to the nebula in the constellation of Draco. The nature of the nebulae was then wholly unknown. For years astronomers had speculated about these

20.4. The nature of the gaseous nebulae

Fig. 20.5. Nebulosity in constellation of Monoceros, photographed in red light. 200-inch Hale telescope. (*Mount Wilson and Palomar Observatories.*)

little hazy patches among the stars. Some regarded them as vast aggregations of stars so distant that they appeared like a tiny cloud. Others thought they might be the fiery mist out of which the universe had been born. Huggins realized that the spectroscope, by its power to analyze light, might reveal the true nature of the nebulae at a single glance. We can imagine, therefore, the feeling of excited suspense mingled with awe with which, after a brief hesitation, he put his eye to the spectroscope. It was like looking into some secret place of creation.

No spectrum such as he had expected appeared—only a single bright green line. At first he thought something must be wrong with his spectroscope, that one of the prisms was displaced. Then the true interpretation flashed upon him. The whole light of the nebula consisted of but one color emitted by a luminous gas. The riddle of the nebulae was solved—and at a single glance! *

We now know that both types of nebulae exist: the gaseous nebulae in our own galaxy, such as Huggins first observed, and the nebulae far outside our galaxy composed of great stellar systems. Later

* This is not an imaginary reconstruction of Huggins' sensations on this occasion but is taken almost verbatim from his own account.

Fig. 20.6. The "Horse Head Nebula," a dark nebula in Orion. Note the relatively small number of stars in the left half of the picture. Only those between us and the cloud can be seen. (Mount Wilson Observatory.)

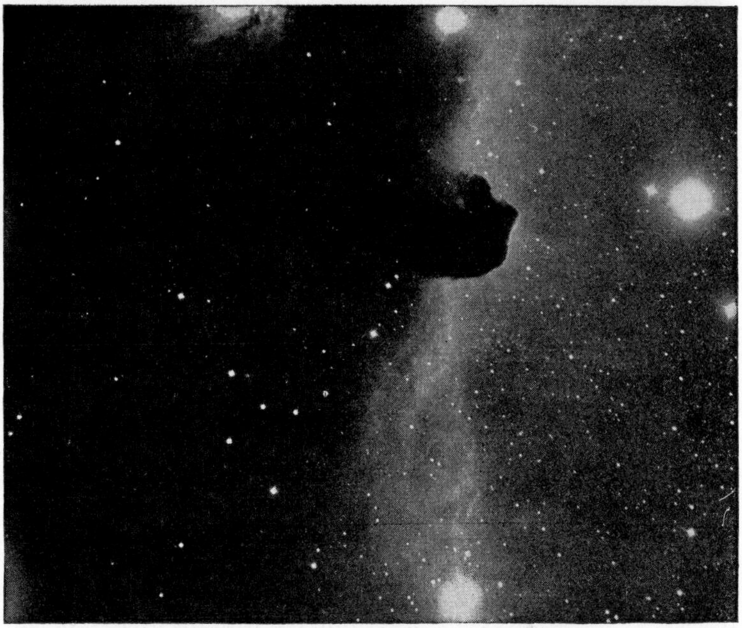

investigation also revealed additional bright lines in the spectra of the gaseous nebulae, among them the yellow line of helium and the familiar lines of hydrogen. There were several others that could not be identified which Huggins suggested might originate in an element peculiar to the nebulae and unknown upon the earth. He occasionally referred to this mysterious element as *nebulium*. The name became popular and was retained for convenience of designation long after the idea of an unknown nebular element was discarded. The nebulium lines were finally identified in 1927 as originating in forbidden transitions in atoms of the elements oxygen, nitrogen, neon, argon, and sulfur.

Obscuring Clouds

In many parts of the Milky Way obscuring clouds of sometimes inky blackness cut off our view of the more distant stars in our own galaxy. Only the few stars, which lie between us and these obscuring clouds, are visible, sparsely dotting the darkened background (Figs. 20.5 and 20.6).

20.5. Dark nebulae

It was formerly thought that these dark spots against the sky were holes through which we could look out into the emptiness beyond the stars. Such an assumption is now known to be unreasonable, for the stars have been found to possess a great deal of motion in all directions, which would obviously have filled such "holes" during the past millions of years of random movement. There can scarcely be more doubt that stars lie beyond an obscuring cosmic cloud such as that

Fig. 20.7. Spiral nebula HV19 Andromedae. It would probably appear spiral if seen from a different part of the universe. (*Mount Wilson Observatory.*)

seen moving forward in Figure 20.6, than that hills and trees lie beyond a cloud bank seen on the horizon.

20.6. Dark matter in extragalactic nebulae

Furthermore, we can by analogy infer obscuring clouds in the Milky Way. Many of the extragalactic nebulae, which are now assumed to be distant counterparts of our stellar system, show unmistakable evidence of a central belt of dark matter surrounding and probably intermingled with the system of stars (Figs. 20.7 and 20.8). Some also seem to show such material existing as more restricted clouds here and there throughout the body of the nebula.

20.7. The nature of obscuring matter

Since much of the material that obstructs our view of more distant stars and star systems is wholly invisible, its nature can be learned only by inference. Objects as large as planets or dark stars would be effective in cutting off light if there were enough of them. Enough very small particles, though, will shut out the light as effectively as larger ones so long as the particles are large in proportion to a wave length of light. Dust in sufficient amounts will dim the light of the sun. The smoke of a coal fire, rendered black by millions of floating particles of soot, is nearly as opaque as a lump of the coal itself.

Fig. 20.8. The dark-lane nebula in Virgo (NGC 4594). Slipher, in 1913, discovered the high velocity of recession of spiral nebulae. This one had the highest velocity then known, 685 miles a second. Notice the dark, absorbing matter. (*Lowell Observatory.*)

Fig. 20.9. The same region as Figure 20.10 but photographed in blue light. Only about one third of the stars shown on the red photograph appear. Blue light from the more distant stars is absorbed and scattered by fine dust particles before reaching the photographic plate. Red light is scattered less and so can penetrate further into intervening cosmic dust. (*Mount Wilson and Palomar Observatories.*)

And a shovelful of coal can make a very great volume of smoke. It is far more reasonable to suppose that the obscuring areas, whose volumes can be measured only in hundreds or thousands of cubic light years, contain finely divided matter rather than large bodies.

20.8. Scattering of light

There has recently been gathered much direct evidence that a large part of the obscuring matter of space (within our galaxy) is due to particles *too small* to stop the light completely or to reflect it back. Such particles scatter light—that is, send it in all directions. The proof of light scattering is found in the fact that stars at a great distance, in or near the Milky Way, are reddened. That is, the blue, short-wave light is scattered and lost more readily than the longer wave red and orange light (Figs. 20.9 and 20.10).

Our atmosphere, even at its clearest, always scatters a larger proportion of blue light than of red. This takes from the sun and stars

Fig. 20.10. Photograph with the 100-inch telescope of the Mount Wilson Observatory taken in red light, showing for the first time the great concentration of faint stars at the nucleus of our galaxy. The number of stars shown on this photograph is estimated to be 800,000 per square degree. Only globular star clusters show a higher concentration. The area covered by the photograph is about the size of the full moon. (*Mount Wilson and Palomar Observatories.*)

the bluish white glare they would otherwise have. It is this scattered blue light that we see when we look at the sky in any direction except that directly toward the sun. In other words, it is the predominance of scattered blue light that makes the sky blue. If it were possible to heat an object close at hand to a temperature of 10,300° F or more, as the sun and stars are heated, its light would be much whiter than that of the sun, because of its larger proportion of blue and violet light.

The reddening of starlight, however, is different from that produced by the tiny molecules of our atmosphere. Particles as small as molecules scatter light powerfully. The reddening of starlight as it passes through space is attributed to larger solid cosmic grains which are not so effective as molecules at scattering light. The grains are so far apart that even in the densest dark nebulae we would have to sweep through a region equal to the volume of the earth to find a thousandth of an ounce.

20.9. The greater the distance the redder the stars
Measures have been made with extremely sensitive recording instruments on the light of the globular clusters, which are the most distant objects visible in the galactic system. Their intense, far-reaching light is due to the fact that each one is composed of some 10,000 stars or more, many of them very bright. Here, as might be expected, is found a high degree of reddening. The case seems to be well proved. There is evidently much partially obscuring matter in the galaxy, especially along the Milky Way. No globular cluster is found within 4000 light years of the galactic plane.

Interstellar Gases

There is another way in which distant objects of the sky may be partially obscured besides by the obstructing and scattering effect of dust particles. Gases absorb *certain wave lengths* of light—certain lines of color. This is the cause of the dark Fraunhofer absorption lines of the solar spectrum.

Calcium atoms make their presence known in interstellar space more clearly than do atoms of any other element. Starlight shining through this gas comes to the spectroscope deprived of its natural quantity of light at certain wave lengths. At the places in the spectrum where these wave lengths should fall, dark lines, due to absorption, are found.

20.10. The gas not a part of stars
It might be thought that these lines are due to calcium in the star's own atmosphere. Such is the cause of the Fraunhofer lines of the sun's spectrum. But these lines of calcium are *slightly* displaced from the positions they would occupy if the absorbing gas were a part

270

of the star, and therefore moving with the star. The Doppler shift proves that the calcium is in interstellar space, and does not share the motion of the star.

The spectral lines made by calcium atoms existing in interstellar space were discovered years ago by Hartmann. He was observing the spectra of a binary, in which the lines shift from side to side as the component stars go around each other. Hartmann noticed that the H and K lines of calcium were exceptionally sharp instead of being wide and diffuse, as they usually are. Also, these sharp lines failed to show any back and forth shift, as the other lines of the spectrum did. Evidently the calcium atoms absorbing the lines of light lay between the star and the observer, not in the star. Their sharpness was due to the lack of any to-and-fro motion, such as gases have in a star. The Doppler effect of such motion widens stellar lines.

20.11. Discovery of interstellar calcium

The H and K lines of interstellar calcium have now been observed between us and hundreds of white stars of very high temperature. These early-type stars are favorable for this observation, for they have no calcium lines of their own to blot out the faint, sharp interstellar lines.

After Hartmann's discovery of the two interstellar violet lines of gaseous calcium, no new lines were observed until twenty years later, when four lines produced by sodium were detected. A search for interstellar lines begun in 1936 added twenty new lines to the list.

Lest it might seem that astronomers are unduly concerned about the clouds of dust and gas pervading the stellar system, their solicitude about so apparently trivial a matter should be explained. For many years the *size* of the galaxy has been a subject of great interest and of changing estimates. When Shapley investigated the globular clusters he first fixed upon 300,000 light years as the greatest diameter of the slightly flattened sphere which they occupy. Later some 200,000 light years came to be more commonly accepted as the value of the stellar system's diameter. The recent work of Stebbins and others upon the effect of obscuring matter seems to be bringing the figure down to 78,000 or 100,000 light years.

20.12. The significance of obscuring clouds

Distance is estimated from the apparent brightness after the probable *actual* brightness is discovered in some indirect way. The fainter a star or a cluster of stars of a certain intrinsic luminosity *appears,* the farther away it will be estimated to be. If a part of this dimness is due to obscuration rather than to distance, the star may be much closer than dimness ascribed to distance alone would indicate.

20.13. How obscuring matter affects measurement of distances

20.14. Cosmic static

The name "cosmic static" has been applied to very short radio waves (microwave radiation) coming from the Milky Way. The waves were first detected by K. G. Jansky of the Bell Telephone Laboratories, in 1931, while investigating thunderstorm static. He noticed that when other noises in his apparatus were low he still picked up small disturbances of unknown origin. At first he attributed them to the sun but later observations convinced him that the waves came from outside the solar system from the direction of the Milky Way.

Jansky's work was continued in 1937 by Grote Reber, at that time a young amateur astronomer, who built a "radio telescope" in his backyard out of whatever odds and ends he could find. This pioneer work by Jansky and Reber, which was done entirely "on their own," now appears likely to develop into one of the most important contributions to observational astronomy of this century.

Besides the general microwave radiation from the Milky Way, there are small regions where the emission is exceptionally intense. Radio telescopes are unable to determine the positions of these regions accurately enough to identify them with particular objects in the sky. But by cooperating with observers using ordinary optical telescopes, four intense sources of microwave radiation have been identified with extended nebulous clouds. The most interesting is Cygnis A, a queer-looking object which apparently consists of two extragalactic nebulae, or stellar universes, which are in collision. The other three sources are believed to be glowing gas clouds in our own galaxy.

The origin of cosmic static is still unknown.

QUESTIONS AND EXERCISES

1. Look at Figure 20.2. How many differences can you detect between these exposures taken 15 years apart? What might cause differences in the two exposures besides actual changes in the nebula itself?

2. Count the number of stars in half a square inch on the right and left sides of the nebula in Figure 20.2. Can you think of a reason for the difference?

3. Notice how sharply defined are the "Gulf of Mexico" and the "Atlantic Coast" in the photograph of the North American Nebula in Figure 20.1. If these regions are darkened by obscuring clouds what do we know about the distances of stars in them?

4. How can the spectral lines of interstellar sodium and calcium be distinguished from these same lines in the spectrum of a star?

5. How can we tell from the spectrum of a star whether its light is red because of its temperature or because its light has been reddened by passing through obscuring matter in space?

6. Name as many different types of objects as you can in our galaxy, such as planets, stars, etc.

21 GALAXIES

21.1. A confu-
sion of names IT IS unfortunate that the gaseous clouds of our own galaxy, and
the immensely larger stellar systems far beyond our Milky Way system should have both been called by the same name, *nebulae*. In
appearance they are indeed similar, but in their essential character
they are almost as unlike as the similarly named stars and "shooting
stars."

The isolated star systems now known to be far beyond even the
outlying stars of our own system are sometimes called SPIRAL NEBU-
LAE (Fig. 21.1). This sets them apart from our nearer, gaseous
nebulae, and would be a good name except for the fact that many of
these distant systems show no sign of spiral form. Another name that
has been widely used is *island universe*. But this violates the accepted
definition of "universe." Among astronomers the name extragalactic
nebulae is much used. Thus the original name is preserved and the
adjective shows that they are beyond the Milky Way.

21.2. Appear-
ance of nebulae Extragalactic nebulae are usually flattened objects, and
therefore their appearance differs greatly, depending on the angle at
which we see them. Seen edgewise, or nearly so, the outlying portions are very thin, and even the denser nucleus shows polar flattening, due apparently, to rotation (Fig. 21.2). If the plane of the nebula is perpendicular to our line of vision, the nebula is nearly circular. Often there are two arms, which emerge from opposite sides of
the nucleus, and spiral around it (Fig. 21.3). Naturally we see many
nebulae at an angle, neither edgewise nor flat side toward us. These
have an elliptical appearance, such as we see in the Great Nebula in
Andromeda (Fig. 21.4).

A striking feature of an edgewise nebula is the dark lane of obscuring matter, which, in some cases, cuts it into two parts. This

Fig. 21.1. The spiral nebula M81, NGC 3031, Ursa Major. Exposure 4 hours, 15 minutes, with 60-inch reflector. (*Mount Wilson Observatory.*)

Fig. 21.2. A spindle-shaped extragalactic nebula (NGC 3115) flattened by rotation. Exposure 1 hour, 40 minutes. (*Mount Wilson Observatory.*)

Fig. 21.3. A nebula (M101) unusually well placed to show the spiral arms. (*Mount Wilson Observatory.*)

evidently corresponds to the obscuring clouds in our Milky Way, which separate it into two parts throughout a part of its length.

Obviously if we could view a nebula from some other point in the sky its form might appear very different. But any motion of ours, even if we could travel as fast as light, would be too slow to carry us to a perceptibly different point of vantage in the course of a lifetime. Our motion would be insignificant in comparison with the vast distance of nearly a million light years that separates us from even the nearest extragalactic nebula.

Measuring Distances to Nebulae

Until telescopes large enough to reveal individual stars in the so-called spiral nebulae were used, distances to the nebulae remained a mere matter of conjecture. Some astronomers thought they were within our stellar system, others were of the opinion that they were separate systems, more distant than our stars. As early as 1917, novae were discovered on photographs taken of spirals, especially in

Fig. 21.4. The Great Spiral Nebula in Andromeda, M 31. A satellite of Andromeda, M 32, is the small round white patch to the right and below the main nebula. The white oval patch above the main nebula is NGC 205, another satellite. Photographed with the 48-inch Schmidt telescope. (*Mount Wilson and Palomar Observatories.*)

the Andromeda Nebula. These new stars seem very dim, of about sixteenth to seventeenth magnitude. Novae in our own system are exceedingly bright in absolute magnitude. Assuming that ordinary new stars and those of the nebulae are, on the average, equally bright intrinsically, it became evident that the nebulae must be very far away.

We have seen that the luminosity of a cepheid variable depends upon its period, a relationship expressed by the period-luminosity curve (par. 18.3). The period of the cepheid is found by observing the changes in its apparent magnitude as the star goes through its light cycle. When the period has been determined, we can go to the curve and read off the absolute magnitude of the cepheid. Then, knowing both the apparent magnitude and absolute magnitude of the cepheid, its distance can be calculated at once.

21.3. Type I and Type II Cepheids

When the absolute magnitudes of the cepheids that form the period-luminosity curve were originally determined, about 1918, it was assumed that all cepheids with the same period have the same luminosity. Not until 1952 did astronomers realize that there are two different types of cepheids which give two different period-luminosity curves (Fig. 18.1). Cepheids of Type I are four times brighter (1.5 magnitudes) than cepheids of Type II of the same period. The two period-luminosity curves run parallel to each other separated by 1.5 magnitudes.

Astronomy would be much simpler for astronomers as well as elementary students of astronomy if there were only one type of cepheid in the universe.

Recognition of the two types of cepheids came through the discovery that there are two distinct types of stars, or *stellar populations*. As early as 1923 the outer spiral arms of the Andromeda nebula had been resolved into individual stars, but all efforts to resolve the central portion of the nebula had failed. Even on the best photographs it appeared simply as a uniform cloudy mass. These photographs had been taken on blue-sensitive plates which were the only kind then available. In 1943 the central portion of Andromeda was resolved into stars by Walter Baade with the 100-inch telescope using red-sensitive plates. The reason the central portion of Andromeda could not be resolved into stars before now became apparent: whereas the brightest stars in the spiral arms are *blue,* the brightest stars in the central nucleus are *red.*

21.4. Stellar Populations I and II

Baade concluded from the study of other galaxies and our own that stars can be divided into two broad general types, which he called POPULATIONS I AND II.

The most luminous stars of Population I are the blue supergiants

100,000 times as bright as the sun found in the spiral arms of galaxies like Andromeda. The presence of blue supergiants in the Milky Way indicates that these stars also occur in the flat spiral arms of our own galaxy. Their spatial arrangement in our own galaxy, however, is much harder to determine than in Andromeda, owing to the heavy obscuring dust clouds through which we can see only short stretches of the spiral arms. The fact that the blue supergiants are invariably associated with clouds of dust and bright nebulosity, suggests that either they have been recently formed from the dust or that it supplies the stars with nuclear fuel. The brightest stars of Population II are red supergiants 1000 times as bright as the sun. Less luminous stars of all colors, however, occur in both populations. Stars of Population II are numerous in our galaxy and in Andromeda. They are especially abundant in the nucleus and form a spherical halo which surrounds the flattened disk of Population I stars and penetrate into the vacant spaces between them in the spiral arms. The globular clusters, which also occupy a roughly spherical space around our galaxy, consist of stars of Population II. Figure 21.5 shows the positions of various kinds of stars of Populations I and II in the spectral class-luminosity diagram.

Stars of Population I are revolving in circles around the dense central nucleus of our galaxy. The sun and most of the stars near us are Population I. The sun *seems* to have a low velocity with respect to these stars but this is because they are all moving along together at nearly the same rate like cars in the same lane of traffic. The globular clusters and the halo of Population II stars are really revolving at a much slower rate in more elongated paths around the central nucleus. Here again appearances are deceptive for they *seem* to be moving at a high velocity relative to the stellar traffic near the sun. A Population II star in our vicinity might be compared to a man driving slowly but in the wrong direction down a one-way street.

21.5. Results of observations of cepheids in Andromeda

Differences in the characteristics of stars in the two populations has proven of exceptional interest. In particular, the investigation of cepheids has resulted in discoveries of far-reaching and fundamental importance, owing to their use as distance indicators (par. 18.3). From observations of the periods of cepheids in the spiral arms of Andromeda the distance to this nebula, in 1929, was found to be 900,000 light years. When a correction was made in 1944 for dimming due to obscuring dust in our galaxy the distance was reduced to 750,000 light years. This value was generally accepted until 1952 when it was announced that the distance to Andromeda had to be changed again. It was now 1,500,000 light years away—just

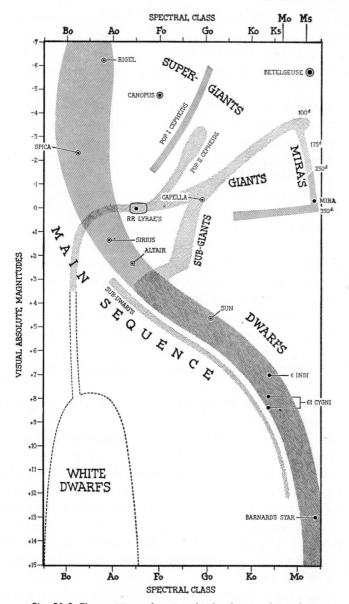

Fig. 21.5. The positions of various kinds of stars of Populations I and II in the spectral class-luminosity diagram. The positions of some star groups are still uncertain, especially the cepheids. Pop. I = parallel lines. Pop. II = dotted areas.

double the previous figure! In fact, the size of the whole universe outside our galaxy had to be doubled. The question immediately arose: how could astronomers have been so wrong?

The explanation is rather long and involved besides being a bit

279

embarrassing. But the events leading to the doubling of the distance scale have played such an important part in the development of astronomical thought in the first half of this century, that they seem worth recounting at length. They may be summarized roughly as follows:

1. Study of the variable stars in the Lesser Magellanic Cloud resulted in the discovery of the period-luminosity curve in 1912. Since the distance of the cloud was unknown only the relative luminosity of the cepheids as shown by their apparent magnitudes could be used in forming the curve.

2. The average absolute magnitude of 11 cepheids in our galaxy was determined from a statistical method. This study served to fix the "zero point" on the period-luminosity curve; that is, the absolute magnitude of a cepheid in the Lesser Magellanic Cloud of a particular period and apparent magnitude. Once this point was fixed the apparent magnitudes of all the other cepheids on the curve could be converted into absolute magnitudes.

3. The period-luminosity curve was extended to include other pulsating stars such as the RR Lyrae variables with periods of less than a day. Because these stars are found so often in the globular clusters of our galaxy they are frequently referred to as "cluster type variables."

4. The size of our galaxy was determined from observations of the RR Lyrae stars in globular clusters.

5. No RR Lyrae stars had ever been observed in Andromeda, presumably because they were too faint to show on photographs taken with the 100-inch telescope. But it was confidently expected that they would appear on photographs taken with the 200-inch telescope. Yet the best photographs taken with the 200-inch telescope failed to show any RR Lyrae stars. In fact, only the brightest stars of Population II appeared on the plates. Something was radically wrong. Evidently the Andromeda nebula was much farther away than had been supposed.

6. Satisfactory agreement between distance and magnitude was finally obtained on the assumption that there is—not one—but *two* period-luminosity curves for cepheids (Fig. 18.1.) There is a period-luminosity curve for Type I cepheids of Population I and another for Type II cepheids of Population II. The cepheids in our galaxy such as Delta Cephei and Polaris, and those observed in the spiral arms of Andromeda, belong to Population I. Cepheids of Population II include stars such as RR Lyrae and W Virginis (Fig. 18.2). The absolute magnitude of the cepheids of Population I is 1.5 magni-

tudes less than that of cepheids of Population II of the *same period*. The absolute magnitudes determined for the old period-luminosity curve were about right for the cepheids of Population II.

7. The absolute magnitude of cepheids of Population I wherever they occur in the universe must be decreased—made brighter—by 1.5 magnitudes. A decrease of 1.5 magnitudes corresponds to a fourfold increase in luminosity. But the apparent magnitudes of these stars remain the same. (The stars of course look no different than they did before!) Now the brightness of an object decreases inversely as the square of the distance. Therefore, if the cepheids of Population I are *four* times more luminous than before, then they must be *twice* as far away, in order to keep their apparent brightness the same.

Since all our determinations of extra-galactic distances are ultimately tied to the period-luminosity curve, the result was that the size of the universe was doubled at one stroke! Only the size of our galaxy remains unchanged. (Except that all the cepheids of Population I are twice as far away as before.)

The Andromeda nebula and our galaxy belong to a cluster of some sixteen nebulae called the "local group," which lie within less than 2 million light years of us. Vast as this distance seems, it is a mere step compared with the universe of nebulae extending out to 2000 million light years, which is the distance astronomers hope to reach eventually with the 200-inch telescope.

21.6. The local group of nebulae

MEMBERS OF THE LOCAL GROUP OF GALAXIES

NAME	TYPE	DIAMETER (LIGHT YEARS)	DISTANCE* (LIGHT YEARS)
Our galaxy	Sb	78,000	. . . . .
M 31 (Andromeda)	Sb	84,000	1,500,000
Large Magellanic Cloud	I	30,000	144,000
M 33 (Triangulum)	Sc	28,000	1,560,000
Small Magellanic Cloud	I	23,400	164,000
M 32 (a satellite of Andromeda)	E2	. . . .	1,500,000
Fornax system	E	13,600	920,000
NGC 205 (a satellite of Andromeda)	E5p	7,200	1,500,000
NGC 6822	I	6,200	1,050,000
IC 1613	I	7,200	1,468,000
Sculptor system	E	5,800	450,000
NGC 185	E	5,600	1,330,000
NGC 147	E	5,400	1,330,000

* Corrected for absorption in space.

21.7. Progressive stages in a nebula's history

It must not, of course, be supposed that all nebulae are exactly alike, or exactly similar to the stellar system. Planets differ from each other, and stars are found in all stages of apparent development. Nebulae have been classified according to their form, and this classification may represent also their progressive stages of development. Figure 21.6 represents some of these *forms,* and perhaps also the *stages,* through which a typical nebula advances from an unorganized, quiescent, globular cloud to a rapidly whirling, flattened system of stars.

The various forms are of interest chiefly because they suggest a possible order of development, and because they help to point out *processes* taking place within the nebula, giving rise to such forms.

1. IRREGULAR NEBULAE. Some 2 or 3 per cent of the nebulae which are near enough to show any special structure are, like the Magellanic Clouds, formless and structureless. If, as is generally agreed, the Magellanic Clouds are outside of the galactic system, and independent of it, they must be of this irregular class.

2. ELLIPTICAL NEBULAE. Perhaps as many as a third or a fourth of the nebulae, although showing no sign of spiral structure, are of elliptical form, or, more rarely, almost or quite globular. These show the usual structural characteristic of condensation toward the center and rarefaction at the edges.

3. SPIRAL NEBULAE. Those showing spiral arms are divided into two classes, NORMAL SPIRALS and BARRED SPIRALS. In the normal spirals the two arms, which spring from opposite sides of the central nucleus, begin immediately to spiral around the denser center. But in barred spirals the two opposite arms extend straight out at first on either side, and then the spiral portions spring from the outer ends of these arms (Fig. 21.7).

These nebulae contain distinctly different stellar populations. Nebular forms such as the first four in Figure 21.6 are composed of Population II. Forms such as 5 and 6 contain stars of both Populations I and II. Stars of Population I predominate in systems 7 and 8.

21.8. Other indirect estimates of distance

Not only do cepheid variable stars provide a method of determining the absolute magnitude, and hence the distance, but other classes of stars that can be seen in nebulae, such as novae, and the very hot, blue-white stars of great brightness, furnish methods of roughly estimating distances. The average brightness of any class of stars in nebulae is thought to be similar to the average brightness of the same class of stars in other systems; our own system, for example.

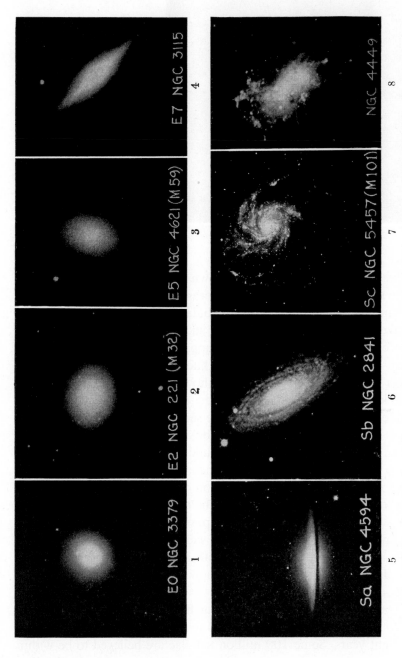

EO NGC 3379
1

E2 NGC 221 (M 32)
2

E5 NGC 4621 (M 59)
3

E7 NGC 3115
4

Sa NGC 4594
5

Sb NGC 2841
6

Sc NGC 5457 (M101)
7

NGC 4449
8

Fig. 21.6. Nebulae of various forms, illustrating the progressive stages through which a nebulae probably passes, according to Hubble's classification. E0 to E7, before spiral form is observable, he calls elliptical nebula. Sa, Sb, and Sc are spirals more or less highly developed. There are a few of irregular form, as number 8, which seem to have developed without spiral form. The Magellanic Clouds are thought to be examples of the irregular form. (Mount Wilson Observatory.)

Hence the absolute magnitude of *new stars,* or of the three or four *brightest stars* in a nebula of unknown distance, may be assumed to be the same on an average, as the average absolute magnitude of such stars in our own system, or in a nebula of known distance. Finding the average distance to stars of any such given class becomes, then, a mere matter of comparing their apparent brightness with the apparent brightness of similar stars to known distance. In this way distances to nebulae too far away to show cepheid variable stars may be at least roughly estimated if a few of the blue-white giant stars, brighter, even, than cepheids, can be seen in the nebula.

21.9. Finding distances from size and luminosity

Since it is in only a few nebulae that cepheid variables are visible, and in little more than a hundred that *any* individual stars can be seen, other criteria of distance are needed that can be applied to the many thousands of nebulae too distant to show stars. From a study of those whose distances can be determined by observation of their stars, it is found that nebulae possess an average luminosity of 400 million suns. There are "dwarf" stellar systems with a luminosity of 40 million suns, and "giants" with a luminosity of 4000 million suns. The brightest stellar system known is Andromeda with a luminosity of 10,000 million suns.

The faintest nebulae which so far have been photographed with the 200-inch telescope are estimated to be at a distance of 1600 million light years. Some 100 million nebulae are believed to be within this range. They occur singly, in pairs, clusters, and clouds. Preliminary counts made on plates taken with the 48-inch Schmidt telescope on Palomar Mountain indicate a marked tendency for galaxies to occur in clusters instead of being spread uniformly through galactic space, as was previously supposed.

Although we spoke of the nebulae as lying in all directions, from the chart of their positions (Fig. 21.8) it would seem that they shun the Milky Way. Where stars are most numerous not a nebula of this extragalactic sort can be seen. Being at such immense distances from our stellar system it is ridiculous to imagine that their distribution should be in the least affected by the fact that the thin edge of our flattened system happens to point in a certain direction.

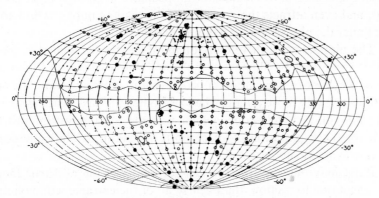

Fig. 21.8. Distribution of extragalactic nebulae. The diagram is based on counts on photographs distributed at intervals over the whole northern sky. The irregular strip from left to right is the Milky Way. It is free from these nebulae. (*Mount Wilson Observatory.*)

It is much more reasonable to suppose that clouds of obscuring matter lying along the Milky Way, and perhaps just beyond it, shut off our view of whatever lies farther out.

In parts of the sky toward the poles of the Milky Way, extragalactic nebulae are most numerous. In these directions space seems to be practically free from a screen of any sort of obscuring matter.

The Red Shift, or Apparent Recession, of Nebulae

Another measureable quantity which is closely correlated with the distances to nebulae is the radial velocity that the nebulae possess, if we can assume that the red shift of their spectra indicates velocity. By *red shift* is meant that all lines of the spectra are removed from their normal positions toward the red end of the spectrum. The most remarkable thing about this shift is that the more remote the object the greater is the shift—the farther away the nebula the faster it recedes. This is a characteristic suitable for use as far out in space as nebulae give light enough to make a spectrum that can be photographed. And, strange to say, the farther away the nebula is, the smaller becomes the precentage error in its measurement. This is because the apparent velocity becomes so great that small individual differences in motion become proportionally less.

21.11. Velocity of nebulae

Aside from the vast *extent* of the extragalactic nebulae and their enormous *distances,* the *velocity* at which they seem to travel is one of their most interesting and peculiar characteristics. Their marvelous speed astonishes astronomers who observe it, furnishes data for speculation to scientists who specialize in cosmological problems, and even attracts the attention of the reading public, who know of it under the phrase "our expanding universe."

The pioneer work in velocity of spiral nebulae as related to their distance was done by Slipher, of the Lowell Observatory, at Flagstaff. But as the work of measurement progressed to more and more distant members of this most remote class of bodies the task was taken up with the 100-inch telescope, which was the most powerful instrument for the exploration of space until the 200-inch Hale telescope became available about 1950.

If we may interpret the red shift of the spectrum as a true Doppler effect due to motion, then nearly all of the extragalactic nebulae of which it has been possible to photograph spectra are moving at a high rate of speed *away from* the earth.

21.12. Increase of velocity with distance

The nebulae whose distances can be measured by a study of the stars they contain recede at the rate of somewhat more than 100 miles a second for each 1,000,000 light years of their distance. This increase of rate is found to continue as far out as spectra can be taken. One particular nebula at 144,000,000 light years is found to be traveling at 7300 miles a second; another one at 300,000,000 light years seems to go about 15,000 miles a second (Fig. 21.9). Recent photographs obtained with the 200-inch telescope on faint nebulae show apparent velocities of recession of 38,000 miles a second.

It should be noticed that these figures are referred to as *apparent* velocities of recession. All astronomers are by no means agreed that the universe is expanding as the red shift would indicate. There may be some new principle of physics involved which is not thoroughly understood at present. Until more observational evidence is available we can only theorize as to the nature of this remarkable effect.

21.13. Theory of an expanding universe

It does, indeed, seem strange that nebulae in all directions seem to be *receding* from us. Why should the direction of their motion be governed by a point in space of such little cosmic significance as the point occupied by the solar system? But if we admit that all space is expanding, then everything in all space is receding from everything else in space. Consider a growing watermelon; as it grows all the seeds get farther from each other. It makes no difference which seed, if any, is actually stationary. A microscopic observer on any one of the seeds would see all the other seeds receding from him. And, moreover, the more distant seeds would recede more rapidly than the nearer ones. The speed of recession would be in direct proportion to the distance.

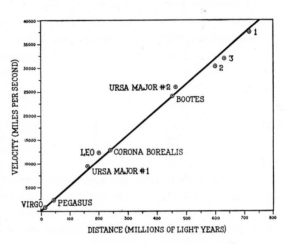

Fig. 21.9. The apparent velocities of recession of nebulae at different distances from our galaxy. The points 1, 2, and 3 correspond to velocities observed in 1951 in three nebular clusters which are more distant than any clusters in which spectra have been previously obtained. The distances of 1, 2, and 3 are provisional estimates.

Such would be exactly the case in an expanding universe, with galaxies instead of seeds. Every one would be receding from us, and the observed speeds would be in direct proportion to the distance. If the red shift does indeed indicate velocity, then the entire universe is expanding. This explanation of the red shift, however, is not deterring scientists from trying to find some other reason for it.

IF the universe *is* expanding as the apparent outward velocities of the nebulae indicate, and IF this expansion has always been the same, then there must have been a time in the remote past when the matter now distributed over the nebulae was compressed into one huge primeval atom. Then "something" happened analogous to a cosmic explosion that sent this matter flying outward at different speeds in all different directions. (This idea is referred to by its opponents as the "big bang" hypothesis.) The age of the universe estimated from the time when this hypothetical explosion occurred is 4000 million years, or double the figure given before 1953. From the relative amounts of certain heavy elements found in the earth physicists believe that the stars and galaxies cannot be older than 5000

21.14. Age of the universe

287

million years at the most. The two estimates agree tolerably well considering the uncertain nature of the problem.

21.15. The future   Scientists are sometimes criticized because they seem to believe in one idea today and something quite different tomorrow. This is only because they try to keep an open attitude of mind and alter their theories to conform with the latest facts based on observations. Thus astronomers were not in the least dismayed when they recently had to double the size of the universe. (The situation also has its brighter side. If the universe is twice as old doesn't that make us all twice as young as we were before?) A subject is much more interesting if it is in a state of rapid development so that new and unexpected discoveries are being made. It seems incredible that only a century ago astronomy was regarded as an "exhausted" science. Now there seem to be more problems pressing for solution than ever before.

QUESTIONS AND EXERCISES

1. Why can we tell more about the structure of the Andromeda nebula than our own galaxy?

2. How many features can you see in Figure 21.4 that resemble those in our galaxy, such as star clusters, obscuring matter, etc.?

3. Let the class vote secretly on which side of the Andromeda nebula (Fig. 21.4) they think is the nearer. How many agree?

4. How would the spectra of galactic and extragalactic nebulae differ?

5. It has been found that the nebulae appear to be receding from us. What do you think is the reason that the Andromeda nebula shows a velocity of *approach?*

6. On a clear dark night the Andromeda nebula can be seen by the unaided eye as a hazy patch of light. Is this the farthest that our eyes can see without optical aid?

7. Would you expect to observe any stars like the sun in the Andromeda nebula? What type of stars would you expect to observe in Andromeda?

APPENDIX

Books Recommended for Supplementary Reading

Astronomical Society of the Pacific. Leaflets about 2000 words long written in a popular style by various astronomers are issued each month. For fuller information write to the Secretary at 675 Eighteenth Avenue, San Francisco 21, Calif.

Bonestell, Chesley and Ley, Willy, *The Conquest of Space*. New York, 1950, The Viking Press, 160 pp. Beautifully illustrated with colored paintings by Chesley Bonestell.

Baldwin, Ralph B., *The Face of the Moon*. Chicago, 1949, The University of Chicago Press, 239 pp.

Clarke, Arthur C., *Interplanetary Flight*. (An introduction to astronautics.) New York, 1951, Harper & Brothers, 164 pp.

Gamov, G., *Atomic Energy*. (Atomic energy in cosmic and human life.) New York, 1947, The Macmillan Company, 161 pp.

Gamov, G., *The Birth and Death of the Sun*. (Stellar evolution and subatomic energy.) New York, 1940, The Viking Press, 238 pp.

Harvard Books on Astronomy. Written by members of the staff of the Harvard College Observatory. Excellent semitechnical accounts of the planets, Milky Way, astronomical instruments, etc. Philadelphia, The Blakiston Company.

Hoyle, Fred, *The Nature of the Universe*. New York, 1950, Harper & Brothers, 142 pp.

Hubble, Edwin, *The Realm of the Nebulae*. New Haven, 1936, Yale University Press, 210 pp.

Jeans, Sir James, *The Universe Around Us*. New York, 1944, The Macmillan Company, 351 pp.

Jones, H. Spencer, *Worlds Without End*. New York, 1935, The Macmillan Company, 329 pp.

Kuiper, Gerard P., *The Atmospheres of the Earth and Planets*. A symposium by experts in astronomy, geology, chemistry, etc. Chicago, 1951, The University of Chicago Press, 434 pp. with photographs.

Ley, Willy, *Rockets, Missiles, and Space Travel.* New York, 1951, The Viking Press, 436 pp. Illustrated.

McCrea, W. H., *Physics of the Sun and Stars.* London, W.1, 1950, Hutchinson's University Library. 192 pp.

Skilling, W. T. and Richardson, Robert S., *Sun, Moon, and Stars.* (Astronomy for beginners.) New York, 1946, Whittlesey House, McGraw-Hill Book Company, Inc., 274 pp.

Sky and Telescope. Published monthly by the Sky Publishing Corporation, Harvard College Observatory, Cambridge 38, Mass. Devoted primarily to popularizing astronomy.

Smart, W. M., *Foundations of Astronomy.* New York, 1942, Longmans, Green and Co., 268 pp.

Smart, W. M., *The Origin of the Earth.* Cambridge, England, 1951, The Cambridge University Press, 239 pp.

Smart, W. M., *Some Famous Stars.* New York, 1950, Longmans, Green and Co., 219 pp. Illustrated.

Whitrow, G. J., *The Structure of the Universe.* London, W.1, 1949, Hutchinson's University Library, 171 pp.

Urey, Harold C., *The Planets.* (Their origin and development.) New Haven, 1952, The Yale University Press. 245 pp.

Journal of the British Astronomical Association. Contains excellent articles on observation methods, recent discoveries, etc. 303 Bath Road, Hounslow West, Middlesex, England.

Journal of the British Interplanetary Society. The British Interplanetary Society was founded in 1933 to promote the development of interplanetary exploration and communication by the study of rocket engineering, astronomy, electronics and other associated sciences. Often rather technical. Secretarial address: 12, Bessborough Gardens, London, S.W.1.

A catalogue listing the price of photographs and lantern slides from the Mount Wilson and Palomar Observatories may be obtained by writing to the California Institute of Technology Bookstore, 1201 East California Street, Pasadena 4, California.

Information on rental of *The Story of Palomar,* a 16 mm moving picture in color and sound, running time 40 minutes, may be obtained by writing to the California Institute of Technology, Office of Public Relations, Pasadena, California.

GLOSSARY

(These explanations are not intended as complete definitions, but merely as aids to the understanding of technical terms used in the book.)

Aberration of light, apparent bending due to our motion.

Absolute magnitude, real brightness.

Achromatic lens, one that gives an image theoretically devoid of color (not completely possible in practice).

Albedo, percentage of light reflected.

Altitude, distance above horizon.

Angstrom unit, a unit of light-wave measurement.

Angular motion, a measure of change in direction.

Annular eclipse, center of sun covered—a ring shows.

Apex of sun's way, point toward which the sun is moving.

Aphelion, point in orbit at greatest distance from the sun.

Apogee, point in orbit farthest from the earth.

Apparent magnitude, brightness as observed on earth.

Astrophysics, a relatively new branch of astronomy dealing principally with the physical and chemical nature of heavenly bodies.

Azimuth, angular distance west from south point on the horizon.

Binary stars, true double stars.

Black body radiation, perfect radiation, such as comes from a black substance.

Celestial, referring to the sky or universe.

Cepheid variable star, one, like Delta Cephei, which fluctuates probably on account of internal changes.

Chromatic aberration, blurring of image by separation of colors by a lens.

Chronograph, instrument for recording time.

Circumpolar, around the pole.

Coelostat, a mirror which makes the sky seem to stand still.

Collimator, lenses to make rays of light parallel.

Comparison spectrum, one produced in the laboratory by known elements, and photographed beside the stellar spectrum.

Conic sections, figures made by sectioning (cutting) a cone.

Conjunction, in a position toward or beyond the sun.

Constellation, a pattern of stars.

Coordinates, two or more values locating a point in space.

Copernican system, sun at center.

Cosmogony, theory of the origin of the parts of the universe.

Declination, angular distance from celestial equator.

Diffraction of light, the spreading of a beam of light into the shadow, causing a light and dark pattern because of interference of the light waves.

Diffraction grating, a reflecting or transparent surface ruled with many parallel lines for giving a spectrum by means of interference.

Direct tide, one under the moon.

Dispersion of light, into its colors.

Doppler effect, change in frequency of sound or light due to motion.

Ecliptic, the path of the sun in the sky during its apparent annual motion around the earth.

Elongation, angular distance from the sun.

Enhanced lines, new or strengthened spectral lines due to higher temperature or voltage in the light source.

Ephemeris, a book of tables of daily positions of heavenly bodies.

Epicycles, "circles" upon a circle—an ancient conception.

Equation of time, the amount that the sun is faster or slower than its mean time.

Equinoxes, the two points at which the sun crosses the celestial equator.

Excited atom, one in which an electron is lifted to a higher orbit.

Extragalactic, beyond our galaxy.

Faculae, "torches," bright spots near edge of sun.

Flocculi, solar markings photographed with aid of spectroheliograph.

Galactic, an adjective referring to our galaxy.

Galaxy, one great system of stars, as our milky way system or a spiral nebula.

Granules on sun, the smallest visible markings.

Group of stars, those having the same direction and speed of motion.

Harmonic law, Kepler's law relating distance of a planet to its time of revolution around sun. Applies to all such revolving bodies.

Hour angle of heavenly body, angular distance it is past our meridian.

Infra-red radiation, with waves too long to be visible.

Interference of light, light and dark patterns due to mutual interference of *two* light beams coming from a *single* source.

Interstellar, among the stars.

Ionized atom, one having lost one or more electrons.

Ionosphere, a layer of ionized air high up that reflects radio waves.

Kinetic energy, energy due to motion.

Latitude (celestial), angular distance from ecliptic.

Latitude (terrestrial), angular distance from equator.

Libration of the moon, apparent "rocking" of moon.

Limb, edge (of sun, moon, etc.).

Local system of stars, a star cloud of perhaps $\frac{1}{30}$ the diameter of the galaxy containing most of the naked eye stars.

Magellanic clouds, two small irregular nebulae near our galaxy.

Magnitude of a star, degree of brightness on some selected scale.

Main sequence stars, those of any type whose brightness is usual for stars of that type. (Neither white dwarfs nor red giants.)

Meteor, synonym for "shooting star"; light produced by a high-speed particle in our atmosphere.

Meteorite, body too small to be called minor planet.

Nadir, the point in the sky directly beneath the observer.

Neap tides, the lowest in the month.

Nebula, literally "cloud." Applied to gaseous clouds among the stars, and to other star systems beyond ours.

Nodes of the moon's orbit, the two points where it goes through the plane of the earth's orbit.

Nova, a "new" star—one suddenly becoming brighter.

Objective prism, used in front of the telescope.

Oblate, flattened at the poles.

Occultation, of a star by the moon.

Opposite tide, one opposite the moon.

Opposition, in a position opposite to the sun.

Parabolic velocity, velocity just sufficient to carry a body to an infinite distance.

Parallax of an object, the angle made at the object by two lines of sight.

Parsec, the distance to a point that would have a parallax of $1''$ of arc.

Penumbra, partial shadow.

Perigee, point in orbit nearest earth.

Perihelion, the point in orbit nearest sun.

Perturbation, the disturbing effect of a third body.

Phase (of moon or planet), the quantity and form of its illuminated disk that is visible.

Photosphere, the visible surface of the sun or star.

Planetary nebula, one resembling a planet in appearance.

Precession, westward motion of the crossing point of equator and ecliptic.

Proper motion of a star, across the sky.

Ptolemaic system, earth at center.

Quadrature, at right angles to the sun.

Radial motion of a star, the amount by which it increases or decreases its distance.

Radiant point of meteors, from where they all seem to come.

293

Radioactivity of elements, radiation due to changes in the nucleus of the atoms.

Radius vector, a moving radius.

Red shift, shift of spectral lines toward red in extragalactic nubulae.

Resolving power of a telescope, power to separate two points close together.

Retrograde motion, backward (westward) motion.

Reversing layer of sun's atmosphere, a thin layer accountable for most of the spectral lines.

Revolution, motion around a point.

Rotation, motion on an axis.

Right ascension, distance east of a north-south line through the vernal equinox.

Saros, a period of about 18 years between eclipses.

Satellite, a body going around a planet.

Shooting star, a meteor.

Sidereal period of moon, time needed to make one revolution around the earth with respect to stars.

Sidereal time, time by the stars.

Solar constant, amount of heat from sun in a unit of time for a unit of space at earth's mean distance.

Solstices, the summer and winter points of sun's greatest distance from the equator.

Spectroscopic binary stars, those that can be detected only with the spectrograph.

Spectroscopic parallax, parallax deduced from character of spectrum.

Spherical aberration, blurring of image due to the failure of lens (or mirror) to bring rays from its center and edge to a common focus.

Spiral nebula, one beyond our galaxy that is visibly spiral.

Spring tides, those highest during each month.

Star cluster, a group apparently close together.

Star group, stars all moving in the same direction at the same speed.

Subatomic energy, energy from changes in the nucleus of an atom more radical than chemical changes.

Supernovae, new stars exceptionally bright.

Synodic period of the moon, time needed to make one turn around earth with respect to sun.

Tangential motion, cross motion.

Telluric lines of the spectrum, those due to our atmosphere.

Thermocouple, gives a current when a joint of two metals is warmed.

Transit, motion of a small body across the face of a larger.

Triangulation, computing a great distance by measuring a short base line and angles of sight.

Tropical year, the ordinary year.

294   **Ultraviolet radiation,** with waves too short to be visible.

Umbra, complete shadow.

Vernal equinox, the point (or date) at which the sun crosses the equator in the spring.

White dwarf stars, those much whiter than is usual for stars of their low absolute magnitude.

Widmanstätten figures, marks of crystallization on a meteorite.

Zeeman effect, the splitting of spectral lines due to a light source in a magnetic field.

Zenith, the point in the sky directly above the observer.

Zodiac, a strip 9° wide on each side of the ecliptic.

Zodiacal light, reflected from particles along the zodiac.

INDEX

DIRECTIONS FOR USING MAPS

If you hold the map face down, with the center above your head, and the words North, South, East, and West toward those directions on the horizon, then the stars will be in place. But a more convenient way is to face the direction in which you want to look, and hold the map vertically in front of you, with that direction down. (These maps are planned for use at latitude 40° north, but they may be used in any north temperate latitude.)

The celestial equator, the line above the earth's equator, is the heavy line across the map from east to west. The intersections of the equator and the horizon are always due east and west of the observer. When Orion is visible the equator may be found, for the belt of Orion is on the equator. When the square of Pegasus can be seen, extend its east side its own length southward. This brings us, not only to the equator, but to the vernal equinox, on the equator (almost).

The ecliptic is the dash line, crossing the equator at the vernal equinox, at an angle of 23½°. It is the apparent annual path of the sun. The 12 "signs of the Zodiac" lie along it. The east and west ends of the ecliptic may lie far to the north or to the south of east and west. This accounts for the sun's rising and setting far to the north or south.

The "hour circles, which meet at the poles, are, for simplicity, shown only by a dash where these circles cross the horizon and the equator.

The "galactic equator" is the heavy line crossing the equator at an angle of 62°. It therefore passes within 28° of the pole. As nearly as can be estimated, it is the center line of the milky way.

Star clusters, nebulae, and star magnitudes are shown by the symbols at the lower left.

For telescope users the map for every third month gives additional information. Underlining means a double star. A double line shows a triple or multiple star. Distance given in seconds of arc shows separation of a double. Figures after Greek letter show magnitude of star.

1 JANUARY STARS

The sky is very symmetrical this month, as a glance at the map or the stars themselves will show. The brightest half of the great circle called the Milky Way is in the winter sky. It extends this month from northwest to southeast, and passes almost through the zenith, the observer's overhead point. The sparsely populated poles of the galaxy contrast noticeably with the Milky Way itself, which is so luminous with star clouds. The south pole is in a dim constellation called Sculptor, near the southwestern horizon. Only one star of this little constellation is shown. The north pole, 90° from Sculptor, is in the northeastern sky, but is now hidden below the horizon, back of the Dipper. It will rise next month. It is in Coma Ber-e-ní´cēs, "Bernice's Hair," which consists of scattered, faint stars. The region around this pole is a famous hunting ground for astronomers with giant telescopes, for the sky is so clear of obstructing dust clouds that great numbers of extragalactic nebulae can be seen.

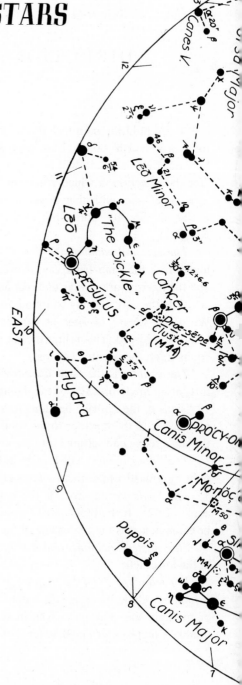

SYMBOLS of MAGNITUDE (brightness)
1 2 2½ 3 3½ 4 4½ Clus. Neb.

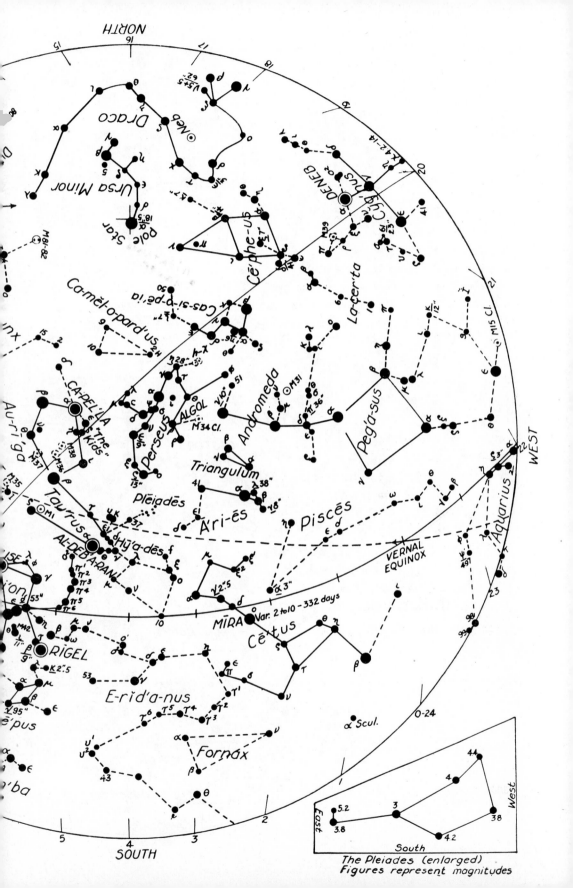

The Pleiades (enlarged)
Figures represent magnitudes

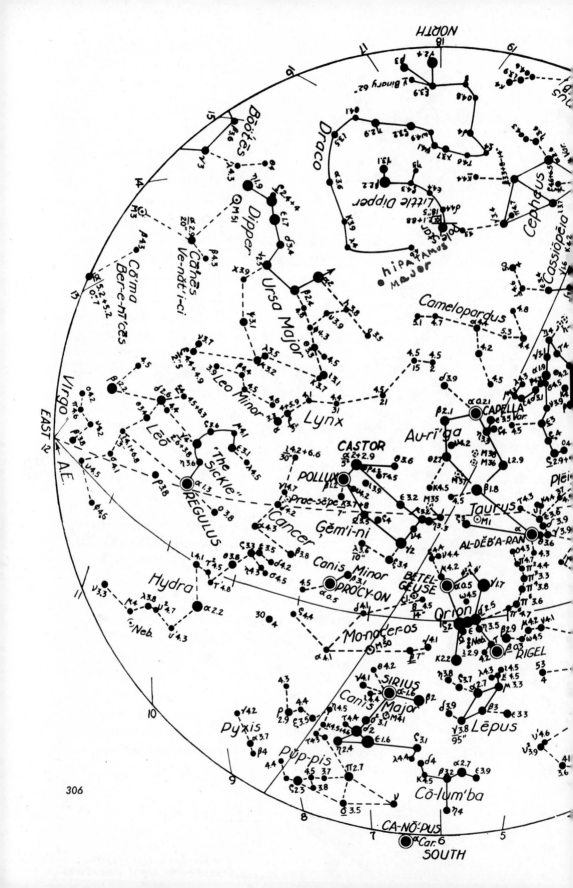

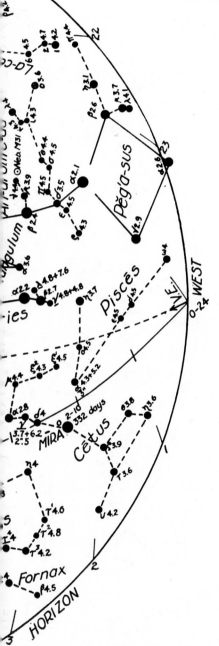

FEBRUARY STARS 2

With the galactic equator still nearly overhead, as in January, this month will be a favorable time for a tour along the Milky Way. By starting from Cyg'nus, the Swan, in the extreme northwest, and following the milky band of lighted highway to Ca-no'pus, in Ca-ri'na, the Keel of a Ship, we shall go through or close by no fewer than a dozen well-worthwhile constellations containing nine first-magnitude stars. Like a prospective celestial navigator, we can give our memories practice in learning the successive constellations and their most outstanding stars.

Leaving Cyg'nus, the Swan, with its flaunting tail, Deneb, we come first to Ce'-phe-us, with its dim but very famous and useful star, Delta; then to Cas-si-o-pe'ia, with no marked stars, but well marked by its letter W. Next An-drom'e-da, a little to one side, and the many-starred Per'se-us.

After all these stars of only medium brightness, we are lured on by Ca-pel'la, twice as bright as an average first-magnitude star, welcoming us to Au-ri'ga, the five-sided constellation. Then in quick succession Gem'i-ni (Cas'tor and Pol'lux), Tau'-rus, O-ri'on, the two dogs, Ca'nis Minor and Major, and finally to Ca-no'pus for southern observers, in its constellation Ca-ri'na.

SYMBOLS of MAGNITUDE (brightness)
1   2   2½   3   3½   4   4½   Clus.   Neb.

Now that the Big Dipper is coming close to the highest point in the evening sky this is a good time to observe two *apparent* motions of the stars around the pole. Once in 24 hours and once a year, the northern stars seem to circle around the celestial pole in a left-handed direction as we look northward. There is another such motion around a point in Draco that is $23\frac{1}{2}°$ from the pole of daily and annual rotation (see August map). But this motion is too slow to observe. Its discovery in the first place required comparison of recorded star positions reaching back over some hundreds of years. This long-period motion causes the westward precession of the equinoxes. It requires 25,-800 years for the stars as well as the equinoctial points to make one complete circuit.

The apparent *daily* rotation of the stars results from the real eastward rotation of the earth on its axis once a day. The apparent *annual* star motion is due to the earth's annual motion around the sun. The long-period motion around the pole of the ecliptic is the result of the gravitational pull of the moon and the sun upon the great $13\frac{1}{2}$-mile thick equatorial ring of the earth. This pull tends to straighten up the earth's axis, which is tilted $23\frac{1}{2}°$. In half of the 25,800-year period, our north pole will shift $47°$ into the south and stars will be seen $47°$ farther south then than now. The earth's axis traces a circle on the sky as the peg of a top traces a circle on the ceiling. This real motion makes the stars seem to move oppositely.

SYMBOLS of MAGNITUDE (brightness)
1 2 2½ 3 3½ 4 4½ Clus. Neb.

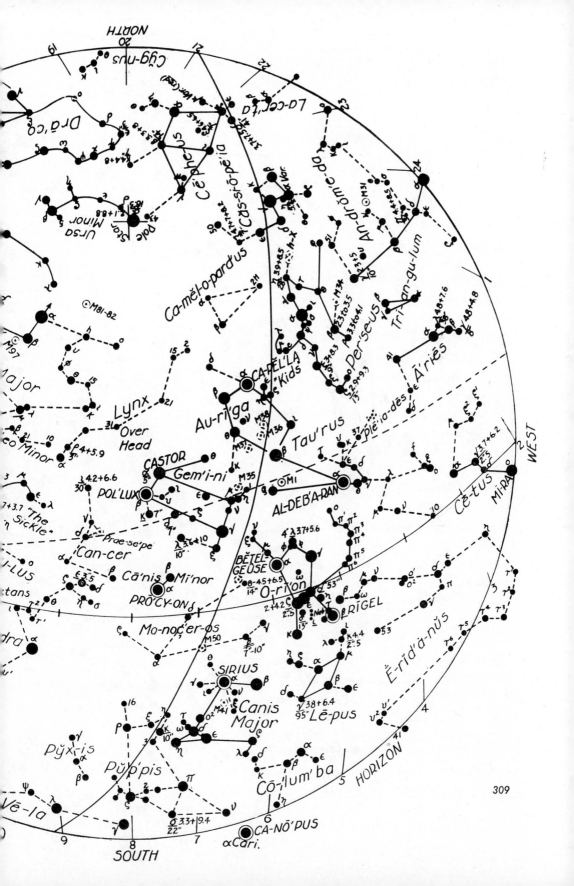

309

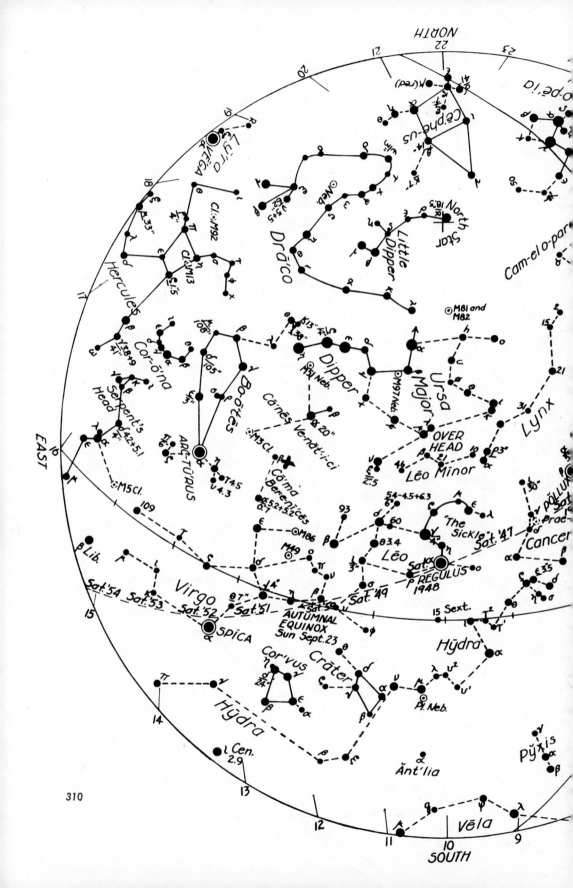

NORTH

Cepheus

Dra̅co

Little Dipper

North Star 1.8:5

M(red)

Camelo-par-

Do-pe'l'q

Lyra

VEGA

Cl.∴M92

Cl.∴M13

Hercules

Corona

Serpent's Head

Y 38+9 4:1

Neb. 2:5

Neb. 2:5

M81 and M82

Dipper

Neb.

M97 Neb.

Ursa Major

Lynx

Bo-o̅tes

Ca'nes Ve-na̅t'i-ci

OVER HEAD

Le̅o Minor

Cancer

M3 Cl.

ARC-TU̅RUS

T 4.5 v 4.3

Co̅ma Berenı̅ce̅s 2.5:2+5.2 0.7

93

54-4.5+6.3

"The Sickle" Sat. '47

POLLUX

Prae

EAST

M5 Cl.

109

M5 Cl.

M86

M49

Le̅o

Sat. '48

REGULUS 1948

β Lib.

Virgo

Sat. '54 Sat. '53 Sat. '52 Sat. '51

θ 7"

Sat. '50

15 Sext.

Hy̅dra

SPICA

AUTUMNAL EQUINOX Sun Sept. 23

Corvus

Cra̅ter

Hy̅dra

ι Cen. 2.9

Pl. Neb.

Ǎnt'lia

Py̆xis

310

14

13

12

11

10

9

Ve̅la

SOUTH

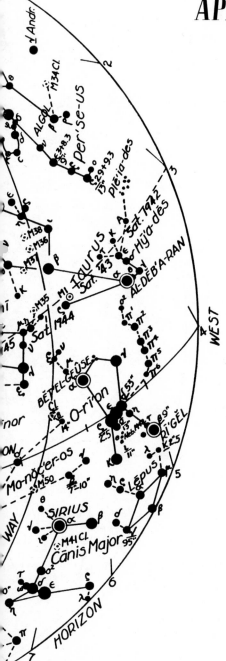

This month we have some return engagements. Arcturus and Spīca, on opposite sides of the equator, having disappeared from view last September, are now in the east. After a half year's absence they rose in March, and are now well up in view, together with their retinues of stars in the constellations Bō-ō'tēs and Virgo. Stars near the equator spend half their time in the night sky, and half with a sunlighted background against which they are invisible. Stars near the north pole are visible at night all the year or nearly so. But those far to the south, such as Canopus, are in our night sky but a short time or not at all. Our astronomers must go to South Africa, South America, or Australia to study south polar stars.

Leo, the Lion, is on the meridian this month, south of the overhead point. Leo is always almost south of the Dipper in Ursa Major, and the two go across the sky from east to west, with the Lion a little ahead of the Bear.

Corvus, the Crow, is an interesting little constellation just ahead (west) of Spīca. Its four main stars look like an inverted cup, but a little star near the upper left corner turns it into a crow, with this star as its beak.

SYMBOLS of MAGNITUDE (brightness)
1   2   2½   3   3½   4   4½   Clus.   Neb.

5   *MAY STARS*

The Dipper is upside down. As always, it is on the meridian of the autumnal equinox, the crossing point of the sun's path over the equator, where the sun leaves us in September for its six months' stay in the southern hemisphere. Remember that Cassiopeia is on the opposite side of the North Star from the Dipper handle, both at nearly the same distance from the pole. You may use the Dipper to locate many constellations and bright stars. For instance, follow the curve of its handle till you come to Arc-tu'-rus, then about the same distance on around the curve to Spi'ca, in Virgo. Also, as is so well known, the end stars of the bowl point to the North Star. Leo, mentioned with the April stars, is straight *back* of the Dipper, about as far as the pole star is in front of it. Leo is often spoken of as the Sickle, just as Ursa Major is called the Dipper, its most recognizable feature. Another constellation is easily found from the Dipper by remembering that the curve of the "little dipper," Ursa Minor, reaches out from the North Star toward the handle of the Big Dipper. Constellations may often be remembered from some natural connection, such as that the Dragon's head is under the heel of the mythological Greek hero, who performed twelve feats of great daring and strength. Incidentally, notice the "keystone" making Hercules easy to find.

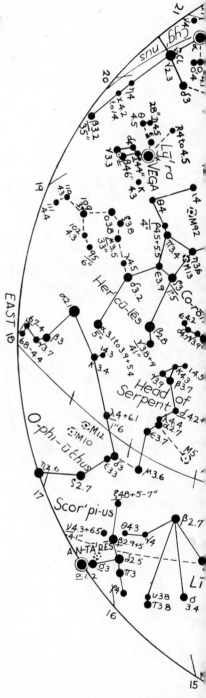

SYMBOLS of MAGNITUDE (brightness)
1   2   2½   3   3½   4   4½   Clus.   Neb.
●   ●   ●   ●   ●   ●   •   ⁝   ⊙

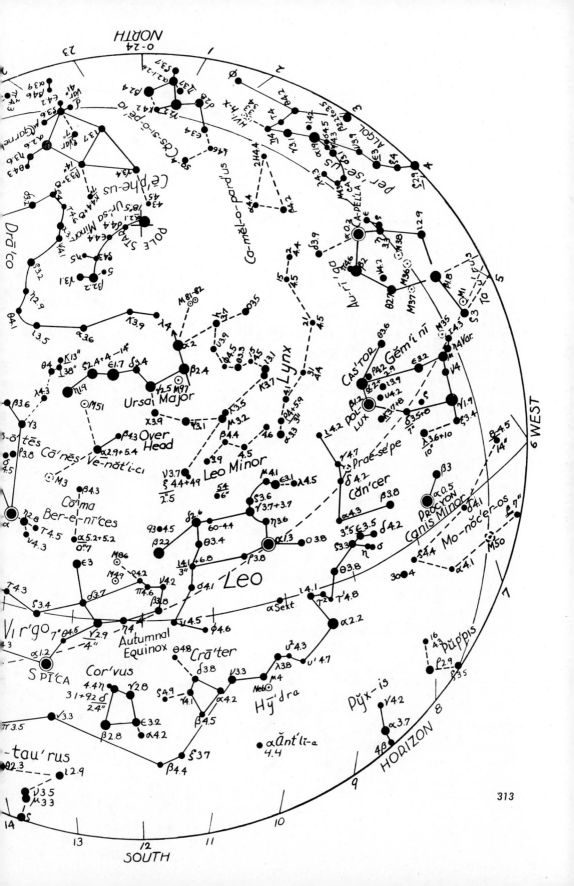

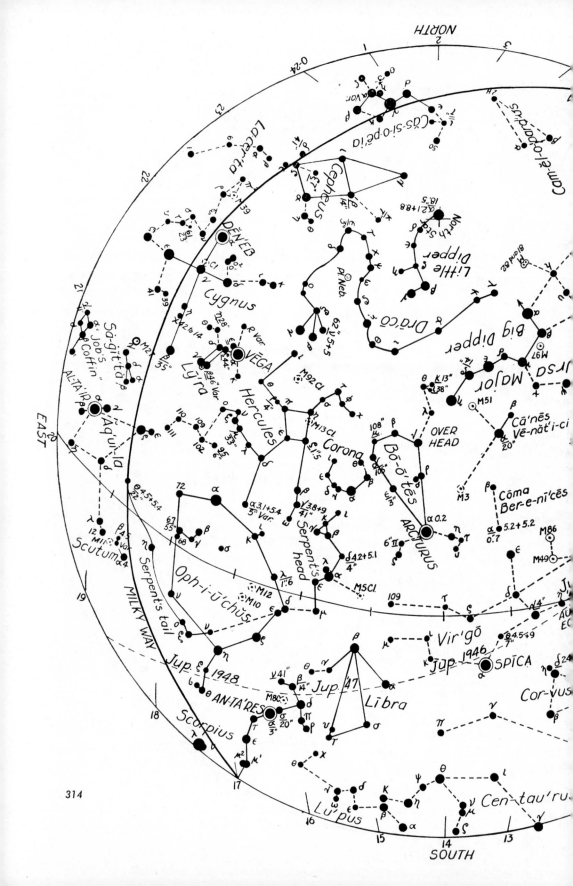

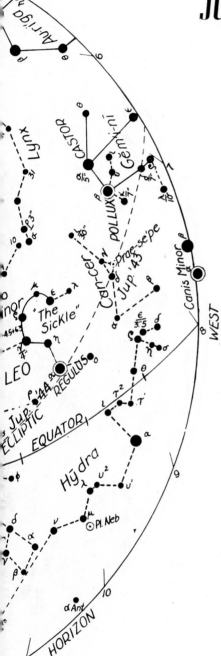

JUNE STARS

Since the northern part of the Milky Way swings around the north star within 28° of the pole, parts of some of its constellations never set at all, or not for long, each year. Between winter and summer, especially in May, the summer part of the Milky Way rises in the northeast before some of the winter constellations such as Canis Minor and Gemini have disappeared. By June there is little left of the splendid winter section, and practically all of the summer constellations have come into view. Even the far southern Scorpion is lifting its head above the southeastern horizon. Cyg'nus, the Swan, Ly'ra, the Harp or Lyre, and Aq'uil-a, the Eagle, all characteristically summer constellations, containing a first-magnitude star in each of them, now dominate the eastern sky. Also, two little constellations near these large ones deserve mention. They are "Job's Coffin" and the Arrow, otherwise called Del-phi'nus, the Dolphin, and Sȧ-ġit'tȧ, the Arrow. "Job's Coffin," especially, is distinctive and easily recognized by its diamond-shaped pattern.

SYMBOLS of MAGNITUDE (brightness)
1 2 2½ 3 3½ 4 4½ Clus. Neb.

7

JULY STARS

In June, the whole 180° of the summer Milky Way came into view well above the eastern horizon. The whole of Scorpius, with its curled-up tail is seen by July, followed closely by Sag-it-ta′ri-us, the Archer, (remember that among the June stars we spoke of Sa-git′ta, the Arrow). Scorpions seem small game to hunt even with a bow and arrow. The end star of the handle of the "Milk Dipper" is the end of the bow, as shown in the map. The arrow seems aimed nearly at the red heart, An-ta′res, of the scorpion. Antares is a supergiant star, and for that reason is bright enough in appearance to be one of our twenty first-magnitude stars although it is much farther away than most of them (171 light years). The constellations of Sagittarius and Scorpius are of great interest because it is among the tremendous star clouds off in that direction that the center of the whole stellar system has been located in recent years. Our *solar system* is between this center and the constellation of Au-ri′ga. If we picture the Milky Way as being a great wheel, with its hub at Centaurus, then the same spoke from hub to rim that goes through our little solar system, goes also through Auriga, which is between us and the rim. Turning of the wheel carries us toward Cygnus.

SYMBOLS of MAGNITUDE (brightness)
1 2 2½ 3 3½ 4 4½ Clus. Neb.

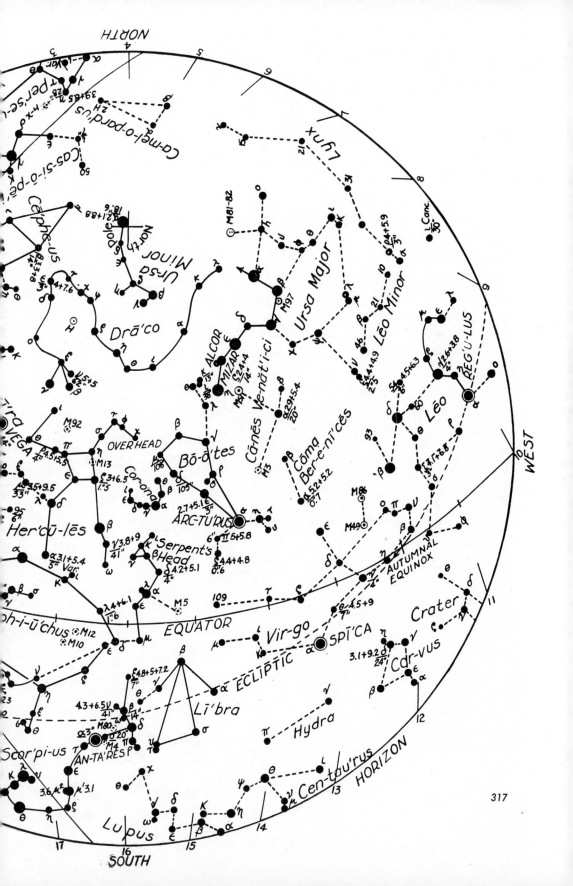

317

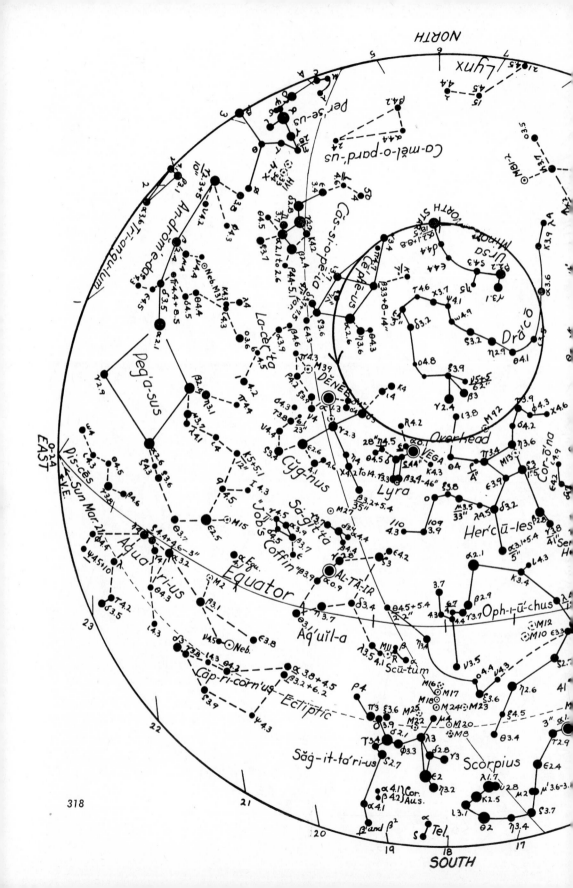

AUGUST STARS

8

The Milky Way in its summer section lies on our meridian, and runs as nearly north and south as it can ever do. Looking to the south along the meridian, we can see the stars and star clouds of Scorpius and Sagittarius near the horizon, or farther up if we live in the southern states. A little above them is the wide-spread but not well-marked constellation of O-phi-u'ehus, meaning the serpent holder. On each side of it is a constellation bearing the name Serpens; Serpens Caput on one side and Serpens Cauda, on the other, the Snake's Head and Snake's Tail. Old pictures show a man holding the snake in his two hands. Up along the meridian near the zenith are Lȳra, marked by its great white giant star Vēga, and Hercules, which can be found from the "keystone." See if you can see M 13, the most magnificent globular cluster in the northern hemisphere. It is near the northwest corner of the keystone. It is 34,000 light years away, but its 50,000 stars look like one. No single star can be seen or photographed at that distance except with unusually powerful instruments. One other constellation not before mentioned has come into view during the summer, A-qua'ri-us, in the east. The word is related to water. From a pitcher near the equator water is supposed to be poured, falling down toward the south in a spray (of dim stars).

SYMBOLS of MAGNITUDE (brightness)
1 2 2½ 3 3½ 4 4½ Clus. Neb.

9   SEPTEMBER STARS

The first stars to make sure of before they set in the west are An-ta′res, the red first-magnitude giant star far to the southwest in Scor′pi-us, and Arc-tu′rus, north of west, in Bō-ō′tēs. All stars move 30°, two hours to the west with respect to the sun, in a month. Arcturus will disappear until March, and Antares till May.

Three first-magnitude stars forming a triangle overhead are Vē′ga, in Lȳ′rà, Dĕn′ĕb, the tail of the Swan, and Al′ta-ir, the middle one of three in line in Aq′ui-la, the Eagle. All three of these great stars are white-hot.

Two other first-magnitude stars are just rising, Capel′la, far to the northeast, and Fo′mal-haut, almost equally far to the southeast. (The latter *may* be pronounced fo′mal-o.) The reason that so many first-magnitude stars are present this month is partly accounted for by the fact that we see a full half circle of the Milky Way at this time of year. (See the August map for stars that have recently set.)

SYMBOLS of MAGNITUDE (brightness)
1   2   2½   3   3½   4   4½   Clus.   Neb.

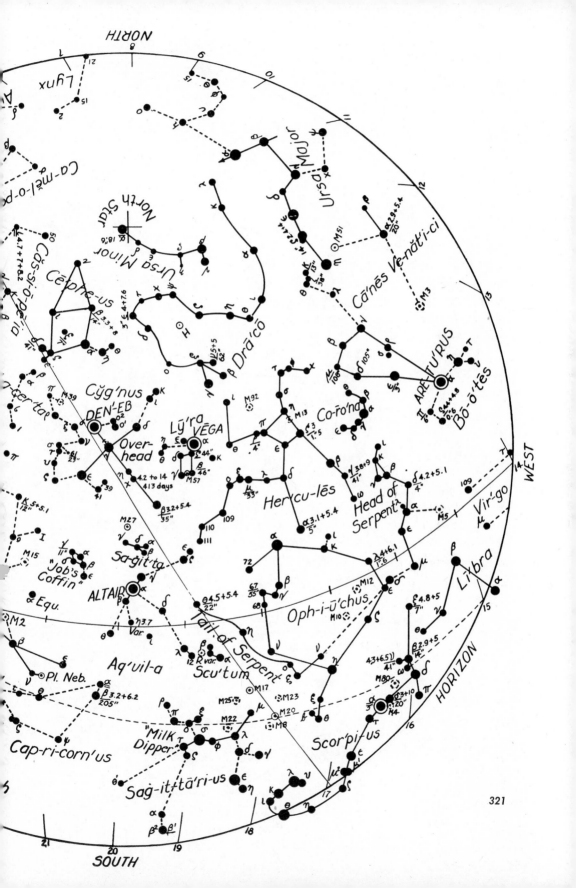

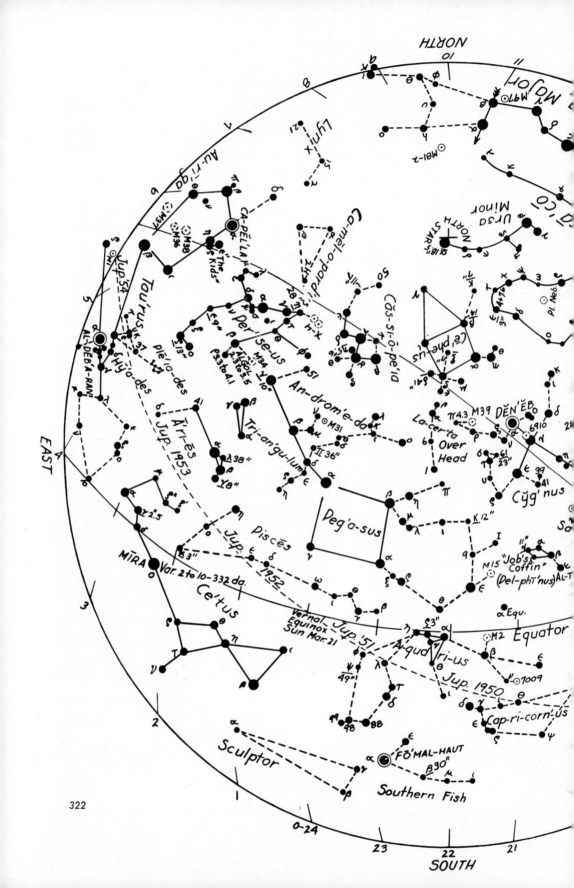

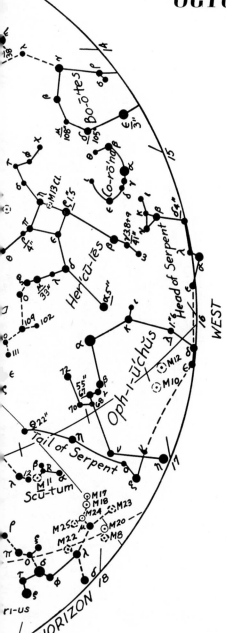

OCTOBER STARS

Coming up from the east, following behind the triangle of first-magnitude stars mentioned in connection with the September map, is the great square of Peg'asus. The square is a landmark with reference to which many other stars can be located. Pegasus is approaching the meridian, leading An-drom'e-da. Indeed, the northeast corner star of the square is considered a part of Andromeda. It is like a coupling pin that holds two cars together.

Near Andromeda are three other constellations, Ce'phe-us, Cas-si-o-pe'ia, and Per'se-us, which should be studied together, for they and Andromeda are associated in mythological lore. Cepheus, the king, leads Cassiopeia the queen, and she is followed by Andromeda, their daughter. Close by Andromeda is her lover, Perseus, who had rescued her from the sea monster that had chained her to a rock. The sea monster, the whale, Ce'tus, may be seen off a little way to the south. Cassiopeia is sometimes spoken of as "Cassiopeia's Chair," because of some resemblance to a chair, but a stronger likeness is to a letter W. These constellations stretch from south of the zenith to far into the north, where Cepheus is a circumpolar constellation.

SYMBOLS of MAGNITUDE (brightness)

1 2 2½ 3 3½ 4 4½ Clus.   Neb.
● ● ● ● ● • •   ⋮⋮   ⊙

11 NOVEMBER STARS

This map, like every third one of the twelve for the year, has an additional feature. The magnitudes of stars are given, to one-tenth of a magnitude. This helps to correct any misconceptions of brightness as judged merely by the sizes of the spots used for the stars. Now will be a good time to become familiar with star magnitudes:

First Magnitude: Aldeb'aran, in Taurus, mag. 1.06, is nearest of any stars on the map to being a standard first. Indeed, there is but one other star in the whole sky (Alpha Crucis) that comes so near to being an exact first as this star Aldeb'aran.

Second Magnitude: The North Star is quite a good example of a second. Alpha, the brightest star in Andromeda, the one that connects it with the great square of Pegasus, lacks only 10 per cent of the light necessary to make it a perfect second.

Third Magnitude: The star in the Big Dipper connecting the bowl with the handle is a rather weak third magnitude.

Fourth Magnitude: The handle of the Little Dipper, adjacent to the Pole Star, and also many of the stars in Draco, the Dragon, winding around the Pole, are in the neighborhood of being fourth-magnitude stars.

Few fifth-magnitude stars are shown on the maps, and sixths are at the limit of vision, averaging 100 times dimmer than firsts.

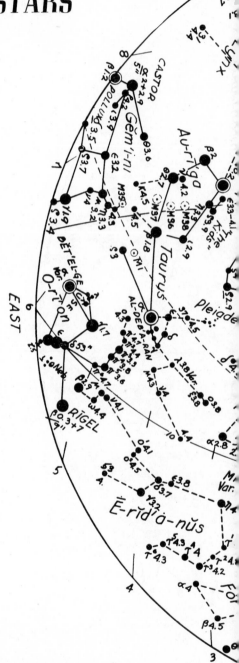

SYMBOLS of MAGNITUDE (brightness)
1 2 2½ 3 3½ 4 4½ Clus. Neb.

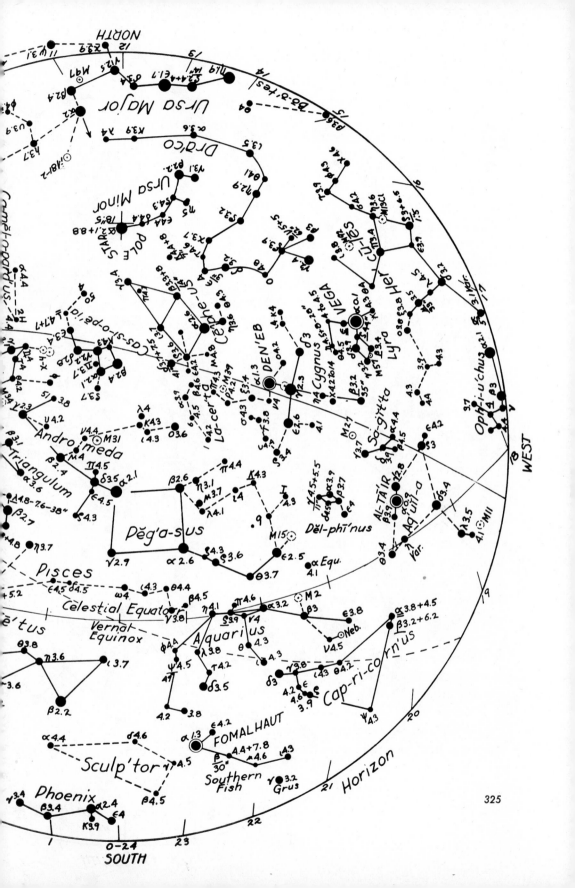

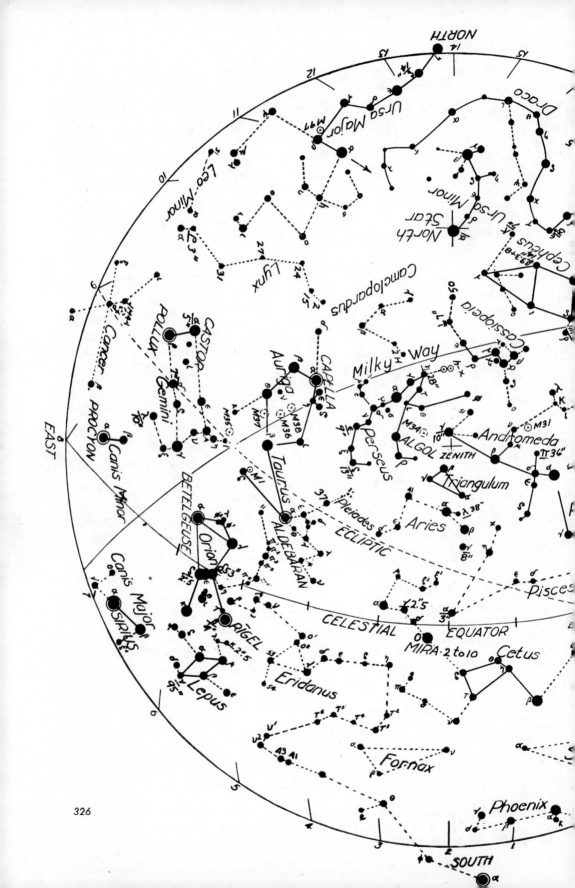

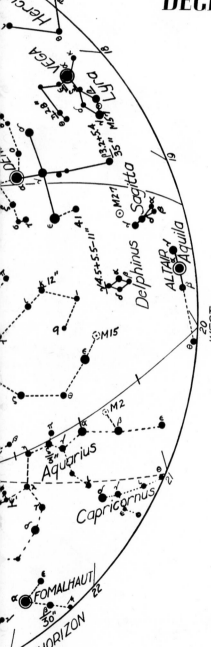

DECEMBER STARS

This month's skies are the most gorgeous of the year. Orion, followed by his two dogs are rising well up in the east. Taurus, the Bull, Gemini, the Twins, and Capella in Auriga, the pentagon, are farther to the north, and will pass close to the zenith. The Milky Way extends as nearly east and west this month as the ecliptic does. If we could see the Milky Way farther south, as tropical observers can do, the sky would be still more thickly strewn with remarkably bright stars. As the well-known constellations mentioned above come into the eastern sky to lend interest to the winter view, four first-magnitude stars are getting ready to drop out of sight in the west. These are Vega, Deneb, Altair, and Fomalhaut.

For residents of the southern third of the United States, Ca-no'pus, second only to Sirius in brightness, can be seen low in the southern sky. For those north of the 37th parallel, Canopus crosses the meridian below the horizon and is not seen at all. Even as far south as the Gulf States, this star, looked for by many, rises to only some 10° or 15°, just above the tree tops in the south, then soon descends to its southwestern setting point.

SYMBOLS of MAGNITUDE (brightness)
1   2   2½   3   3½   4   4½   Clus.   Neb.